AGRICULTURE AND THE LAW

AUSTRALIA

The Law Book Company
Brisbane • Sydney • Melbourne • Perth

CANADA

Carswell
Ottowa • Toronto • Calgary • Montreal • Vancouver

Agents

Steimatzky's Agency Ltd., Tel Aviv;
N.M. Tripathi (Private) Ltd., Bombay;
Eastern Law House (Private) Ltd., Calcutta;
M.P.P. House, Bangalore;
Universal Book Traders, Delhi
Aditya Books, Delhi;
Macmillan Shuppan KK, Tokyo;
Pakistan Law House, Karachi, Lahore.

Agriculture and the Law

edited by

EDWARD S. WALSH,
Barrister-at-Law

ROUND HALL
Sweet & Maxwell
1996

Published in 1996 by
Round Hall Sweet & Maxwell,
Brehon House, 4 Upper Ormond Quay,
Dublin 7.
Typeset by Gough Typesetting Services,
Dublin.
Printed by Genprint, Dublin.

© Round Hall Sweet & Maxwell

ISBN 1 899738 19 3

A catalogue record for this book
is available from the British Library.

ROUND HALL
Sweet & Maxwell
1996

To my father,
LIAM A. WALSH

PREFACE

Farming and agriculture-related business is a mainstay of the Irish economy:

- agriculture comprises approximately 10 per cent of the Gross National Product;

- there are 120,000 full-time farmers in the Republic of Ireland;

- a large proportion of the Irish workforce is directly or indirectly employed in the agriculture industry;

- in 1994 an estimated 5,270 students were enrolled in agricultural courses (which range from the three-year certificate in farming to farm apprentice-ships), and an estimated 4,745 people completed such courses of agricultural training in 1994.

Ireland's membership of the European Union, and particularly the Common Agricultural Policy, has had a major impact on farming. Based on projections for 1997, the recently introduced Rural Environment Protection Scheme (R.E.P.S.) grants will amount to a sum of £230 million alone with a proposed total expenditure during the period of operation of R.E.P.S. of £750 million. There are already some 13,000 participating farmers under the R.E.P.S. scheme who have been paid a total of £45.6 million as of April 1996.

Contemporary agricultural practice is increasingly subject to regulation, such as planning regulations, environmental controls, those regulations made pursuant to Acts of the Oireachtas (for example the Disease of Animals Acts), or those regulations imposed by European Community law.

As a consequence of the Common Agricultural Policy, farmers are subject to the quota system which regulates production. New schemes have been introduced, such as area aid, rural environmental protection schemes, an early retirement scheme, and other aids to production, all of which have a legal basis with even further complexity for the farmer. Separate and apart from this, farmers are, in common with all other citizens, subject to the normal obligations imposed by law but because of the nature of the operations carried on farmers are now exposed to an increasing liability both in respect of the way in which land is now used and in relation to their stock and off-farm effects which the operations may cause, such as in nuisance. The increasing complexities and burdens imposed by the legal system require the farmer, the agricultural advisor and indeed any person connected with farming or related agricultural industries to be properly acquainted with his legal obligations and legal issues which may arise in the day-to-day running of a farm or agricultural enterprise.

It is intended that this book will provide a wide ranging and comprehensive account of the principal aspects of law relating to farming and agriculture and will be of particular interest to the farmer or agricultural advisor or any person involved in agriculture. In attempting to provide a comprehensive guide, the overall purpose has been to ensure that the principal areas which may be of concern to a farmer have been covered. Certain subjects are sufficiently broad in scope to justify an entire book. Insofar as each subject which has been discussed in the book, the contributor has endeavoured to provide all necessary information sufficient to ensure that the reader has a working knowledge of that area such as should satisfactorily answer any general inquiry. Inevitably, if the reader encounters a problem, or for that matter falls foul of any regulatory provisions, recourse to a lawyer is in all instances advisable.

The law unless otherwise stated is as of March 31, 1996.

The work of the editor has been greatly lessened by the diligence and effort of the contributors and by the quality of their contributions.

I wish to record my appreciation to Bart Daly and Michael Diviney for their sterling efforts and enthusiasm in ensuring the publication of this work.

My thanks to Elaine Hanniffy, Elizabeth Mullins, Elva Kearney and Simon McDonald for their considerable efforts in expediting and assisting in the completion of this book.

Finally, a special thanks to my wife Constance and to our children Elanor, Harald and Kate.

Edward S. Walsh
Law Library
Four Courts

April 24, 1996

TABLE OF CONTENTS

Preface vii

1. **Basic Concepts of Land Law**
   by *Peter Bland* 1

2. **Agriculture and Environmental Law**
   by *Dr Yvonne Scannell* 15

3. **Planning Law**
   by *T.C. Smyth (Jnr.)* 38

4. **Planning Law and Agriculture**
   by *T.C. Smyth (Jnr.)* 57

5. **Banking**
   by *Edward S. Walsh* 71

6. **Contract**
   by *Simon McDonald* 96

7. **Employment Law**
   by *Paul Greene* 108

8. **Employers' Liability**
   by *Elizabeth Mullins* 122

9. **Occupiers' Liability**
   by *Edward S. Walsh* 135

10. **Nuisance**
    by *Edward S. Walsh* 148

11. **Animals**
    by *Edward S. Walsh* 156

12. **Fire**
    by *Elaine Hanniffy* 168

13. **Defamation**
     by *Edward S. Walsh*. 173

14. **Succession**
     by *Elaine Hanniffy* 185

15. **Leasing of Farms**
     by *Henry Abbott, S.C.*. 193

16. **Tax**
     by *Sean McKiernan*. 209

17. **Control and Eradication of Animal Diseases**
     by *Michael MacGrath*. 233

18. **Milk Quotas**
     by *Michael MacGrath*. 243

19. **Financial Aid to Farmers**
     by *Peter Bland*. 256

Index. 267

CHAPTER 1

BASIC CONCEPTS OF LAND LAW

Peter Bland, Barrister-at-Law

Introduction

Land has historically been the primary means of generating wealth in Ireland. Our land law emerged to control and protect the economic and political positions of land owners and to resolve the disputes which arose as to the possession and transfer of land. This law has not remained static but has been shaped and developed by centuries of social, political and economic changes. A striking example is the agricultural tenancy. The law once reflected a policy to eliminate agricultural tenancies. Agricultural tenants were given rights which made it commercially unattractive for landowners to lease out their land. Due to the radical programme of social engineering by land acquisition undertaken by Irish Land Commission between 1881 and 1992 the agricultural tenancy is now very rare in Ireland. In recent times it has become recognised that it is difficult to become a farmer without the capital to purchase land. The response was to jettison some of rights of agricultural tenants in order to encourage the return of the lease of agricultural land.

Despite revolutionary changes of the laws which apply to land, much of Irish land law remains recognisable from its historical origins. Indeed, without a basic knowledge of the the early history of the land law of Ireland it is not possible to understand the fundamental concepts of Irish land law.

The starting point for an overview of Irish land law is the concept that the law is not so much concerned with who owns land but rather who has the right to possess it. We may speak of a person as the owner of the land, and indeed he has those rights we associate with ownership, yet technically every acre in the Republic of Ireland belongs to the State. This principle is a vestigial remnant of the feudal society which existed in medieval western Europe. Feudal concepts which applied in Normandy were modified by Norman custom in England and then exported almost fully developed to Ireland after the Anglo-Norman Conquest. The French-speaking adventurers who conquered England created a system whereby all land belonged to the King. Land was granted in parcels by the King to his followers who held as tenants-in-chief. These magnates then divided their estates out to sub-tenants. Land was thus the subject of a pyramid of interests under the Crown. By controlling who could profit from the use of the conquered land the Crown secured allegiance throughout the conquered society. The land of Ireland was similarly claimed by the King and granted to the French-speaking adventurers who crossed the Irish sea to hold as tenants-in-chief. Just as all the land of Ireland ultimately belonged to Henry II after 1169, under Article 10 of the Constitution all the land of Ireland ultimately belongs to the State. Henry II's concern was in keeping control over Norman barons. The same concept today provides the State with a constitutional basis to interfere with the citizen's use of land in the name of the common good.

Tenure

In the medieval pyramid of landholding the tenant undertook to provide a service to his superior. For example, in return for the possession of land the tenant of the Manor of Dalkey was required to provide one hawk annually. Malta was held under similar terms, hence the term "Maltese Falcon". There is a record of a tenant who was obliged to "make a leap, a whistle and a fart" on Christmas Day. Our Dalkey tenant did not fully "own" the land in the same way as he owned his cows. He *held* the land from his feudal superior. The idea of one person holding land from another under certain terms and conditions is called *tenure*. His feudal superior did not fully "own" the land either, as he could not repossess it if the tenant continued to send him his yearly hawk. What the Dalkey tenant had acquired was a better right than any one else to possess the land. As a result of this concept of tenure, the law recognises that several persons can simultaneously have rights in the same piece of land, even though only one of them may be in possession.

Estates in Land

The permanent nature of land makes it a crude exercise to think in simple terms of who owns a particular portion of the earth's surface. Law is a means of resolving disputes. A dispute as to who owns a tractor is relatively easily solved by tracing backwards, the owners of the vehicle until one reaches the day on which it rolled off the assembly line. To trace back through all the owners of a field of land would require records stretching back to the Book of Genesis. The feudal doctrine of *estate* avoids this impossibility. An imaginary entity called the estate is placed between the person who possesses the land and the land itself. The word "estate" in this context should not be confused with the use of the same word to describe a large unit of land or the property of a deceased person. Estate here describes the period of time for which the holder is entitled to exercise those rights which we associate with ownership. By treating the ownership of land in this manner, lawyers have been able to devise elaborate schemes which can realise the desires of their clients as to who should enjoy their land over lengthy periods of time and depending on each feasible eventuality.

The person we commonly describe as the owner of a piece of land has a particular estate in that land. When he instructs his solicitor to sell his land the thing that the solicitor puts up for sale is that imaginary estate. It is in this way that a person does not buy land but buys the right to occupy it. A person has a right to hold land only for as long as his estate in the land lasts. Estates in land therefore differ according to the duration of time for which they can be held. Estates in land can be broadly categorised as *freehold* or less than freehold (otherwise described as *leasehold*). An estate is freehold if its duration is not known; it is less than freehold if the duration is certain. A lease of land for five years would be an estate less than a freehold estate because the right to hold the land will last for that certain period of five years.

Freehold estates

There are four main types of freehold estate:

1. estate in fee simple;

2. estate in fee tail;

3. life estate;

4. estate *pur autre vie*.

The *fee simple* estate is the largest and best estate in land. There is a fee simple estate held by some person in every piece of land (except, arguably, land that is vested in the State). It is out of that person's estate that other, lesser estates may be created. The vast majority of Irish farms are held in fee simple by the farmer. Fee means that the estate can be inherited and simple indicates that there is no restriction other than that imposed by statute as to who can inherit the land. A fee simple estate may be absolute or modified by, for example, a condition that the estate shall revert to the grantor should a specified event occur.

Possession in itself is not proof of the right to possess – the man who steals my horse has no right to keep it. In the language of land law the fact of occupation or possession of land is called *seisin* of land. He who has seisin of land derives his entitlement from the particular estate which he holds. Unlike the man who steals my horse the man who steals my land may eventually acquire a right to possess it. The squatter who is in wrongful possession of land has a better right than any person other than the rightful holder of the appropriate estate in the land. It may appear confusing at first, but the squatter acquires a fee simple estate by just going into possession. This is because estate relates to the duration of the possession and a squatter could potentially hold the land for ever unless the rightful owner brings a claim to recover the land within 12 years: section 13 of the Statute of Limitations 1957. To acquire land by adverse possession the occupation must be without 'the permission or leave of the true owner. Tenants or persons taking land by conacre or agistment cannot acquire the land by adverse possession. Adverse possession "is possession of land which is inconsistent with the title of the true owner: this inconsistency necessarily involves an intention to exclude the true owner, and all other persons, from the estate or interest which is being acquired": *Murphy v. Murphy* [1980] I.R. 183, *per* Kenny J.

Fee tail indicates that only specified descendants, such as male heirs or issue by a particular wife, can inherit the land. The land was then described as entailed. Today the estate in fee tail is rare and is held by very few farmers.

The third type of freehold estate is the *life estate*. At the time of the Anglo-Norman Conquest an estate could not be inherited so that the life estate was the largest interest in land recognised by Irish law. If you hold a life estate in a field that means that it is held for your life only and it is not inherited by your successor. A life tenant may be prevented from destroying the land by the person entitled to the land after the death of the life tenant. The doctrine of waste protects the person who will become entitled by restricting injury to the land, whether this injury is by a positive act such as cutting timber (voluntary waste) or by neglect such as allowing the hay shed collapse through disrepair (permissive waste).

The doctrine of waste also applies to an estate *pur autre vie*. An estate *pur autre vie* is an estate limited in its duration to the life of another person. If A leaves in his will his house to B "for the life of C" then B has the right to possess the house only for as long as C remains alive.

Estates Less than Freehold

As mentioned earlier an estate less than freehold is an estate in land which is demised, or leased, for a definite period of time. Even if the land is leased for as long as 999 years it is considered to be a lesser estate than freehold. These estates are generally categorised as follows:

(a) leases for a term certain;

(b) periodic tenancies;

(c) tenancies at will; and,

(d) tenancies at sufferance.

A lease for a term certain (or a "term of years") is a leasehold estate where there is a certain period of time, such as the five years minimum term required under the Early Retirement Scheme, up to which the lease can continue. That does not mean that it is certain that the lease shall last for that period of time.

Under the terms of the lease a party could be able to determine or put an end to the lease if the other party has done something entitling him to do so. The relationship of landlord and tenant is created where the tenant acquires the right to exclusive possession of the land for the defined period of time. Simply put, exclusive possession means that the tenant has such control of the land that he can keep his landlord off it for as long as the tenancy exists. For this and other reasons, the question of whether an agreement creates this relationship has important legal consequences for both the landlord and the tenant.

A lease for longer than one year must be in writing: Landlord and Tenant Law Amendment Act (Ireland) 1860, section 4. For the purposes of the Rural Environment Protection Scheme or the Early Retirement Scheme, the Department of Agriculture will require the production of a copy of a written lease. To facilitate an increase in agricultural leases the I.F.A. and Allied Irish Banks p.l.c. produced a document entitled "Master Lease of Agricultural Land" which is available free of charge to I.F.A. members and for the sum of £5 to non-members. This is intended to serve as a standard form draft document. Individual parties may have specific requirements which are not covered in the master lease, in which case the document can be used as a basis for discussion as to the eventual contract to lease agricultural land.

In the other major categories of leasehold estates there is no legal requirement to reduce the agreement to writing. A lease which runs for a period such as week-to-week is called a periodic tenancy. Unlike the lease for a term certain there is no certainty as to the period for which the lease can continue. The lease will run for a certain fixed minimum period such as a week or month, and continue thereafter for an indefinite number of these periods until a party decides to determine the lease. A periodic tenancy is determined by the clear communication of the intention to end the relationship at a certain time ("the notice to quit").

Strictly speaking a tenancy at will and a tenancy at sufferance are not actually estates in land. They represent the holding of land from another (*leasehold tenure*) but without a right to hold for a definite period of time (*leasehold estate*). A tenancy at will is created when there is an agreement to create the relationship of landlord and tenant but there is no agreement as to how long the relationship will last. It can be ended at any time by either party. A *tenancy at sufferance* is the legal description of the situation which exists when a tenant remains in possession after the determination of the previous tenancy.

Leases for lives and *fee farm grants* can be described as the jinnets of this classification of estates, being examples of interests in land which possess both freehold and leasehold characteristics. Due to the Land Purchase Acts, they are found today mostly in urban areas. The fee farm grant is an interest unique to Irish law where the holder of the fee simple is obliged to pay a rent to the grantor of his estate. The obligation continues for all time to bind the successors in title of the grantee of the fee simple to pay the rent to the successors in title of the grantor. Leases for lives which are renewable forever can no longer be created. A lease for lives renewable forever conveyed a freehold estate in land which lasted for the lives of three people. In this respect it resembles the estate *pur autre vie*. When one of the three died the life of another person is substituted on the payment to the lessor of a sum of money. It is still possible to create a lease for lives which is not renewable forever but is limited to a fixed term, such as 99 years.

Future Interests in Land

A fee simple absolute in possession is the closest to the full ownership of land that the law recognises. It is *absolute* because there is no limited estate, such as a life estate, carved out of it. If an estate in land is held *in possession* it may be enjoyed at the present time. As we have seen the fee simple can be modified and the possession and enjoyment of an estate in land can be projected to some time in the future. A is the fee simple owner of a field; where A grants a lease of the field for a term of one year to B, he cannot without cause disturb the right of possession that B has acquired. He does not stop holding the fee simple estate however but is said to hold it *in reversion*. After the year has elapsed he is entitled to go back into possession of his field. Possession reverts to him; he again holds his fee simple in possession.

Another means by which the enjoyment of an estate in land is postponed is when it is held *in remainder*. In this situation A conveys his fee simple estate to B for life, remainder to C in fee simple. This means that A no longer has any interest in the estate, B holds a life estate and C holds a fee simple estate which he cannot enjoy until B dies. B is called the remainder man.

Co-ownership

The farmer who leaves his farm to his three sons creates a situation where the estate in the land is held by a co-ownership. The sons become simultaneously entitled to the possession of the land. There may be taxation advantages to co-ownership or it may spare the farmer from the difficult choice of which of his children will inherit the family farm. There are two frequently used ways of co-owning land: the *joint tenancy* and the *tenancy in common*. Different results arise on the death of a joint tenant and the death of a tenant in common. In a joint tenancy the other co-owners automatically share in the whole of the land. So, on the death of the third brother, the other two increase their share of the farm from a third to a half each. This automatic right is called *the right of survivorship*. In a tenancy in common there is no such right of survivorship: the deceased co-owner's share passes to the beneficiaries under his will, or on intestacy if he has made no will. If the third brother leaves his share to his wife and two daughters in equal shares, they will be entitled to a ninth share each in the farm. The natural progression in a joint tenancy is to one person becoming the sole owner of the property simply by living longer than the other co-owners. In a tenancy in common the likelihood is that the number of co-owners will increase with each death. It is possible for a joint tenant to convert the joint tenancy into a tenancy in common; this is referred to as severance of the joint tenancy The co-ownership may be brought to an end by the sale of the farm or by physically dividing the farm into units to be held in the sole ownership of the previous co-owners. The co-ownership will also end when one co-owner has acquired all the shares of the other co-owners.

How to Acquire an Estate in Land

Estates in land are most commonly acquired by purchase and by succession, *i.e.* by the terms of the will of the deceased owner or on intestacy if there is no will. It is also possible to acquire an estate in land by adverse possession, by gift, by forfeiture and by grant from the State, the ultimate owner of all land. As we have seen a person may also acquire a lesser interest from another's estate. Thus A, who is entitled to the fee simple estate of a field, may grant a life estate in it to B, B may then grant a leasehold interest in it to C and C could mortgage the leasehold interest to D. A, B, C and D would all then hold estates in the same field, though only C in this example would be entitled to possession. The abstract notion of estates thereby facilitates the freedom to make the best use of what is an obviously limited but valuable and practically eternal resource.

Title and Title Deeds

Whatever way the right to possess land is obtained, it obviously must be proved. The record, deeds or tradition which establishes the fact of that right is the *title of the possessor*. The title to land is either registered or unregistered. If the land is registered the title may be found on a folio at the Registry of Deeds where it may be inspected by the public. If the land is unregistered the title is found in the documents (referred to as the "title deeds") which establish how the estate has been acquired. Before land is bought, the title of the vendòr should be examined, for it may be that another person has a greater right to possess the land than the vendor.

Farmers are often asked to bring in their title deeds to the bank. This is a request which should be treated with caution. It is unlikely that the bank is volunteering to store the documents in it's safe so that they will not get lost. The deposit of title deeds is a means of creating an equitable mortgage. No written contract is required. To eventually enforce the mortgage the bank must prove the borrower's intention to enter into a verbal contract. The borrower is often asked to read a declaration that the deeds are deposited by way of security. The seasonal nature of farming requires credit facilities and lending institutions legitimately require security for their risk; however, the informality of the transaction could disguise the enormity of the consequences. The farmer who mortgages his land has transferred his fee simple estate to the bank. Technically the bank is now the owner, subject to the farmer's right to defeat the mortgage by repaying the loan on time. He remains in possession but the lending institution can apply to the Circuit Court for an order for possession if he defaults on the repayment of the loan. Once it has achieved vacant possession of the property the lending institution has no impediment to a quick sale of the land. Mortgages are subject to what is called the *equity of redemption* or the right to the difference between the value of the farm and the amount of the mortgage (and the bank's ubiquitous costs).

Conacre and Agistment

In Ireland it is far more common for a farmer to enter into a contract to "take" land than to enter into a lease. By "taking" or "letting" land what is meant is that an arrangement is entered into where one farmer acquires the right to enter upon another's land for an agreed purpose. Where there is a *right of conacre* the agreed purpose is to till, plant or sow and harvest crops and where there is a *right of agistment* it is to graze livestock. These arrangements are considered to be licence agreements. They are permissions to do things which would otherwise be trespass. By analogy, when a person goes to the All-Ireland Final he purchases a ticket permitting him to enter Croke Park to watch the match. He does not acquire an estate in the football ground, just a licence or permission to be there for the agreed purpose. If he entered the ground without the permission given by the ticket, he is trespassing.

Conacre and agistment must be distinguished from leases of land. Like the supporter in Croke Park the farmer who enters into a contract of conacre or agistment has no right of exclusive possession of the land and thus cannot prevent the owner from entering. However Irish law has recognised the reality of a conacre or agistment contract and it has been stated that the person who takes land under such an arrangement enjoys "a special possession for a particular purpose" which does not oust the owner's "general possession". His use of the land is restricted to that particular purpose: therefore a farmer who takes land on agistment would not be entitled to use the land as a site for car boot sales.

Conacre and agistment arrangements are usually for a short term, such as the customary 11 months. It is this short-term nature which has led to criticism of such arrangements. The farmer who takes land for 11 months is unlikely to be concerned as to grassland management or inputs, nor is there any incentive to do any improvement of fencing other than stopping gaps. Conacre and agistment arrangements do not therefore lend themselves to intensive farming. The farmer who takes the land cannot control his future farming operations as he has no security of tenure: in other words, in the absence of a specific term of the agreement the farmer who takes the land has no right to renew the arrangement for another term. Against this it, must be stated that conacre and agistment arrangements give the opportunity of a relatively cheap entry into farming and for temporary or seasonal enlargements of holdings when such are required. The advantage for the farmer who enters into a conacre or agistment arrangement is that the relationship of landlord and tenant is not created. A farmer may hold a lease of land subject to a covenant against subletting: a conacre or agistment contract would not be in breach of such a covenant. Of more importance has been the avoidance by conacre and agistment contracts of statutory restrictions in respect of the letting, subletting and subdivision of agricultural and pastoral land.

Land

The maxim *cujus est solum, ejus est usque ad coelum et ad inferos* expresses the general rule that "whose is the soil, his is also that which is up to the sky and down to the depths of the earth". There are a number of exceptions to and limitations of this general rule. It would indeed be a great pleasure for farmers to prevent politicians of the opposing colours from travelling in helicopters over their land. Unfortunately section 55 of the Air Navigation and Transport Act 1936 prevents any action for trespass or nuisance unless the aircraft flies at an unreasonably low height. Statutory restrictions to the owner's enjoyment of his land below the soil are contained in the Mineral Development Act 1979. The Local Government (Planning and Development) Acts 1963 to 1992 provide the greatest restrictions on the use of land: see below, chapters 2, 3 and 4. At common law the State is entitled to treasure trove, being objects of gold or silver the true ownership of which is unknown and which have been concealed underground.

Land is generally understood to mean the earth's crust; in law the term "land" has a wider definition. Land is regarded by the law as including not only the physical surface of the earth but also those things which are fixed to the surface ("fixtures"). Thus trees, buildings and other permanent structures form part of the land. Whether objects are sufficiently connected is decided by a two part test. The first question is the degree of annexation, or how securely it is attached to the land. Bags of fertiliser stored on pallets at the gate to a field would not form part of the land, whereas fertiliser that has been spread on the land obviously has become part of the land. Farmyard manure stored in a field would not be a fixture but may become part of the land if it becomes overgrown with weeds. The second part of the test relates to the purpose of *annexation*: is the thing fixed for its convenient use as it was or for the more convenient use of the land. It has been said that a dry stone wall is a fixture of the land but the same stones piled on top of each other in a builder's yard would not constitute a part of the land. Even when such things do not form part of the land there is a legal presumption that the fee simple owner in possession is the owner. It is important when buying land to determine what things are fixtures. One would not expect the movable furniture of a house to be included in the sale, but what about the alarm and the satellite dish? Whether a thing is a fixture is also important when one holds a lease of land. A building erected by a tenant becomes part of his landlord's land. Some fixtures however may be removed by the tenant; for example, under section 3 of the Landlord and Tenant Act 1851 or under section 17 of the Landlord and Tenant Law Amendment Act (Ireland) 1860 an agricultural tenant may remove certain fixtures such as a cattle crush or a tractor shed provided he complies with certain conditions.

In law, land is that which is contained in the ownership of an estate in land. Along with the particular rights of possession, the owner of an estate in land may also acquire certain property rights. It is for this reason that the legal definition of land includes some rights which are connected with the physical extent of the land. These rights are referred to as *incorporeal hereditaments* and by this it is meant simply that they will remain attached to land after it is sold or the owner dies. The right of way is an example of such a right that most farmers will be familiar with. Not all farming operations have the use of a right of way across their neighbour's land but when the right exists, it is included in the estate of that farm for potentially time without end. The two most important incorporeal hereditaments, *easements* and *profits à prendre*, are discussed below, page 12.

The ownership of land also includes the right to catch and appropriate wild animals on that land, so that a pheasant shot by B which falls to the ground on A's land belongs to A. The water in ponds and lakes on a farm is part of the farmer's land. When water runs in a defined channel so that it forms a natural river or stream over the land of a farmer, that farmer owns the soil of the stream or river bed, unless another person can prove a better title. If the river is the boundary between two farms each owner is presumed to own the soil of the bed up to the half way point. The owner of the banks of a river is known as the *riparian owner*. Riparian owners do not own the water itself. However they are entitled to have access to the water which touches their lands and to have the water reach them in its natural state in flow, quality and quantity so that they can take the water for their ordinary purposes connected with their lands. A riparian owner also has a right not to have his banks eroded by changes caused by some other person upstream. If the river is tidal then the soil of the bed is owned by the State. At common law the owner of land adjoining the sea is entitled to the seashore to the ordinary high tide mark, but thereafter the shore is vested in the State.

Boundaries

Disputes often arise between farmers of adjoining lands as to the boundary line between their properties. The fact that one farmer maintained the ditch, fence, wall or hedge does not necessarily mean the boundary structure is on his land: a certain and unambiguous description of the extent of the land in the conveyance is conclusive of ownership. In the title deeds to the property there should be a map on which the boundaries to the property are marked. Photocopies of the Ordnance Survey map upon which are marked the boundaries to the conveyed property are used in practice. Should the dispute not be resolved by reference to the documents of title, it is necessary to look to other evidence which could include other relevant legal documents or the evidence of witnesses, as intention of the parties and the purpose and subsequent maintenance of the particular boundary. The physical features of field boundaries can give rise to certain presumptions. Where two fields are separated by a ditch and hedge, the boundary is presumed to be on the far side of the hedge. This is because it is presumed that he who dug the ditch also planted the hedge on the earth that was thrown up, and that all these works would have been done on his own land. However the practice of the Ordnance Survey is to draw the boundary lines across the centre of the hedge so that, if the lands have been purchased in a conveyance which relies on an Ordnance Survey map, the presumption is ousted by the agreement of the parties to the line marked on the map.

Roads

Roads usually form the boundary of some part of a farm. A road which the public have a right to pass over is called a highway. At common law there is a presumption that the soil of the highway belongs to the owners of the adjoining land on each side. The highway does not automatically extend to the hedge that encloses it. A public right of way is created by statute or by express or implied dedication to the public of the way by the owners of the underlying soil. When a road authority declares by order a road over which a public right of way exists to be a "public road", the road authority becomes responsible for its maintenance. Unless the land under the road has been acquired by the authority, this statutory authority to maintain highways does not extend beyond the limits of what was originally a path long before the automobile age. For this reason the practice of road authorities of treating the verge as the property of the County Council may in some cases be misconceived and illegal.

Incorporeal Hereditaments

A farmer may have traditionally passed over his neighbour's field in bringing his sheep to graze a mountain. In crossing his neighbour's land he could be

exercising a right called an *easement* which he possesses by virtue of the
ownership of his particular farm; in grazing the mountain he exercises a right
called a *profit à prendre*. Easements and *profits à prendre* are rights which a
person can acquire over the land of another. As stated above, they are rights
which attach to land and are not personal to the owner. They automatically pass
to the successor in title to the land and are included as part of a conveyance of
land under section 6(1) of the Conveyancing Act 1881. These rights are
therefore considered to be part of the land itself. To the farmer, the most
important of these rights is the *right of way*, which entitles the owner or occupier
of land to the right of passage over his neighbour's land. A right of way is an
example of an easement. Other recognised easements include the right to
support, to light, to store manure, to put a drain across and to take water from
another's land. It is even possible to have a easement to use a lavatory on
someone else's land.

The principal difference between an easement and a *profit à prendre* is that
a *profit à prendre* involves the taking, off another's land some part or some
produce of that land, such as sand, gravel, grass, turf, fish, wood or wild animals.
An easement includes the right to use the land of another in a particular way,
or to restrict the owner using his land in a certain way, but does not extend to
the taking off of any part or produce of the soil. The most relevant *profits à
prendre* to farmers are the right to cut turf (*turbary*), the right to graze land
(pasturage or, as it is traditionally described in Ireland, "*commonage*"), the right
to fish (*piscary*) and sporting and mining rights. Rights of pasturage are
included as land farmed for the purpose of participation in the Rural Environment Protection Scheme: a farmer who has a right of pasturage may claim
R.E.P.S. payments in respect of a proportionate share of the land grazed, but a
farmer will not receive payments for land over which he exercises a right of
turbary. The overgrazing of land "in commonage" has caused environmental
concerns particularly in the West of Ireland.

Easements

The land which is accommodated or benefited by an easement is called the
dominant tenement and the land which provides the benefit is called the *servient
tenement*. The benefit must be for the land as opposed to the landowner,
although it obviously follows that what benefits the land will benefit the
landowner. The right must be certain and capable of definite expression. A right
of way cannot be expanded into a general right to wander about at will. An
easement is described as negative if the right is to restrict the servient owner
from doing something on his own land. The right to light and the right of support
are negative easements. Easements which unduly inhibit the development of
land are not recognised by the courts. A right to a view or to provide shelter for
animals by retaining a hedge have been held by the courts not to exist as
easements. A right in the nature of an easement is recognised in having one's

fence maintained by one's neighbour. This easement is unusual in that it involves the expenditure of money by the servient owner. It must be stressed that the existence of a fencing easement is rare and would be difficult to prove. In the general course every farmer is legally obliged to fence his land to stop his animals escaping.

Profits à prendre

There are two classes of *profits à prendre*: *profits à prendre in common* and *several profits à prendre*. A profit in common is a profit which may be either enjoyed by two or more persons in common with the owner of the dominant tenement. A sole or several profit differs in that it is enjoyed to the exclusion of all persons, including the owner of the dominant tenement. Thus, where an owner of bog-land confers a grant of a several profit to cut turf from his bog to a commercial turf extractor he is not entitled to cut turf from his own bog. But where a number of people enjoy rights of common of turbary in respect of the bog, the owner of the bog is not prevented from cutting turf. The several profit is of infrequent occurrence and the profit in common is of much greater importance to the farmer. Most Irish rights of common of turbary arise out of grants contained in leases and survived the vesting of the lands in the tenants under the Land Purchase Acts.

Most rights in common are *appurtenant*: the right runs with the dominant tenement to which it is attached. As turf is a fuel, common of turbary is always appurtenant to the house and not the land of the commoner. The needs of the tenement sets the limit on the amount of turf which can be extracted in the exercise of a right of turbary. Similarly the exercise of common of pasture is limited by the amount of stock that can be outwintered on the dominant tenement. Unlike easements some profits can exist *in gross* or without a dominant tenement.

Acquisition of Easements and Profits

Easements and *profits à prendre* are said to *lie in grant*. The grant may be express, implied or presumed. An express grant at common law was created by a deed, but oral agreements to grant a right may be recognised in equity. A grant may be implied when it was intended to be created but was omitted from the conveyance. An *easement of necessity* is implied when the right is necessary to give effect to the common intention of the parties, such as where a field is bought which is landlocked. An easement can also be acquired by implied grant under the rule in *Wheeldon v. Burrows* [1879] 12 Ch.D. 31 where a portion of a farm is sold. Easements and profits are also acquired by presumed grant, or prescription. *Prescription* is a means of giving legal recognition to rights which have been enjoyed for a long time without interruption. There are three different modes of acquisition by prescription:

(a) at common law, where use must be proven since 1189;

(b) by lost modern grant, where the courts indulge in a fiction that use of the right for 20 years is taken as proof of a grant which has been lost; and,

(c) under the Prescription (Ireland) Act 1858, where uninterrupted use for 30 years for profits and 20 years for easements defeats proof that the user began after 1189 and uninterrupted use for 60 and 40 years respectively makes the claim absolute and indefeasible. A right to light which is enjoyed for 20 years without interruption becomes absolute and indefeasible.

Extinguishment of Easements and Profits

There are three ways in which an easement or profit can be extinguished: by statute, by *unity of seisin* or by release. Unity of seisin is where the fee simple of both tenements is held by the same person. Thus if A enjoyed a right of way over B's land, the right of way is extinguished, if B purchases the fee simple in A's land. It obviously makes no sense to speak of a right of way over one's own land. That right of way is also extinguished if the dominant owner, A, executes a deed of release. Release can also be implied by the abandonment of the right. It can be difficult to tell when an easement or profit has been abandoned. The fact that the dominant owner has ceased to exercise the right may not be enough and it is often necessary to examine the surrounding circumstances to see if there is an intention to abandon the right. So in *O'Gara v. Murray*, unreported, High Court, McCarthy J., November 10, 1988, it was held that the fact of the cessation of use of a right of way coupled with the surrounding circumstances of the building of a wall and the use of the path as a vegetable patch and dumping ground was indicative of release. The courts have also interpreted significant alterations of the dominant tenement to indicate an intention of abandonment.

CHAPTER 2

AGRICULTURE AND ENVIRONMENTAL LAW

Dr Yvonne Scannell, Law School, Trinity College, Dublin*

Introduction

Environmental law is probably the area of law which impacts more on the farming community in its everyday activities than any other area. This chapter will try to describe the more important environmental controls over farming activities and the potential liabilities of the farmer who is not careful to comply with land-use laws and to avoid polluting the environment.

Environmental law is sometimes extremely complex and it changes very rapidly. Appropriate specialist advice should be taken in concrete situations as this chapter is the merest outline of some of the more important controls.

Land-Use Plans

In recent years a number of what can be called land-use plans have been made or prepared in Ireland. A short description of the various plans is given below. These plans are particularly important for farmers because provisions in them may increase or decrease the value of their lands or operate to restrict the way farming is carried on.

Development Plans

These are plans in which local authorities set out what they want for their areas. The most important provisions in these are usually land-use zonings where land

---

*Dr Yvonne Scannell was born in Tralee, County Kerry. She lectures in environmental law in the Law School, Trinity College, Dublin and is a consultant in environmental and planning law to Arthur Cox, Solicitors. She is the author of four books including *Environmental and Planning Law* (1995) and is a director of Tara Mines Ltd., the Irish National Petroleum Corporation and the Educational Building Society. She represents Ireland on the European Council for Environmental Law.

is zoned for particular purposes, for example, for residential or industrial development. Other provisions may state that a particular area is of special scenic importance or of particular importance for archaeological reasons. Farmers will usually not mind their land being zoned residential or industrial but they might object if their lands are zoned for amenity purposes because this usually reduces land values. Local authorities could make development plans and special amenity area orders which de-exempt agricultural developments, especially in areas of special amenity value and special interest, but few have done this to date.

It is very difficult, and frequently impossible, to get planning permission for any development which materially contravenes the provisions of a development plan. Farmers should check draft development plans when they are put on public display to see if anything in them could affect their lands for better or worse. They have rights to object if they do not like the local authority proposals. Most agricultural land is not zoned for any particular use but all development plans state the sort of development they consider acceptable and unacceptable in the countryside.

Special Amenity Areas and Conservation Orders

A planning authority is empowered sections 42 and 43 of the Local Government (Planning and Development) Act 1963, as amended, to make a special amenity area order where it appears to them that by reason of:

1. its outstanding natural beauty,

2. its special recreational value, or

3. a need for nature conservation,

an area should be declared an area of special amenities.

It is again, very difficult and frequently impossible to get planning permission for any development which materially contravenes the provisions of a special amenity order. Certain types of agricultural development which are normally exempted development are not exempted in a special amenity area. Compensation is not payable when planning permission is refused or when very strict conditions are attached to planning permissions for development in these areas. If a farmer appeals to the Minister for the Environment against an order, the Minister must hold a public inquiry and he or she may refuse to confirm the order after hearing the case against it.

Planning authorities may make conservation orders to protect special flora or fauna in special amenity areas. There is an appeal to An Bord Pleanála against these orders.

Tree Preservation Orders (T.P.O.s)

Most tree felling is exempted development but planning authorities have several powers under planning legislation to preserve and protect trees and woodlands. Section 45 of the Local Government (Planning and Development) Act 1963, as amended, provides for the preservation of trees, groups of trees or woodlands by means of tree preservation orders. A T.P.O. may prohibit the cutting down, topping, lopping or wilful destruction of trees except with the consent (which may be conditional) of the planning authority. Typical conditions require the replanting of trees.

As a general rule compensation is payable for damage caused by a refusal of consent or for a conditional consent. However, compensation is not payable in numerous circumstances especially where the trees have a special amenity value or interest.

There may be a right of appeal against the order to An Bord Pleanála which may confirm it with or without modifications or which may annul it. Contravention of an order is an offence punishable by a maximum fine of £1,000.

Orders under the Wildlife Act 1976

Sections 15, 16 and 17 of this Act establish a procedure whereby the Minister of State at the Department of Finance may make:

1. an establishment order establishing nature reserves on lands owned by him or the State;

2. a recognition order, recognising nature reserves in private ownership; and

3. a designation order, designating land as a refuge for a particular species of fauna which should be specially protected.

Before publishing notice of intention to make orders for nature reserves or refuges for fauna, the Minister is obliged to consult, and in some cases to obtain the consent of, authorities whose interests may be affected. Owners and occupiers of lands to be covered by designation orders must be notified. There is a right of appeal to the Minister against the order and compensation may be payable if land will be devalued. Over 173,000 hectares or 0.22 per cent of the Republic of Ireland is covered by nature reserves.

Under section 18 of the Wildlife Act, the Minister or any other person with his approval, may enter into an agreement with any person having an interest in or over land as to the user or management of the land in the interests of protecting or conserving wildlife. Compensation may be paid to any person having, or claiming to have, an interest in the land to which the agreement relates.

The Minister also has power under section 21 of the Act to make an order declaring a particular species or particular species of flora protected either throughout the State or in a particular area or areas. There are about 1,300 flora protection sites in the country.

Section 12(2) of the Act requires Ministers of State, local authorities and certain other public bodies to *consult* the Minister of State at the Office of Public Works before taking decisions which might adversely affect the wildlife values of nature reserves or refuges for fauna set up under sections 15, 16, 17 and 18 in the interests of eliminating or reducing potential damage and to take all practicable steps to avoid or minimise effects or interferences with the suitability of nature reserves or refuges or with the management of land covered by a section 18 agreement. Other public bodies also have to take account of the effects of their decisions on wildlife.

Special Protected Areas (S.P.A.s)

E.C. Directives 79/409, 85/441 and 91/244 on the conservation of wild birds in so far as relevant to land-use controls, seek to protect the nests and habitats of birds and require the State to ensure the provision of a sufficient diversity and area of habitats so as to maintain the population of all species.

Annex I, as amended, lists particularly vulnerable bird species for protection. Ireland was *obliged* to classify the most suitable areas (on land and sea) as special protection areas (S.P.A.s) for these species. Similar measures are to be taken for regularly occurring migratory species not listed in Annex I. In all these areas the State is obliged to take "appropriate steps" to prevent pollution, deterioration of classified habitat and disturbance to the birds. Outside these areas, Member States are to "strive to avoid" pollution or deterioration of habitats generally. These obligations necessarily have implications for land-use, air and water use and may in appropriate circumstances require the prevention or control of a wide range of activities, including agricultural activities, on or near an area which is the habitat of a protected bird. So, for example, there have been objections to people trying to establish shellfish farms because this could interfere with bird life in a S.P.A. About .001 per cent of the State is covered by S.P.A.s. It is now a condition of E.U. grants for activities in areas important for birds that appropriate steps are taken to protect the birds.

Planning authorities are notified of S.P.A. designations and they have to take them into account when considering whether to allow or carry out developments which might damage them or cause disturbances to birds.

Areas of Scientific Interest (A.S.I.s)

An inventory of areas of scientific interest, *Areas of Scientific Interest in Ireland* was published in 1981 and updated in 1989 by the Office of Public Works which has responsibility for these areas. In 1977 An Foras Forbartha published a national inventory of landscapes, *Inventory of Outstanding Landscapes*, and in

1980 a report, *Peatland Sites of Scientific Interest in Ireland* was published for the Wildlife Advisory Council.

Areas of interest in the inventory are listed by county, classified by habitat and described according to their value (geological, ecological or geomorphological or a combination of these). Ecological sites are further classified into those with particular botanical, ornithological or zoological features. Each listing is accompanied by a brief description of the areas and location and an indication of whether its importance is international, national, regional or local. About one million acres have been identified as areas of scientific interest. The designation of land as an A.S.I. may affect private property rights. For example, forestry grants are usually not payable for afforestation in these areas and planning authorities are likely to be less willing to permit development which they think could damage them.

Strictly speaking, there are no legal controls over A.S.I.s unless a development plan states that they are to be preserved or protected. Developments which could damage any such area may be prohibited or conditions may be attached to any permission granted to prevent or minimise any damage if the development plan states that they are to be protected. Owners of quarries have been prevented from developing them becasuse they were in an A.S.I. Much development likely to have a detrimental effect on these areas is exempt from planning control, particularly agricultural and forestry developments.

Coillte is obliged under section 14(1) of the Forestry Act 1988 to consult with the Minister for Finance concerning forestry development in A.S.I.s. It refers applications for grant assistance in these areas to the Wildlife Service of the Office of Public Works. Grant aids for unsuitable agricultural and forestry developments in these areas are usually refused or made conditional on compliance with restrictions designed to preserve them. The names and general locations of certain valuable species of flora are contained in the *Red Data Book* published by the Office of Public Works in 1988.

Natural Heritage Areas (N.H.A.s)

The Minister for State at the Department of Finance has announced proposals to replace A.S.I.s with natural heritage areas. These areas will contain the rarer wildlife habitats, endangered species of flora and fauna and areas of geological interest. Farmers in designated areas may be eligible for higher rural environment protection scheme payments under the Agri-Environment Programme of the Department of Agriculture, Food and Forestry. Grants may be available to farmers who contract to engage in environmentally friendly farming in these areas. The legislation necessary to designate these areas has not been passed. It is likely that planning permissions will be difficult to obtain in these areas.

Environmentally Sensitive Areas (E.S.A.s)

E.C. Regulation 797/85 allowed the State to give special aid to farmers in "environmentally sensitive areas". These areas are defined as being "of recognised importance from an ecological and landscape point of view". Farming methods compatible with "conserving the natural habitat" must be adopted in these areas and farmers receive grant aids conditional on agreements not to intensify production and on setting stocking densities at a level compatible with the specific environmental needs of the area.

An Agri-Environment Programme for Ireland, known as the "Rural Environment Protection Scheme" (R.E.P.S.) was approved in 1993 under which expenditure of up to £230 million is envisaged. Farmers will be paid a premium of 125 Ecu per hectare up to a maximum of 40 hectares. An additional 20 per cent is payable to farmers who undertake special environmentally friendly practices such as preserving areas of scientific interest/natural heritage areas.

Special Areas of Conservation (S.A.C.s)

E.C. Directive 92/43 on the protection of natural and semi-natural habitats and of wild flora and fauna was adopted in December 1991. The purpose of this Directive is to establish a comprehensive network of special areas of conservation (S.A.C.s) of European significance for rare, endangered, and vulnerable species and habitats across the Community. The network will be known as Natura 2000 and will consist of sites of international importance. It must include S.P.A.s designated under E.C. Directive 79/409 (see above). S.A.C.s must be designated by the year 2004. Normally they must be designated by Member States but there is provision for Community designation in exceptional circumstances. The Directive also enshrines the Berne Convention on the Conservation of European Wildlife and Natural Habitats into the Community's legal framework. Funding is available for conservation projects. It is likely that certain agricultural activities which could interfere with these areas will be prohibited and that it will be difficult to get planning permission for activities which could affect them.

National Parks

Five large parks owned by the State and administered by the Office of Public Works have been established. A national environment park, for which there is no statutory basis, was established in 1988 by agreement between local authorities and tourism interests in the Slieve Bloom Mountains.

Plans have been announced to establish national parks in the Burren, Co. Clare and in Co. Wicklow. Until recently, the practice was to establish national parks on State-owned lands but a new and legally undesirable practice of declaring national parks on privately owned lands commenced in 1991. There are reports that this has already affected land values in these areas.

Planning Law

Planning permission is required from a local authority for all "development" of land except what is called exempted development. Development of land is defined as:

1. the carrying out of any *works* on, in or under land; or

2. the making of any *material change in the use* of any structures or other land.

Theoretically, therefore, almost anything you do to land could be development and planning permission could be required for it. However, life would be impossible if you had to get planning permission for everything you do to land so the the law provides that development by certain persons (*e.g.* local authorities) or certain kinds of development (*e.g.* using land for agricultural purposes) is exempted, *i.e.* does not require planning permission. The lists of exempted developments are contained in section 4 of the Local Government (Planning and Development) Act 1963 as amended or in the Local Government (Planning and Development) Regulations 1994, 1995 and 1996 (these are referred to hereafter as the "1963 Act" and the "1994 Regulations".) In addition, some Acts of the Oireachtas can create more exempted developments.

It is usually relatively simple to see what *works* are exempted development but it is difficult to determine what is a *material change* of use. Broad categories of land use have been identified by planners, for example residential, commercial, industrial, agricultural, amenity and recreational uses. These are subdivided (sometimes in development plans) into more detailed categories: for example, apartments, hostels, hotels and guest houses are all residential uses of land. A change of use *from* one of the broad categories of use (*e.g.* the change from agricultural to residential when a shed is converted into an apartment) will normally be a material change of use but a change *within* a broad category may not be, for example, using three bedrooms in a house for bed and breakfast. It depends upon whether it is a "material" change or not.

The 1994 Regulations provided that certain named changes of use and certain temporary changes of use may be exempted development in certain circumstances – basically because such changes are considered immaterial in that they are unlikely to affect the environment greatly.

Whether or not a particular activity is or is not exempted development is a matter of fact and degree to be determined by the local planning authority or, if there is a dispute about the matter, by an Bord Pleanála. Courts rarely overturn the decisions of these bodies when they say that planning permission is required for a particular development.

Exemption for Agricultural Developments

Exemptions in the 1963 Act

Section 4(1)(a) of the 1963 Act provides that exempted development shall include "development consisting of the use of any land for the purposes of agriculture or forestry (including afforestation), and development consisting of the use for any of those purposes of any building occupied together with the land so used". Section 2 of the 1963 Act defines "agriculture" so as to include:

> "horticulture, fruit growing, seed growing, dairy farming, the breeding and keeping of livestock (including any creature kept for the production of food, wool, skins or fur, or for the purpose of its use in the farming of land), the use of land as grazing land, meadow land, osier land, market gardens and nursery grounds, the use of land for turbary, and the use of land for woodlands where that is ancillary to the farming of land for other agricultural purposes, and 'agricultural' shall be construed accordingly".

This exemption relates only to the *use* of land for agriculture or forestry purposes and not to *the carrying out of works* for such purposes. Planning permission is not necessary for the change of use of any land *to* agricultural use or for the change of use of any buildings *to* agricultural use provided they are "occupied together with land so used".

Section 4(1)(i), as amended, provides that the following shall also be exempted development:

> "development consisting of the carrying out of any of the works referred to in the Land Reclamation Act, 1949, not being works comprised in the fencing or enclosure of land which has been open to or used by the public within the ten years preceding the date on which the works are commenced."

Exempted in the 1994 Regulations

Further exemptions for agricultural *works* are contained in the 1994 Regulations, but whereas there are no further conditions to be fulfilled to be able to rely on the exemptions granted in section 4(1) of the 1963 Act, the exemptions granted by regulations are subject to a number of restrictions, *i.e.*:

1. With few exceptions, these developments are only exempted if carried out in what may loosely be called "rural areas". These are defined in article 9(3) of the 1994 Regulations as areas other than "county boroughs, boroughs, urban districts and towns specified in the First Schedule to the 1963 Act, and the excluded areas defined in section 9 of the Local Government Reorganisation Act, 1985". Eighty-six towns are specified in the First Schedule so that the definition of "rural" is very broad including many towns, villages and groups of houses which are not specified in the First Schedule.

2. Anyone claiming an exemption under the 1994 Regulations must comply with the various limitations and conditions specified with the exemption, otherwise the development will not be exempted.

3. An agricultural development which might be listed as exempted in regulations will not be exempted if it would not satisfy certain requirements in article 10 of the 1994 Regulations or if it is listed under Article 24 of the European Communities (Environmental Impact Assessment) Regulations 1989 as a development for which an environmental impact assessment (E.I.A.) is required. It is always essential to read article 10 before claiming that a development is exempted.

Exempted in all areas   The types of agricultural development which are usually exempted in all areas include erecting a gate, plastering a concrete wall, fencing, painting, sinking a well, works for providing an approved group water scheme, and the carrying out of development in compliance with notices under section 12 of the Local Government (Water Pollution) Act 1977, or section 26 of the Air Pollution Act 1987, or in compliance with a condition (or conditions) attached to a fire safety certificate granted in accordance with Part III of the Building Control Regulations 1991 other than the construction or erection of an external fire escape or water tank. But even then, certain conditions must be fulfilled before some of these are exempted.

Exempted in rural areas   Exempted developments in rural areas include:

1. *Land Reclamation:* development consisting of the carrying out on land used only for agriculture or forestry of the following works:

   (a) field drainage;

   (b) land reclamation;

   (c) the removal of fences;

   (d) the improvement of existing fences;

   (e) the improvement of hill grazing; or

   (f) the reclamation of estuarine marsh land or of callows where the preservation of such land or callows is not an objective of a development plan for the area.

This exemption for land reclamation works extends the exemption given in section 4(1)(i) of the 1963 Act covering land reclamation by the Minister for Agriculture to land reclamation carried out by any other person. However, as indicated in the next section, large scale land reclamation may be subject to planning permission and environmental impact assessment procedures (E.I.A.s).

The other important exemptions for agricultural works in the 1994 Regulations consist of exemptions for agricultural buildings erected in "rural" areas only. These are specified in classes 6, 7, 8, 10, 11, and 12 of column 1 of Part III of the Second Schedule to the 1994 Regulations. Planning permission is not required for these works unless they are subjected to E.I.A.s.

2. *Roofed Structures for Housing Certain Animals*

Class 6 exempts: Works consisting of the provision of a roofed structure for the housing of pigs, cattle, sheep, goats, poultry, donkeys, horses, deer or rabbits having a floor area not exceeding 300 square metres (whether or not by extension of an existing structure) and any ancillary provision for effluent storage. This exemption is subject to six conditions which must be complied with if the works are to be exempted:

> Condition 1 prohibits the use of any such structure for any purpose other than the purpose of agriculture. It should be noted that to be exempted the structure must be a *roofed* structure housing the *listed* animals. Thus, for example, fish farms, mink farms or alligator farms would not be covered by this exemption. The loophole which existed under the 1977 Regulations whereby several adjacent structures could be erected provided none of them exceeded the specified floor area (then 400 metres) has been closed off.

> Condition 2 states that:

>> "the total area of such structure together with any other such structures situated within the same farmyard complex or within 100 metres of that complex shall not exceed 450 square metres floor area in aggregate".

> Thus the maximum floor area that can be used as an intensive livestock unit for pigs, cattle, sheep, goats, poultry, donkeys, horses, deer or rabbits in a "farmyard complex" without planning permission is 450 square metres. In computing the 450 square metres account should only be taken of other *roofed* structures for housing the *specified* animals; the area occupied by other agricultural structures such as barns, sheds etc. not so used can be discounted. So also can structures occupied by animals other than those listed in class 6. This is because the 450 square metre limitation only applies to "other *such* structures" *i.e.* structures listed in class 6.

> It is not difficult to foresee that there will be problems in defining exactly what a "farmyard complex" is. Presumably it means the area on a farm which is the centre of farmyard activities. This is a question of fact to be decided in each individual case and the local authority should be consulted on the matter.

> Condition 3 provides that:

"effluent storage facilities adequate to serve the structure having regard to its size, use, location and the need to avoid water pollution shall be provided".

Condition 4 provides that:

"no such structure shall be situated, and no effluent from such structure shall be stored, within 10 metres of any public road".

Condition 5 provides that:

"no such structure within 100 metres of any public road shall exceed 8 metres in height".

The regulations specify how height is to be calculated.

Condition 6 provides that:

"no such structures shall be situated, and no effluent from such structure shall be stored, within 100 metres of any dwelling house (other than the dwelling house of the person providing the structure) or other residential building or school, hospital, church or building used for public assembly, save with the consent in writing of the owner and, as may be appropriate, the occupier or person in charge thereof".

This condition is obviously designed to protect the amenities of neighbours who might be affected by smells and other nuisances associated with agricultural structures housing large numbers of animals. A structure of 300 square metres is capable of housing a large number of pigs. It can be difficult to eliminate smells associated with intensive livestock rearing units (especially those containing pigs and poultry) and the 100 metre *cordon sanitaire* is presumably intended to eliminate complaints about smells and other nuisances from those who do not consent to them. The idea behind the *cordon sanitaire* is a good one but experts argue that the distances are not far enough in Ireland. It should be noted that condition 6 does not, for example, protect the amenities of persons occupying industrial or commercial developments, or visitors to national monuments, or places of pilgrimage adjacent to intensive livestock units.

In order to establish the "adequacy" of effluent storage facilities, farmers would be well advised to consult with their local authority and Teagasc adviser. If effluent facilities are inadequate, the development will not be exempted and will therefore be illegal if built without planning permission. The developer could also be served with a notice under section 12 of the Local Government (Water Pollution) Act 1977, ordering the provision of what the local authority considers to be adequate effluent storage facilities. Regulations made under section 21 of the Local Government (Water Pollution) Act 1990 may also be made to control the collection, storage, treatment and disposal of slurries.

Just providing effluent storage facilities will not, of course, ensure that water pollution is prevented. They will have to be properly managed and controlled and their contents will have to be disposed of in accordance with good agricultural practice. If slurry is causing or liable to cause water pollution the farmer can be prosecuted and sued for damages under pollution legislation described below.

3. *Roofless Structures and Open Areas*

Class 7 exempts: Works consisting of the provision of roofless cubicles, open loose yards, self-feed silos or silage areas, feeding aprons, assembly yards, milking parlours, sheep dipping units, effluent storage facilities or structures for the making or storage of silage, or any other structures of a similar character or description, having an aggregate floor area not exceeding 300 square metres, and any ancillary provision for effluent storage.

The conditions and limitations on which these structures are exempted are exactly the same as those described for class 6.

4. *Miscellaneous Structures*

Class 8 exempts: Works consisting of the provision of any store, barn, shed, glass-house or other structure, not being of a type specified in class 6 or 7 and having a floor area not exceeding 300 square metres.

Condition 1 prohibits the use of any such structure for any purpose other than the purpose of agriculture or forestry but excluding the housing of animals or the storing of effluent. So, for example, a person cannot try to meet condition 2 of class 6 by putting some livestock in structures listed in class 8.

Condition 2 provides that the total area of a class 8 structure together with any other such structures situated within the same farmyard complex or within 100 metres of that complex shall not exceed 900 square metres floor area in all. If this area is exceeded, the development will not be exempted.

Condition 3 provides that no such structure shall be situated within 10 metres of any public road.

Condition 4 provides that no such structure situated within 100 metres of any public road shall exceed 8 metres in height and the final condition is the same as condition 6 to class 6 developments stated above.

Stables

Class 10 exempts: Works consisting of the provision of a roofed structure for the housing of horses, other than horses kept for use in the farming of land, or ponies, having a floor area not exceeding 100 square metres (whether or not by extension of an existing structure) and any ancillary provision for effluent storage.

Condition 1 prohibits the use of any such structures for any purpose other than the housing of horses or ponies. Conditions 3, 4, 5, and 6 are similar to conditions 3, 4, 5, and 6 to Class 6. Condition 2 specifies that the total area of such structures together with any other such structures within a premises or within 100 metres of that premises shall not exceed 150 square metres floor area in aggregate.

Greyhounds

Class 11 is very similar to class 10 in that it exempts roofed structures for housing greyhounds but the floor area must not exceed 50 square metres (whether or not by extension of an existing structure) and any ancillary provision for effluent storage.

Condition 1 states that the structure cannot be used for any purpose other than the keeping of greyhounds.

Condition 2 provides that the total area of all such structures situated within a premises or within 100 metres of a premises shall not exceed 75 square metres floor area in aggregate

Conditions 3, 4, 5, and 6 are the same as conditions 3, 4, 5, and 6 to class 10.

Yards

Class 12 exempts: Works consisting of the provision of a roofless hard-surfaced yard, or of a roofless hard-surfaced enclosed area, having an area not exceeding 100 square metres (whether or not by extension of an existing yard or area) and any ancillary provision for effluent storage.

Condition 1 provides that no such structure shall be used for any purpose other than in connection with the keeping of horses, ponies or greyhounds.

Condition 3 specifies that the total area of all such structure/s together with any other such structures situated within the same complex or within 100 metres of that complex shall not exceed 150 square metres floor area in aggregate.

Conditions 2, 4, and 5 are the same as conditions 3, 4 and 6 to class 11.

Even if all of the agriculture developments described above comply with applicable conditions and limitations, they must also not contravene article 10 of the 1994 Regulations. So, for example, classes 6 to 12 above are not exempted development in areas to which a special amenity area order relates or if they are subjected to E.I.A. No such development is exempted if it would interfere with a view or prospect of special amenity value or special interest, listed for preservation in a development plan for the area in which the development is proposed or in a draft variation of the development plan or a draft new development plan.

Classes 3 and 4 of Part III of the Second Schedule to the 1994 Regulations specify more exemptions for minor works in rural areas (mainly drainage and fencing) which may be relied on by farmers.

Fees are payable for planning applications for agricultural developments. These are prescribed in Part VII of the 1994 Regulations.

Environmental Impact Assessment (E.I.A.)   Environmental impact statements (E.I.S.s) must be submitted with planning applications for certain agricultural developments specified under Article 24 of the European Communities (Environmental Impact Assessment) Regulations 1989 unless the Minister for the Environment has exempted the development from E.I.A. The following activities, although they are agricultural in nature are subjected to planning permission requirements and E.I.A. irrespective of the identity of the developer:

(a) the use of uncultivated or semi-natural areas for intensive agriculture purposes, where the area involved would be greater than 100 hectares;

(b) initial afforestation, where the area involved would be greater than 200 hectares, or the replacement of broadleaf high forest by conifer species, where the area involved would be greater than 10 hectares;

(c) peat extraction which would involve a new or extended area of 50 hectares or more.

The exemptions for forestry are to be reduced to 70 hectares initial afforestation and other controls may also apply from October 1, 1996. In addition, planning permission and E.I.A. will be required for cumulative afforestation (*i.e.* within 500 metres) by or on behalf of a single developer over a three-year period which results in the total area planted exceeding 70 hectares. Local authorities will also be designating areas sensitive to forestry where it may prove difficult to plant new forests. If the areas covered by the above developments do not exceed the stated sizes, they will be exempted development and no E.I.S. need be prepared for them.

Other specified developments subjected to E.I.A. include poultry rearing, pig rearing and salmonid breeding installations which exceed a certain size. Below this, planning authorities and An Bord Pleanála must only require the submission of an E.I.S. "where they consider that a development would be likely to have a significant effect on the environment". In other words, an E.I.S. may be required even though the size specified is not exceeded.

Pollution Law

Introduction

Legal liability for environmental pollution has also been extended in recent years. At one stage, a polluter was generally only liable to pay damages in negligence, nuisance, trespass or under the rule in the case of *Rylands v. Fletcher* (1868) L.R. 3 H.L. 300. Damages were limited to compensating for personal injuries and damage to property which was owned by an identified person.

Today a polluter could be made liable to pay the costs of preventing, remedying or cleaning up damage to the environment itself, for example, damage to flora, fauna, fisheries and other natural resources for which there is no identified owner. Actions for breaches of water and air pollution laws (and soon, for breaches of waste laws) can be brought by any person, regardless of whether or not he is personally affected. Pollution cases can be brought in all the courts from the District Court up. Cases for breaking planning laws can only be brought in the Circuit or High Court. Prosecutors can get their costs and expenses for taking successful prosecutions, and any person who successfully sues a polluter for water or air pollution can also get their expenses for investigating, mitigating and remedying the pollution.

Common Law Remedies

These are actions which existed before any Act of Parliament (statute) was passed and which can still be used as well as the statutory remedies.

The principal common law remedies for damage caused by pollution are nuisance, negligence, *Rylands v. Fletcher* (see above), trespass, actions for breach of statutory duty and actions for misfeasance of public office. The main advantage of these remedies is that a successful plaintiff may get money for loss suffered, a possibility which does not always exist when statutory remedies are used.

The usual common law action for alleged pollution is the action in nuisance. The most famous nuisance action in recent times is *Hanrahan v. Merck Sharpe and Dohme* [1988] I.L.R.M. 629. The facts of this case are well known. A farmer sued Merck Sharpe and Dohme for damage allegedly caused by emissions from their factory. His action partially succeeded but the importance of this case lies not so much in the outcome as in the enormous psychological effect it had on the public. Since that case, industry and particularly the chemical and pharma-ceutical industry, has been very closely regulated and controlled in this country. The most common nuisance actions threatened against farmers are actions for polluting neighbours' wells and for smells.

Farmers should be careful to carry out their activities as recommended by Teagasc and on any labels and instructions on agricultural products. This is particularly important when they are dealing with chemicals and fertilisers.

Liabilities under Statutes

Ireland's water and air pollution laws were passed to implement European Union requirements but they frequently go further, especially where they deal with matters relating to the enforcement of environmental controls. Irish legislation provides for extensive civil and criminal remedies for all kinds of air and water pollution offences. Controls over waste disposal are being updated.

The Main Criminal Offences

Section 3(1) of the Local Government (Water Pollution) Act 1977, as amended in 1990, provides that it is a criminal offence for any person "to cause or permit" polluting matter to enter waters. A similar offence exists under section 171 of the Fisheries (Consolidation) Act 1959, as amended, of causing or permitting deleterious matter to enter waters. All farmyard wastes (silage, slurry, waste pesticides) could be classified as polluting or deleterious matter. Farmers are frequently prosecuted under this section for letting slurry, silage or less frequently, pesticides or fertilisers, enter waters or for failure to maintain slurry tanks.

Section 24(1) of the Air Pollution Act 1987 obliges the occupier of any premises to use the best practicable means to limit or if possible to prevent, an emission from their premises. Section 24(2) of the Air Pollution Act 1987 provides that it is a criminal offence for the occupier of any premises (other than a private dwelling house) to cause or permit an emission from any premises in such a quantity or in such a manner as to be a nuisance. Premises is defined to include land. Emissions include smells. A few prosecutions have been brought against farmers under section 24 for causing smells from intensive livestock units or by spreading slurry at the wrong time or place. It should be noted that the law allows some tolerance for farming smells in rural areas and it is unlikely that a farmer spreading slurry would be convicted under section 24 unless he flagrantly ignored Teagasc advice on when and how to do so properly. Farmers spraying chemicals and using other agrichemicals should follow instructions to the letter and follow Teagasc advice in order to comply with section 24 and to avoid other legal liabilities.

Defences

The best defences to charges under the Local Government (Water Pollution)

Act 1977 for causing or permitting the entry of polluting matter to water or for breaches of section 24 of the Air Pollution Act 1987 are to have used all reasonable care or the best practicable means to prevent or minimise the discharge. Much advice is available to farmers on how to avoid causing or permitting air or water pollution. It is not a defence to causing or permitting deleterious matter to enter waters under section 171 of the Fisheries (Consolidated) Act 1959, as amended, to prove that all reasonable care was taken. This is why water pollution prosecutions are almost invariably, and sometimes unfairly, taken under this section.

Penalties

Conviction for these offences can result in maximum fines of up to £25,000 and/or five years imprisonment for water pollution and £10,000 and/or two years imprisonment for air pollution. Prosecutions for water pollution offences can be brought by any affected person. If the offences are committed by a farmer subject to integrated pollution control (*e.g.* an intensive pig farmer) the maximum criminal penalties are £10,000,000 and/or 10 years imprisonment. Additional fines can be imposed for continuing offences.

Licences

All discharges of trade and sewage effluents to waters must be carried out under and in accordance with a licence granted under section 4 of the Local Government (Water Pollution) Act 1977. Farmers are rarely required to obtain these licences since they do not usually discharge effluents through a point source. All emissions from new processes listed in the First Schedule to the Air Pollution Act 1987, and from 10 existing processes specified in the Air Pollution Act 1987 (Licensing of Industrial Plant) Regulations 1988, must be licensed under section 32 of the Air Pollution Act 1987. Again, farmers do not usually have to get one of these licences although some agricultural industries do.

Under the Environmental Protection Agency Act 1992 the new activities liable to cause pollution listed in the First Schedule to that Act and existing activities specified by ministerial orders under section 82 of the Act must, instead of being licensed under the Water and Air Pollution Acts, be licensed under Part IV of the Environmental Protection Agency Act 1992. These are mainly what are called intensive farming activities. This licence (an I.P.C. licence) will deal with all aspects of pollution control liable to be emitted from the prescribed activities. I.P.C. licences may soon be required for large scale intensive pig and poultry rearing installations. Failure to obtain the relevant licence, or to comply with conditions in the licence granted, is a criminal offence. Moreover, it can have other very serious consequences especially where required licences have not been complied with. On the other hand, compliance with the conditions in a licence can be a defence to prosecutions and to other actions for polluting.

Civil Liabilities

Water Pollution

Civil liabilities deal with the sort of orders a court can make other than imprisonment and fines. Section 10 of the Local Government (Water Pollution) Act 1977, as amended in 1990, permits any person to apply to the appropriate court (which includes the District Court) where any person is contravening section 3(1) of the 1977 Act (causing or permitting polluting matter to enter waters) or section 4 of that Act (causing or permitting the discharge of trade or sewage effluents except under and in accordance with a licence). The court has extraordinary powers including powers to order the defendant to:

– terminate the entry or discharge;

– mitigate or remedy any pollution caused;

– pay the plaintiffs costs in investigating, mitigating or remedying the effects of the discharge;

– replace fish stocks;

– replace spawning grounds;

– take preventative measures;

– remove polluting matter from waters;

– treat affected waters;

– make or pay for alternative arrangements for water supplies to persons affected by pollution;

– make good, damage to plant or equipment or to water abstraction or treatment works and any *consequential* losses incurred by any person by reason of the entry of polluting matters to waters.

This section was used in *Thornton v. Meath County Council* (unreported, High Court, O'Hanlon J., February 14, 1994) to compel a waste disposal company to provide an alternative source of water for farmers whose wells had allegedly been polluted by his activities. It has also been used to require polluters to restock fisheries.

If the defendant does not comply with the court order, the local authority or

Fisheries Board may carry out the order and bill him. There is no ceiling on the maximum damages that can be awarded in the High Court. The best defence a person sued under this section can have is that he is complying with a statutory licence under section 4 of the Local Government (Water Pollution) Act 1977 or a licence granted under section 171 of the Fisheries (Consolidation) Act 1959, or the Environmental Protection Agency Act 1992 or that the entry of the polluting matter is permitted under section 3(5) of the Water Pollution Act 1977. Farmers are unlikely to be able to use section 3(5).

High Court actions may be taken under section 11 of the 1977 Act, as amended, by any person to prohibit, remedy or prevent past, present or possible future entries or discharges or escapes of polluting matter to waters unless they are made under and in accordance with a statutory licence or unless they are regulated under certain statutes or statutory instruments. The order may be made, for example, against any person having *custody or control* of polluting matter or trade or sewage effluents. This action could be brought against persons who, through no fault of their own, obtain custody or control over polluting matter liable to cause water pollution, for example, farmers on whose lands waste has been dumped. Some farmers have allowed quarries to be used for waste disposal. It could also, for example, be used to order clean-ups of land contaminated by a previous owner if pollutants from the land were likely to escape into waters.

Air Pollution

Air pollution includes smell which could harm human health or interfere with amenities. A similar action to section 11 of the Local Government (Water Pollution) Act 1977 described above may be taken in the High Court under section 28 of the Air Pollution Act 1987 to prevent:

– The continuance of an unlicensed emission which could cause a serious risk of air pollution;

– the continuance of a licensed emission which is not in accordance with the licence;

Under section 28(A)(1) of the Air Pollution Act 1987 action may be taken by any person in *any* appropriate court for an order to:

(a) terminate an emission which contravenes the terms of the applicable licence, or which is unlicensed, or which is not in accordance with a emission limit value specified under section 51 or which does not comply with a Ministerial direction specifying the best practicable means under section 5(3),

(b) mitigate or remedy the effects of the emission concerned,

(c) pay the applicant or any other specified person costs incurred in investigating, mitigating and remedying the effects of the emission concerned.

Local authorities and in the cases of industries subject to integrated pollution control, the E.P.A., have wide powers to serve notices under sections 10(5) and 12 of the Water Pollution Act and section 26 of the Air Pollution Act 1987, to require measures which they specify to be taken for limiting or preventing pollution. They can carry out measures which they have specified themselves if the person served with the notice does not comply with it. They also have powers to take measures to prevent, remedy and clean up the effects of water or air pollution themselves or to assist others (for example environmental associations) to do this and to recover the costs from the person whose acts or omissions necessitated such steps. Again, liabilities under these sections are for damage to the environment and are far wider than traditional common law liabilities. Numerous notices have been served on farmers under section 12 of the Local Government (Water Pollution) Act 1977.

Actions for damages

Liability for environmental damage (for water and air pollution) was greatly expanded under section 20 of the Local Government (Water Pollution) Act 1977 and section 28(B)(1) of the Air Pollution Act 1987, as amended. These sections give *any* person who has suffered any injury, loss or damage to his person or property from water pollution or air pollution to recover damages from:

1. the *occupier* of the premises from which the effluent or pollution originated unless the pollution was caused by an act of God, or by the act or omission of a third party over whose conduct the occupier had no control (usually a trespasser) and which the occupier could not reasonably have foreseen or guarded against or

2. *any person* whose act or emission constitutes, in the opinion of the court, a contravention of any provision of the Water Pollution Acts 1977-1990 or the Air Pollution Act 1987, as appropriate.

These damages will not be awarded where the discharges or emissions were carried out under and in accordance with licences issued under section 4 of the Local Government (Water Pollution) Act 1977, or section 171 of the Fisheries (Consolidation) Act 1959 or section 32 of the Air Pollution Act 1987, or under Part IV of the Environmental Protection Agency Act 1992 or in other defined cases which are unlikely to be relevant to farming activities.

Avoiding Liability

The best way to avoid civil liability for water or air pollution (apart from not releasing pollutants in the first place) is to take all reasonable care to ensure that pollutants do not enter waters or to use the best practicable means to ensure that discharges of pollutants to the air (like smells) are prevented or minimised or, in certain cases, to discharge under and in accordance with a licence. Those who comply with their licences cannot be successfully sued under sections 3, 10, 11 or 20 of the Water Pollution Acts 1977–1990, or section 28 of the Air Pollution Act 1987.

Waste Disposal

This area of environmental law will soon be codified and reformed. Liability for improper waste disposal may exist at common law. Statute law to date is remarkably silent in this respect. Industrial waste disposal is usually regulated under planning legislation and under the European Communities (Waste) Regulations 1979, and the European Communities (Toxic and Dangerous Waste) Regulations 1982 and other regulations. But the more common organic agricultural wastes are exempted from these regulations. The European Communities (Use of Sewage Sludge in Agriculture) Regulations 1991 (S.I. No. 183 of 1991), require persons using sewage sludge to ensure that the quality of the soil or surface or groundwaters is not impaired.

The 1979 and 1982 Regulations oblige those disposing of waste to dispose of it in a manner which will not "endanger human health or harm the environment". But the only penalties specified for not complying with these obligations are prosecutions for minor criminal offences for which the maximum penalty is £600 (£1,000 for toxic and dangerous waste) and/or six months imprisonment. Whether or not a civil action for damages lies for failure to comply with the duty in the regulations has yet to be seen. A High Court action could be brought under section 27 of the Local Government (Planning and Development) Act 1976 for failure to comply with a planning condition regulating waste disposal but damages are not available under this section or any planning legislation. A little known provision in section 107 of the Public Health (Ireland) Act 1878 could, however, be extremely effective for ensuring the remediation of improper waste disposal. Section 107 states that "any accumulation or deposit which is a nuisance or injurious to health" shall be deemed to be a statutory nuisance. Local authorities are obliged under sections 108, 110, 111 of the Act to abate such nuisances by serving a notice requiring remedial works on the owner or occupier of the premises. If the person served with the notice fails to comply with it, the local authority may apply for a District Court order requiring remedial work. Note however that this remedy can only be used where a nuisance or a threat to public health exists. There are no mandatory soil contamination standards in Ireland.

Summary of Main Liabilities

Civil liability for improper waste disposal is a subject at present being discussed by the E.C. which is having grave difficulties in adopting a directive on the subject. Until legislation is adopted, the following is probably the general position in Ireland.

1. A producer of waste has a statutory duty under the European Communities (Waste) Regulations 1979, and the European Communities (Toxic and Dangerous Waste) Regulations 1982, to dispose of it in a manner which will not endanger human health or harm the environment. Whether damages lie for breach of this duty has yet to be determined.

2. A producer of any waste is obliged at common law to dispose of waste so as not to cause personal injuries or damage to property.

3. The statutory duty and the common law duty of care would probably be discharged by giving waste to a *competent* waste disposal contractor *authorised* under the 1979 and/or 1982 Regulations *and* the relevant E.C. Directives to dispose of it. However the waste producer should be satisfied that any authorised waste disposal contractor is genuinely capable of, and is in fact, disposing of waste in a proper manner and that the waste is given to him with the necessary information and in the necessary condition to enable him to do this. If he suspects that his waste is not being dealt with properly, he should normally refuse to deal with the contractor again or until any problems are rectified.

4. If improper waste disposal results in, or is liable to result in air or water pollution, action can be taken under the Air and Water Pollution Acts against the occupiers of land to prevent, remedy or mitigate the effects of the pollution. It could also be a breach of planning control. Several instances have occurred where farmers allowed contractors to dump waste in old quarries. This could be a breach of planning legislation making the farmer liable to £2 million fine and for restoring the land to its condition prior to the dumping.

Important provisions in the Waste Management Bill 1995 include the following:

– A prohibition on a person holding, recovering or disposing of waste "in a manner that causes or is likely to cause environmental pollution".

– A prohibition on the transfer of the control of waste to any person other than one permitted to deal with it.

– A duty to notify the local authority (and the E.P.A., if hazardous waste is involved) of any loss, spillage, accident or other development concerning waste which causes, or is likely to cause, environmental pollution. This duty already exists for incidents liable to cause air or water pollution.

– A requirement that permits be obtained from local authorities for waste collection and licences from the E.P.A. for waste disposal or recovery at facilities.

The definition of waste in the Bill would probably include almost all farm wastes. Some farm wastes would also be defined as hazardous wastes. The Bill does not oblige local authorities to provide facilities for the disposal of hazardous wastes. This is a very serious matter because the definition of hazardous wastes in the Bill is very wide indeed and it includes many wastes which many people consider harmless. It seems that the philosophy of the Bill is to leave hazardous waste disposal to the private sector.

The enforcement provisions relating to the obligations in the Waste Bill are similar to those in air and water pollution legislation, *i.e.* very strict with the possibility for enforcement in lower courts by any individual regardless of his/her interest in the matter. Power is also given to local authorities and/or the EPA to prevent environmental pollution from activities covered by the Bill. Local authorities and the E.P.A., where appropriate, will have powers to order any person *holding recovering or disposing* of waste to take prevention or mitigation measures.

Recently in *Cambridge Water Co. v. Eastern County Leather* [1994] 1 All E.R. 53 the House of Lords held that there is no liability in negligence or nuisance for damage caused by pollution unless the damage was reasonably foreseeable when the acts giving rise to it occurred. This decision was very much motivated by the realisation of the practical effects of deciding otherwise but it means that at common law, liability for pollution damage caused by past activities will not fall on a person if he could not have foreseen the damage at the time. Of course, liability for environmental damage caused by such pollution can lie with the current occupier of the land or any person who has contravened certain environmental legislation.

Directors and managers of companies can be liable as well as the company for all types of pollution. This means that both the company and directors and management in it can be sued or prosecuted.

Bibliography

Scannell, Y., *Environmental and Planning Law* (The Round Hall Press, 1995)
O'Sullivan and Shepherd, *Irish Planning Law and Practice* (Butterworths, Looseleaf)

Chapter 3

PLANNING LAW

T.C. Smyth (Jnr.), Barrister-at-Law

1. Introduction

Planning law is concerned with the way in which physical environments, be they urban or rural, are developed. The objective of planning law is to ensure that the environment is safe, efficient and aesthetically pleasing to present and future users. Inevitably, the law of planning must interfere with the understandable desire of landowners to do as they please with their own property. Constitutional objections have been raised against various provisions of the planning code but, to date, none of these challenges have succeeded; the basic interventionist principle of planning law has survived.

Planning law, which is almost exclusively statute based, works in two ways. The first is by *forward planning*. This is planning in the true sense of the word and involves the formulation, adoption and implementation of a development plan by a planning authority. *Planning control*, on the other hand, requires individuals who wish to develop their land to submit to a regulatory regime. Planning control is the means by which planning objectives are realised. The basic requirement of planning control is that persons seeking to develop land must seek planning permission before they commence such development unless some exemption can be claimed.

2. Development

Development of land can occur in two ways. First, the physical appearance of the land can be changed by "works". This type of development is known as operational development. The term "works" is defined by section 2 of the Local Government (Planning and Development) Act 1963 to include any act or operation of construction, excavation, demolition, extension, alteration, repair or renewal. The other type of development occurs where there is a change in the "use" of land (also known as functional development). "Use" is negatively defined in the legislation as not including such use as occurs when "works" are carried out on land. In other words, the two categories of development are separate and the language of one category should not be used to redescribe what is in fact an example of the other (see *Re Viscount Securities* (1978) 112 I.L.T.R. 17, *per* Finlay P.)

The statutory term "development" is defined in section 3(1) of the Local Government (Planning and Development) Act 1963 as "save where the context otherwise requires, the carrying out of any works on, in, or under land or the making of any material change in the use of any structures or other land".

The 1963 Act gives some assistance as to the meaning of the term "material change of use" by listing some common changes of use which are to be regarded as material. Thus the placing of vans, tents or other objects on land for the purpose of caravanning, camping or for the sale of goods is deemed be a material change of use. The storage of caravans or tents and the deposit of matter such as vehicle parts, old metal and builders' rubble is likewise deemed to be a material change of use; so also is the use as two or more dwellings of a structure which previously was used as one.

In cases where the 1963 Act is silent, it is necessary to go back to first principles. In assessing material change, one is concerned with whether the nature of the use has changed in planning terms by, say, putting greater demands on local amenities, or generating additional traffic burden, etc. Three situations commonly arise is practice.

1. The relevant planning unit of the use may have changed. The "planning unit" is the physical area in which the original use was carried on. If the original planning unit has become fragmented (*e.g.* a private residence has been made into flats) or substantially enlarged (which is often consistent with a change from private to commercial use), the probability is that there has been a material change of the use.

2. The planning nature of the original use may bear no real comparison with the use as it currently exists. The application of the theory is not always straightforward as the original use may have consisted of both a primary use and a secondary use. The primary use of a hotel, for example, would often involve several secondary uses. Secondary uses derive validity from the primary use and so are ignored in determining whether there' has been a material change of use. However, if the original primary use has manifestly been changed (*e.g.* hotel to shopping centre) or has been changed by virtue of intensification (as often happens when small farm quarries are used for intensive commercial extraction) the test for materiality will be satisfied.

3. Where there has been an intentional abandonment of the original use. When this happens, it is not possible at a later stage simply to revert to the original use because the law regards that use as having lapsed. In other words, the

purported resumption would be regarded as a material change of use. A common example is that of the local quarry. Developers often attempt to re-activate such quarries by arguing that periodic local extractions kept the original use alive despite spells of temporary inactivity; objectors will maintain the opposite pointing to derelict buildings and rusted equipment to show that there was an intention to abandon the use permanently. Another situation of abandonment is where a developer obtains a new planning permission, embarks upon its implementation and then finds that finances dry up; such a developer would not be able to revert to the original pre-permission use without a new planning permission.

3. Planning Authority

The planning authority is a statutory body. In effect, it is simply a hat worn by a local authority when exercising planning functions in its functional area. The planning authority for any given area is responsible for the day to day operation and policing of the planning code. The planning authority consists of a manager and elected members. The manager exercises *executive functions* while the elected members exercise *reserved functions*.

The most important of the planning powers, the power to grant planning permission, is executive in nature. This means that the elected members are somewhat disadvantaged when it comes to trying to affect the outcome of planning determinations. Section 4 of the City and County Management Act 1955 permits the elected members to resolve, by special majority vote, that the manager should exercise his statutory function in a certain way (notably, the power to grant planning permission). This provision is usually at the centre of a tug-of-war between the manager (supported by his team of technical advisers) and the elected members. The section 4 procedure has given rise to a wealth of caselaw but it seems clear that if the procedure is properly and validly exercised the manager has no choice but to perform his statutory functions as directed.

3.1 Powers

The planning authority has powers under non- planning legislation to compulsorily acquire land for planning purposes and further, under section 74 of the Local Government (Planning and Development) Act 1963, to appropriate land to planning purposes. It can also deal in such acquired or appropriated land in order to secure planning objectives that are perceived to be in the best interests of the proper planning and development of an area (section 75).

The planning authority is also vested with extensive powers to develop land. In this respect, section 77 of the Local Government (Planning and Development) Act 1963 outlines the areas of the planning authority's competence. There is a general exemption conferred on the local authorities from the requirement of having to obtain planning permission (section 4(1) of the 1963 Act) The usefulness of the exemption has been eroded by the provisions of Parts IX and X of the Local Government (Planning and Development) Regulations 1994 (S.I. No. 86 of 1994) which prescribe public consultation procedures if the proposed local authority development requires an environmental impact statement or if the development is of a prescribed type. Part IX only facilitates an exchange of views on environmental concerns whereas Part X, being in the nature of a planning process, allows the planning merits of the case to be commented upon. The two procedures are mutually exclusive.

4.   Development Plan

The guiding principle of planning law is encapsulated in the phrase "*the proper planning and development of the area*". Numerous statutory powers of the planning authority are circumscribed by this principle and, to a significant extent, the development plan defines what is meant by the term. See generally the Local Government (Planning and Development) Act 1963, sections 19 to 23.

4.1   Contents of the Plan

The development plan consists of a written statement and a plan indicating the development objectives for an area. The legislation lists a number of things that must be included in the plan. In the case of urban areas, the plan must include objectives for;

– the use of particular areas for particular purposes (in practice called "*zoning*");

– the convenience and safety of road users and pedestrians;

– the renewal of obsolete areas, and;

– the preservation, improvement and extension of amenities.

For rural areas, the plan must include objectives for the renewal of obsolete areas; the preservation, improvement and extension of amenities; and the development of water supply and sewerage services. Other objectives, including zoning for rural areas, are optional and can be found listed in Schedule 3 of the Local Government (Planning and Development) Act 1963.

4.2   Planning Authority Bound by Plan

The planning authority is under a duty to take such steps as may be necessary for securing the objectives which are contained in the provision of the development plan (section 22 of the 1963 Act). The statutory prominence of the development plan is further recognised in section 39 of the Local Government (Planning and Development) Act 1963 which states that a planning authority must not materially contravene the provisions of the plan. The usefulness of the rule is apparent where the planning authority is proposing to develop land without planning permission pursuant to its powers under section 4 of the 1963 Act. If the authority wishes to develop beyond the parameters of the plan it must make good its lack of authority by varying the plan in accordance with the procedures discussed below. Failure to do so means that the authority acts *ultra vires* thereby rendering itself open to judicial review.

The courts have been unsympathetic to the authority when issues of material contravention have arisen in the past. The plan has been likened to a social contract between the planning authority and the public which should not be varied by the unilateral and unaccountable actions of one of the parties (*Attorney General (McGarry) v. Sligo County Council* [1991] 1 I.R. 99, *per* McCarthy J.). In recent cases, the principle has arisen in the context of planning authorities purporting to provide halting sites for travellers.

4.3   Procedure for making a Plan

The making of the plan is a reserved function. A plan is newly devised or varied at least once every five years. The planning authority begins the process by making, and advertising the existence of a newly drafted or changed plan. The public are entitled to inspect the relevant draft and to make objections and representations thereon. The planning authority must consider those objections and representations. Accordingly, the relevant draft may or may not be amended. The plan will proceed to completion unless a proposed amendment is considered by the planning authority to be a material alteration of the original draft. If the latter view is taken, further advertisement and consultation is required before the plan can be completed.

5.   Planning Permission

A person wishing to develop land must first ascertain whether the intended course of action is *development* as defined by the 1963 Act (see above). The next step is to determine whether planning permission will be required for the development. The permission requirement, whilst normal, may not apply if it can be shown that the development is *exempted*, or that the development was *commenced before the appointed day* (October 1, 1964). In cases of doubt, a reference can be made to An Bord Pleanála (the Board) under section 5 of the 1963 Act to determine the planning status of the proposed development. Apart from the civil enforcement powers which the planning authority has in cases of *unauthorised development* (see below), it is a criminal offence to develop land without a required planning permission. See generally the Local Government (Planning and Development) Act 1963, sections 24 to 28.

5.1 Development not requiring Planning Permission:

5.1(i) Development commenced before the appointed day Pre-1964 development is a relatively straight-forward category; occasionally, disputes of fact arise as to whether the development was commenced prior to the appointed day or, in the case of a pre-1964 use, whether the use was continued (*i.e.* without abandonment) to the present day.

5.1(ii) Exempted Development Exempted development comprises a large category of development. Articles 8 to 13 and the Second Schedule of the Local Government (Planning and Development) Regulations 1994 deals extensively with the subject. Reference should also be made to section 4 of the Local Government (Planning and Development) Act 1963. In all cases, extreme care should be taken to ascertain the precise nature of the exemption and the qualifications which must be satisfied in respect of it; the consequences of proceeding with non-exempted development are often severe. A common mistake is to think that a "use" exemption also includes a "works" exemption and vice versa. This is only sometimes the case.

Section 4 of 1963 Act exempts local authorities from the requirement of planning permission. It also confers important private exemptions dealing with the use of land for agriculture or forestry, works for the maintenance, improvement or other alteration of any structure (not materially affecting the external appearance thereof), use of curtilage areas (where such use is incidental to the enjoyment of a dwellinghouse), use of land as a casual trading area, and works of land reclamation. Some section 4 exemptions will not be available in particular cases where the submission of an environmental impact statement is necessary.

Articles 8 to 13 of the Local Government (Planning and Development) Regulations 1994 provide instruction on how to interpret the exemptions conferred by the Second Schedule to the those Regulations. The Second Schedule is divided into four parts each of which contain a number of classes (the actual exemptions). The classes are often qualified or limited in some way. Part 1 deals with *general* exemptions (notably dwellinghouse developments and changes of use). Part II deals with *advertisement* exemptions, Part III with *rural* exemptions and Part IV with *classes of use*.

Parts I, II and III of the Second Schedule must be read in conjunction with article 10 of the 1994 Regulations. This provision specifies the circumstances in which exempted development status will be withheld despite the wording of the Second Schedule. Examples are where a condition in a planning permission would be breached, where a special objective of the development plan would be compromised, where public safety would be affected, where the exemption relates to an unauthorised structure, or where the development would require an environmental impact statement; generally, exempted status will be withheld where higher considerations are accorded a legal right of way. Part IV, relating to *changes of use*, is subject to the separate limitations contained in article 11. Part IV permits a change of use *within* classes specified in Part IV. For example, a concert hall would be allowed to move within its relevant use class (class 11) to become a cinema, or a bingo hall. The change must be possible without having to carry out works which require planning permission or which would be in breach of a condition of a planning permission. Part IV does not permit developers to *enter* any of the relevant classes; planning permission would be required for such entry subject to very limited exceptions which can be found in Part I (class 13).

5.2   Development requiring Planning Permission:

5.2(i) Relevant law   In cases where planning permission is necessary, extensive procedures come into play. These can be found in Parts IV to VII of the 1994 Regulations and in various decisions of the courts.

5.2(ii) Applicant   The applicant for planning permission must have the requisite degree of interest to make the application, that is, be the owner of the property or a person duly authorised by the owner (*Frescati Estates v. Walker* [1975] I.R. 177).

5.2(iii) Notice of Application   Notice requirements must be fulfilled by the applicant (articles 14 to 17 of the 1994 Regulations). Notice of intention to make a planning application must be advertised in a local newspaper two weeks prior to the application being submitted. A site notice must be erected and kept in place for at least one month after the application has been made. These notices must give sufficient detail to inform the public of the general nature and whereabouts of the proposed development. The planning authority has power to require the applicant to give further or better notice of his application as appropriate.

5.2(iv) Application   The application must give a number of relevant details and particulars, and be accompanied by plans, drawings and maps of a prescribed standard (see articles 18 and 23 of the 1994 Regulations). Every application requires the payment of a prescribed fee (Part VII of the 1994 Regulations). The application can be for a full or *outline planning permission*.

An outline permission allows a developer to ascertain whether a proposed development is acceptable in broad terms to the planning authority (articles 20 and 21 of the 1994 Regulations). If it is, details will be submitted later as part of an approval application (article 22). It is not possible to have the outline permission altered at the approval stage (*The State (Pine Valley) v. Dublin County Council* [1982] I.L.R.M. 169). In some instances (see below) an outline planning permission cannot be sought.

5.2(v) Public Participation The public is entitled to inspect the application documentation at the offices of the planning authority (article 36 of the 1994 Regulations) and submissions and observations on the application can be made by any member of the public (article 34). Such offerings should be of a planning nature; the planning authority will ignore everything else.

5.2(vi) Determination of Application After a prescribed period of time (two months unless extended), the planning authority must determine the application. Failure to give timely notice entitles the applicant to claim a planning permission by default (section 26(4) of the 1963 Act). The application is determined having due regard to the development plan and the proper planning and development of the area (section 26(1) of the 1963 Act). Three results are possible; a grant, a grant subject to conditions, or a refusal. A favourable decision cannot be implemented until after the appeal period (one month) has expired. If no appeal is lodged, the *decision to grant* permission (with or without conditions) becomes a *grant* of planning permission as a matter of course (section 26(9) of the 1963 Act).

5.2(vii) Appeals to An Bord Pleanála An appeal can be made to An Bord Pleanála against any decision of the planning authority by the applicant or any third party (section 26(5) of the 1963 Act). All appeals must be made within one month of the planning decision; late appeals are invalid (section 17 of Local Government (Planning and Development) Act 1992). Appeals must be in the prescribed form (see section 4 of the 1992 Act). Unless invited by the Board, the appellant has no right to elaborate upon his appeal as presented. Parties and non-parties to the appeal also have one right of submission and observation (sections 7 and 8 of the 1992 Act). Only in exceptional cases, to be determined by the Board upon receipt of a request, will an oral hearing of the appeal be held (section 12 of the 1992 Act).

The appeal may be a full appeal where the Board completely re-determines the original application (section 26(5)(b) of the 1963 Act) or, in cases where the planning authority decided to grant permission subject to conditions, be limited at the discretion of the Board to a review of such conditions as are appealed (section 15 of the 1992 Act). In the latter type of appeal the Board does not re-determine the original application; it merely directs the planning authority to alter or remove a condition from its decision if it considers that such condition was unwarranted.

The Board has four months from the date of receipt to determine the appeal but this period can be extended by notice (section 2 of the 1992 Act). Once the Board makes an appeal decision the planning process is complete. Disgruntled applicants or objectors cannot re-open the planning merits before the courts; the latter is restricted to considering legal matters that may have arisen during the planning process (*O'Keeffe v. An Bord Pleanála* [1993] 1 I.R. 39).

5.2(viii) Interpretation and Implementation of Planning Permission A

planning permission has been described by the courts as an "appendage to title", that is, it enures for the benefit of the land rather than of the person who sought it. Accordingly, the permission falls to be interpreted objectively. To this end, reference can be made not only to the grant itself but also to such documentation that is amenable to public scrutiny, *i.e.* the documents on the planning file. For the same reason, private understandings between developer and planning authority are generally excluded from any exercise of interpretation.

A point of some importance is that a planning permission does not of itself confer any entitlement on its holder to carry out the development (section 26(11) the 1963 Act). The holder may well find that an insufficiency of property rights or a failure to comply with other legal requirements will prevent use being made of the planning permission.

Once granted, an unimplemented permission has a shelf-life of five years (section 2 of Local Government (Planning and Development) Act 1982). The permission will lapse after the expiration of the five years. If substantial works have been carried out on foot of the permission and it is shown that the development will be completed within a reasonable period, the planning authority is required, upon an application being made to it, to extend the life of the permission (section 4 of the 1982 Act).

5.3 Matters Related to Planning Permissions

Thus far, only basic planning permission procedures have been described. It must be emphasised, however, that other factors can alter the process to a significant degree. Some of these factors are applications for permissions which would materially contravene the development plan, retention permissions, environmental impact statements, pollution licences, and building law.

5.3(i) Applications in Material Contravention of Development Plan The

planning authority cannot grant permission in respect of a planning application that materially contravenes the development plan unless and until a notice of such intent is advertised in a local newspaper. Resulting objections and representations must be considered by the authority. Even then, there must be a three quarters majority resolution by the members of the authority to grant the proposed permission (section 26(3) of the 1963 Act).

5.3(ii) Retention Permissions An application for a retention permission is sought to correct situations where a planning permission was required but not obtained or, if it was obtained, was not complied with (section 28 of the 1963 Act). The application can be made both in respect of unauthorised structures and unauthorised uses. Such applications closely follow the procedures for normal planning applications.

5.3(iii) Environmental Impact Statement The preparation and submission of an Environmental Impact Statement (E.I.S.) is a pre-condition to the grant of planning permission in certain cases. An E.I.S. is, as its name suggests, a statement of the likely effects which a proposed development will have on the environment. An E.I.S. is required to contain a number of prescribed matters (see article 25 of the the European Communities (Environmental Impact Assessment) Regulations 1989 (S.I. No. 349 of 1989)) and is usually required if the proposed development is of an environmentally sensitive nature (see articles 24 and 26 of the 1994 Planning Regualtions and the First Schedule to the 1989 Regulations, as above).

There is a prescribed list of potentially unclean developments (*e.g.* nuclear power stations, chemical plant, incinerators for hazardous wastes, etc) that will automatically oblige the developer to submit an E.I.S. with his planning application. In other cases, an E.I.S. will be required only if certain *thresholds* would be exceeded by the proposed development. An E.I.S. will also be required if, the thresholds not being exceeded, the development is one which will require an *integrated pollution control licence*. Threshold developments include certain types of pig or poultry-rearing installations, quarries, shipyards, food plants, abattoirs, racing tracks and skilifts.

Procedurally, the presence of an E.I.S. will affect the manner in which the planning process operates. For instance, it will not be possible to claim "exempted development" benefits in some instances (see above), outline planning permission will not normally be available, different notice requirements will apply and the planning authority, in deciding the application, must in addition to normal planning considerations, have regard to the E.I.S. and to any submissions received on foot thereof.

5.3(iv) Integrated Pollution Control Licences Such licences have more to do with environmental legislation than planning. I.P.C licences deal with such things as emissions into air and water and must be sought in respect of certain listed activities (usually of an environmentally unclean nature) under the Environmental Protection Agency Act 1992. In addition to the indirect relevance of I.P.C. licences to environmental impact statements, there are two further points of notable importance:

1. The developer is obliged, in his newspaper notice, to advertise the fact that an I.P.C. licence will be required for the proposed development.

2. The planning authority, in considering any E.I.S. that is submitted to them, must disregard any matter that touches upon issues of environmental pollution; only the Environmental Protection Agency is entitled to address such issues.

5.3(v) Building law   The importance of building law in the planning process was significantly reduced with the abolition of the Building Bye-Laws and the introduction of the Building Control Act 1990, together with the regulations made thereunder. Planning and building matters are now dealt with by separate and distinct bodies of law. The transitional provisions contained in section 22 of the Building Control Act 1990, should be consulted if building works were carried out between December 13, 1989, and June 1, 1992, as the Building Bye-Laws are still relevant in such cases.

The current regulatory regime applies to the design, construction, material alteration, servicing, fitting, and material change in the use of a building. Article 6 of the Building Regulations 1991 (S.I. 306 of 1991) lists the buildings that are exempt from the requirements, *e.g.* ancillary dwellinghouse developments and agricultural buildings. The requirements with which building projects must comply are different depending on what development is being proposed. A list of the possible requirements that may apply can be found in the First Schedule to the Building Regulations 1991; the list deals with such topics as structure, fire, site preparation, moisture resistance, materials and workmanship, sound, ventilation, etc.

The legislation requires that a *commencement* notice be sent to the relevant building control authority by a person who intends to carry out works or to make a material change in the use of a building (article 6 of the Building Control Regulations 1991). The purpose of the commencement notice is to put the building control authority on notice of the proposed development so that it can take appropriate steps to ensure compliance with the requirements of the legislation. It is an offence not to submit an commencement notice (section 16 of the Building Control Act 1990).

A further building law requirement is that a *fire safety certificate* must be sought before many (commercial) buildings can legally be built (articles 8 and 9 of the Building Control Regulations 1991). The certificate need not be sought for most types of dwellings and agricultural buildings. A fire safety certificate is an indication from the building control authority that the building will be fire safe if it is constructed as proposed. It is an offence not be obtain such a certificate (section 16 of the Building Control Act 1990).

The consequences of not complying with the requirements of building law can be very costly. An *enforcement notice* can be served on the owner or builder of the building up to five years after the completion of works or of the commencement of a new use. Such a notice can require that the building be altered to bring it into compliance with the requirements of the building regulations (section 8 of the Building Control Act 1990). Furthermore, the notice can sterilise the use of whole or part of the building until such time as the notice is complied with. The building control authority can itself enter the building to execute the notice; the expense of such a course of action would be passed on to the owner or builder.

6. Enforcement

Where individuals fall on the wrong side of the planning legislation, the planning authority has three enforcement devices at its disposal; prosecution, notice and court action.

6.1 Prosecution

Under section 24 of the Local Government (Planning and Development) Act 1963, the planning authority can prosecute a person for carrying out any development without a required planning permission. The offence is punishable on indictment by fine not exceeding £1,000,000 and/or two years imprisonment. A separate indictable offence will arise for every day that the original offence is continued after conviction; such offences carry a fine of £10,000 and/or two years imprisonment.

A District Court judge can dispose of both types of offence summarily in an appropriate case. Where there is to be a summary prosecution, a time limit of six months applies; the period can be extended where the prosecutor has no notice of the illegality. The penalties are £1,000 and/or six months imprisonment for the main offence and £200 and/or six months for subsequent offences.

6.2 Notices

6.2(i) Warning Notice (section 26 of the Local Government (Planning and Development) Act 1976) The planning authority may serve a warning notice under section 26 of the 1976 Act. A warning notice is usually a precursor to prosecution. The notice may be served where it appears that development has commenced or is likely to commence without a required planning permission. If the development in question relates to unauthorised use, the notice must be served within five years of the commencement of that use. The owner of the property is served with the notice but a copy may also be given to any other person concerned with the alleged illegality: both parties may be prosecuted if there is a intentional, assisted or permitted failure to comply with the directions given in the notice. The prosecution is dealt with as *per* a prosecution under section 24 of the Local Government (Planning and Development) Act 1963.

The warning notice can also be used to prevent the removal or damage of any natural or physical feature which a condition in a planning permission requires to be preserved. An owner who receives such a notice can defend any subsequent prosecution by alleging that he took reasonable steps to comply with the notice and at all times, acted in good faith.

6.2(ii) Enforcement Notice under section 31 of the Local Government (Planning and Development) Act 1963 This notice is appropriate where development has been carried out (past tense) without a required planning permission or, in breach of a condition of a planning permission. The planning authority is required to consider the proper planning and development of the area, the development plan and, if applicable, the relevant planning permission in deciding whether it is expedient to serve a notice.

The notice can be served on the owner and the occupier of the land within five years of the development being carried out or, where one is dealing with non-compliance with a condition, within five years of the latest date for compliance with that condition. Dates for compliance are rarely stated in the planning permission so it is permitted for the planning authority to give a special notice for this purpose. The special notice must be served within five years of the grant of planning permission. Therefore, if the planning authority serve the special notice towards the end of the five year period the developer may not know whether a section 31 enforcement notice will be served until a further five years expires.

The notice must identify the illegality complained of and specify a date after which the notice is to take legal effect. The notice can and often does require that restorative steps be taken, *e.g.* that a use be discontinued, that a structure be demolished or that works be undertaken. The planning authority has power to enter lands and carry out physical works itself. Naturally, the owner of the land will be obliged to pay the bill in such cases. If the notice requires that a use be discontinued or imposes a condition concerning works or uses and a person fails to comply with the notice in either of those respects, a summary offence is committed (£800 for first offence; £150 for every continuing offence after conviction to a ceiling of £800)).

6.2(iii) Enforcement Notice under section 32 of the Local Government (Planning and Development) Act 1963 Where planning permission was obtained for the retention of a structure (see above) and a condition thereof has not been complied with, the planning authority can serve a notice under section 32 of the 1963 Act on the owner and occupier of the relevant structure. The notice must be served within five years of the latest date for compliance with the condition. If no compliance date is specified in the permission, a special notice, similar to that described above in relation to the section 31 enforcement notice, can be served. The circumstances in which the planning authority can serve the notice, the contents of the notice, the powers of the authority once the notice has been served and the legal consequences of failing to comply with a notice, also follow the section 31 procedure.

6.2(iv) Enforcement Notice pursuant to section 35 of the Local Government (Planning and Development) Act 1963   Where development has been commenced and has or is not being carried out (present tense) in conformity with its relevant planning permission, the planning authority can serve a notice under section 35 of the 1963 Act on the person who commences the development or, on the person who has carried out or is carrying out such development. The notice can be served within five years of the end of the implementation period for the planning permission in question (usually five years). The procedure described above for section 31 of the 1963 Act applies equally to section 35.

6.3 Court Action

The statutory injunction, section 27 of the Local Government (Planning and Development) Act 1976, is a popular and powerful enforcement provision that can be invoked by planning authority and private litigant alike.

Section 27 of the 1976 Act applies where:

(a) development has been or is being carried out without planning permission; or

(b) development has not been or is not being carried out in conformity with a planning permission (whether by reason of breach of a condition contained in the permission or for any other reason).

As regards category (a), the action must be brought within five years of the unauthorised works becomming substantially complete or within five years of the unauthorised use being commenced. Category (b) actions must be commenced within five years of the expiration of the implementation period for the relevant permission (usually five years).

The action can be taken in either the Circuit Court or in the High Court against any person and is brought by motion. Interim and/or interlocutory orders can be sought. The relevant Circuit Court is determined by reference to the location of the subject land. The court will determine how the alleged illegality will be addressed in accordance with judicial discretion rather than in accordance with a statutory planning formula.

7. Compensation and Related Matters

In some instances, where the burden of planning law upon the individual is severe, provision is made for compensation. Alternatively, the individual can take matters into his own hands by requiring the planning authority to buy out his affected interest in the land.

7.1 Compensation

7.1(i) Entitlement to Claim   Where the value of any person's interest in land is reduced by a refusal of planning permission or by a grant of permission subject to conditions, compensation may be claimed, provided the claim is not restricted or excluded by the legislation (section 11 of the Local Government (Planning and Development) Act 1990). The claim must be made to the planning authority within six months of the notification of the relevant planning decision (whether originating from the planning authority or from An Bord Pleanála).

The measure of compensation to be paid by the planning authority is such agreed amount as represents the reduction in value of the claimant's interest in the land or, in the absence of agreement, such amount as may be determined in accordance with the First Schedule of the Local Government (Planning and Development) Act 1990. In addition, the occupier of the land is entitled to be compensated for the damage (if any) to his trade, business or profession which he carries out on the land.

7.1(ii) Restrictions on the Claim (section 12 of the Local Government (Planning and Development) Act 1993)   The right to compensation is capable of significant restriction under the legislation. If the planning authority choose to invoke any one or more of these restrictions the courts require that this should be done in clear and unambiguous language. Parroting the exact wording of the prescribed restrictions is not essential but is perhaps the best way of avoiding ambiguity (*X.J.S. Investments Ltd. v. Dun Laoghaire Corporation* [1986] I.R. 750; *Eighty-Five Developments Ltd. v. Dublin County Council (No. 2)* [1993] 2 I.R. 392). In determining a planning application the planning authority must consider the proper planning and development of the area so any deliberate attempt to defeat a compensation claim for the purpose, say, of saving money would be reviewable by the courts.

There are five types of restriction (section 12 of the Local Government (Planning and Development) Act 1990):

1. Where permission is *refused* because of the proposed nature of the development (see Second Schedule to 1990 Act). Developments which propose a material change of use, the demolition of a habitable house, or the erection of an advertisement structure are instances of where a refusal of planning permission cannot be compensated.

2. Where permission is *refused* for a particular type of reason (Third Schedule to the 1990 Act). Prescribed reasons include cases where the local water, sewerage or road facilities are deficient; where public safety would be endangered by reason of traffic hazard; where the proposed development would case serious pollution or; where a proposed structure would injure local amenities or property values. In such cases, compensation will not be

payable in respect of the refusal of permission.

3. Where planning permission is *granted subject to a prescribed condition* (see Fourth Schedule to 1990 Act) *e.g..* conditions which require the payment of financial contributions for facilitative works to be undertaken by the local authority; conditions reserving or restricting the types of structures that can or cannot be put on specified land; conditions relating to layout of the proposed development and; conditions requiring the preservation of special features. Compensation is excluded in respect of *such conditions* but this does not mean that other conditions contained in the permission could not be used to substantiate a claim for compensation).

4. The fourth category relates to applications under section 28 of the 1990 Act for the retention of unauthorised works and uses. In such cases, whether permission is refused or granted subject to conditions, compensation is not payable.

5. No compensation can be claimed if the planning authority is to acquire the land pursuant to a purchase notice under section 29 of the 1990 Act (see below).

7.1(iii) Blocking the Claim The planning authority can, within three months of the claim being received, prevent the claim from proceeding for a period of five years (or completely) by serving a special notice. The notice will state that in the opinion of the planning authority, the land is still capable of other development in respect of which permission ought to be granted, notwithstanding the previous refusal or grant subject to conditions. "Other" development means development of a residential, commercial or industrial character which involves the construction of one or more named structure types, *e.g.* shops, flats. etc. (see section 13 of the 1990 Act).

The compensation claim will die altogether if no application for "other" development is made during the life of the special notice or if planning permission is in fact obtained for "other" development.

7.1(iv) Minister's Power in respect of the Claim (section 14 of the Local Government (Planning and Development) Act 1990) The Minister for the Environment can, in certain cases where the Board has made a planning decision on appeal, lift the substantive and procedural restrictions placed on a claimant's claim by sections 12 and 13 of the 1990 Act.

7.2 Purchase Notices

In cases where planning permission has, on appeal been refused or granted subject to conditions, an owner of land may serve a *purchase notice* on the planning authority under section 29 of the Local Government (Planning and

Development) Act 1963.

The purchase notice is served where the owner alleges that the land is incapable of reasonably beneficial use in its existing state and that it cannot be rendered capable of such use by the implementation of an existing planning permission (previously obtained). In a case where a permission has been granted subject to conditions, the owner must further allege that the land cannot be rendered capable of reasonably beneficial use by the implementation of that permission.

The purchase notice must be served within six months of the Board's decision refusing permission or granting permission subject to conditions. The effect of the purchase notice, if accepted, is that the owner's interest in the affected land is purchased by the planning authority.

Once served, the planning authority has three months within which to consider the purchase notice. The authority must then serve a notice indicating whether it will comply with the purchase notice or not. If it is willing to comply, the planning authority is under a duty to acquire the interest of the owner and to this end, its notice of reply is regarded as having the same effect as a compulsory purchase order (see below). If it is not so willing, reasons must be given. An Bord Pleanála will be sent a copy of the purchase notice in such a case and may upon being satisfied that the notice is a proper one, confirm the notice and require the planning authority to acquire the owner's interest. Alternatively, the Board may, in order to render the land capable of reasonably beneficial use, choose to grant the permission that was refused, alter the one that was granted or, direct that a new permission be granted in the event of an appropriate planning application being made. The purchase notice will be confirmed by default if the Board does not make a decision within a specified period of time.

7.3   Related Matters

7.3(i) Compulsory Purchase of Land   The planning authority has indirect powers to compulsorily acquire land pursuant to provisions of the Local Government (Ireland) Act 1898, and of the Local Government (No. 2) Act 1960. The compulsory acquisition of land is a separate body of law and is mentioned for the sake of completeness.

7.3(ii) Notices not related to the Enforcement of Planning Control   The planning authority may *revoke or modify an unimplemented planning permission* by serving notice on the owner and occupier of the land and upon any other person who might also be affected (section 30 of the Local Government (Planning and Development) Act 1963). The power must be exercised having due regard to the proper planning and development of the area and to the development plan. A prerequisite to the exercise of the power is that there be a change in the planning circumstances of the case to warrant revocation or modification of the permission. An appeal lies to An Bord Pleanála against the notice of the planning authority. The compensation and purchase notice provisions discussed above apply in modified form to a revocation or modification of a planning permission.

The planning authority may serve a notice on the owner and occupier of land or on any other affected person requiring that *any structure be removed or altered* (section 36 of the 1963 Act). The power must be exercised having due regard to the proper planning and development of the area and to the development plan. The planning authority has power to enter land and take such steps as are specified in the notice. An appeal may be taken against the notice to the Board. The compensation and purchase notice provisions apply in modified form.

Under section 37 of the 1963 Act the planning authority can require that *any use be discontinued or continued only subject to certain conditions*. The notice is served on the owner and occupier of the land and upon any other affected person. Regard must be had to the proper planning and development of the area and to the development plan in exercising the power. An appeal may be taken against the notice to the Board. The compensation and purchase notice provisions apply in modified form.

8. Rights of Action

There are four main causes of action which an individual can pursue if he or she has a planning grievance; judicial review, reference on point of law, section 27 injunction and private action.

8.1 Judicial Review

This action can be taken against a public body (*e.g.* the planning authority or the Board) to quash or compel a certain decision or course of action (see Order 84 of the Rules of the Superior Courts 1986 (S.I. No. 15 of 1986)). Where the action challenges a planning decision or any appeal or reference made under the planning legislation, the action must be brought within two months of the making of the relevant decision (section 82 of the Local Government (Planning and Development) Act 1963). The time limit is strict and as yet, no exceptions exist. If the impugned decision is that of the planning authority, litigants should not wait for the Board to determine any appeal before commencing court proceedings; the two-month period will almost certainly have expired before such appeal is finally determined.

In dealing with planning matters, the courts only have power to deal with legal anomalies that may have arisen during the planning process, *e.g.* where the applicant never had the requisite interest to make the application or, where the Board had regard to matters which were not properly before it. The courts will not re-open or re-determine the planning merits of the case save where this is indirectly necessary in the exercise of its judicial review of the matter. The applicant will only be entitled to apply for relief if he or she can show that substantial grounds exist to justify the contention that the decision is invalid or that it ought to be quashed. The three most common substantial grounds are *ultra vires*, breach of natural or constitutional justice, and actionable unreasonableness.

8.2 Reference on Point of Law

This is a relatively obscure remedy which arises out of the procedure which enables an individual to make a reference to the Board to have the development status of a proposed project determined. The Board can refer a question of law for the determination of the High Court (section 5(2) of the 1963 Act).

8.3 Section 27 Injunction

The section 27 injunction has already been discussed in the context of enforcement. The remedy is also available to private litigants and is the most effective way of dealing with a difficult neighbour or developer. Often, a group of local residents will band together to share the cost of such an action.

8.4 Private Action

There are a plethora of other common law remedies available to litigants which may be of assistance in dealing with the indirect effects of a planning matter. Perhaps the best example is the common law action of nuisance which can be taken against a developer who has caused damage whilst carrying out development, *e.g.* by cracking, subsidence, etc.

CHAPTER 4

PLANNING LAW AND AGRICULTURE

T.C. Smyth (Jnr.) Barrister-at-Law

1. Introduction

In one sense there is nothing unusual about the operation of planning law in the context of farming. Indeed, the general principles relating to such matters as development plans, applications for planning permission, enforcement and compensation, apply as described in the previous chapter. The one area of major concern is the topic of development and, in particular, what types of development require planning permission and what types do not. The provisions of the European Communities (Environmental Impact Assessment) Regulations 1989 (S.I. No. 349 of 1989) are also of importance in that they require the submission, with a planning application, of an environmental impact statement for certain developments of a farming nature.

2. Definition of Farming

Farming is the business or skill of "agriculture", a term which is defined in section 2(1) of the Local Government (Planning and Development) Act 1963 to include:

> "horticulture, fruit growing, seed growing, dairy farming, the breeding and keeping of livestock [but not bloodstock] . . . the use of land as grazing land, meadow land, osier land, market gardens and nursery grounds, the use of land for turbary, and the use of land for woodlands where that use is ancillary to the farming of land for other agricultural purposes".

A reference to An Bord Pleanála in 1994 concluded that the keeping of fish for the production of food comes within the meaning of "agriculture". The term "agricultural" is to be given a like interpretation as the term "agriculture".

3. Development Plans

A development plan for a rural area is not required to zone particular areas for particular purposes. Such a plan need only indicate objectives for the development and renewal of obsolete areas; the preservation, improvement and exension of amenities; and for the provision of new water supplies and sewerage services and the extension of such existing supplies and services (section 19 of Local Government (Planning and Development) Act 1963). The plan, therefore, will be relatively uninformative as to what is meant by the term "the proper planning and development of the area" in any given case. This makes the prediction of planning authority views more difficult where rural areas are involved.

4. Planning Permission

Generally, development associated with farming does not require planning permission, that is, such development is exempted development under the planning legislation. Where the benefits of exempted development do not apply or where such benefits are withheld for one of several prescribed reasons, farmers are no different from other developers of land; they must expend time and money applying for and obtaining planning permission (see chapter 3). The consequences of developing land without a requisite planning permission are serious.

4.1 Exempted Development

Most exemptions, whether conferred by section. 4 of Local Government (Planning and Development) Act 1963 or by the provisions of the Local Government (Planning and Development) Regulations 1994 (S.I. No. 86 of 1994), will be withheld in certain circumstances. It will be remembered that the exemptions contained in the Regulations are arranged into four parts under the headings "General", "Advertisements", "Rural", and "Classes of Use". They are subject to the restrictions contained in article 10 (Parts I, II, and III only) and article 11 (Part IV only).

Two mistakes are commonly made with exemptions. First, exemptions cannot be used to build upon a planning permission. The planning permission must be implemented as granted without pre-empting the exemptions. Secondly, exemptions are usually specific to either "works" or "use" development and only sometimes both.

5.   Specific Exemptions

In this part, specific exemptions as they apply to the different parts of the farm will be discussed.

5.1   The Farmhouse

The farmhouse is both a structure and a dwellinghouse and as such qualifies for two important exemptions under section 4(1) of Local Government (Planning and Development) Act 1963.

5.1(i) Section 4 Exemptions *Works for the maintenance, improvement or other alteration of the farmhouse structure* may be carried out without planning permission (section 4(1)(g) of the 1963 Act). Such works, so far as they affect the exterior of the building, must not be inconsistent with the character of the structure or of neighbouring structures. The interior features of the structure can be freely altered save where a feature is listed for preservation in the development plan because of its artistic, historic or architectural interest (section 4(1A) of the 1963 Act). This exemption only covers such things as replacement of doors, painting, plastering, roof repairs, etc. Additions and extensions to the farmhouse are covered by different exemptions.

Any structure or land situated within the curtilage of a dwellinghouse can be used for the incidental enjoyment of the dwellinghouse (section 4(1)(h) of the 1963 Act). This exemption would cover such things as parking areas and the use of a structure as a garage or as a garden shed (but not as a storage area for wholesale goods). In the case of farms, it is sometimes difficult to identify the curtilage of the dwellinghouse, so common sense should be allowed to prevail. This exemption is an important partner to the various "works" exemptions discussed below.

5.1(ii) Planning Regulation Exemptions Part I of the Second Schedule to the Regulations lists a number of "works" and "use" exemptions that can be carried out within, or within the curtilage of, a dwelling. A number of miscellaneous exemptions, not specifically referrable to dwellings, are also mentioned. In the present context, the relevant grounds upon which Part I exemptions will be withheld under article 10 of the Planning Regulations of 1994 are:

– if a condition in a planning permission would be breached;

– if a view or prospect of special amenity value that is protected by the development plan would be interfered with;

- if the works or use relate to an unauthorised structure or the unauthorised use of a structure;

- if a listed building or other structure would be affected by the works or use; or

- if the works or use would obstruct a public right of way (*e.g.* a mass path).

The exemptions are as follows:

Extension   A rear extension of the dwelling or the conversion (for use as part of the dwelling) of a garage, store, shed or other structure attached to the rear or to the side of the dwelling. (Works exemption, P1/Class 1 – dimension limitations apply.)

Central Heating   Provision of a chimney, boiler house or oil tank for the central heating system of the dwelling. (Works exemption, P1/Class 2 – dimensions of oil tank restricted.)

Curtilage structure   Provision within the curtilage of the dwelling of a greenhouse, garage, store, shed or other similar structure. (Works exemption, P1/Class 3 – location, dimension, and finish limitations apply; also, no such structure may be used for human habitation or for the keeping of hens, horses, pigs, pigeons or ponies.)

TV Aerials   Erection of television antenna (Works exemption, P1/Class 4 – limitations apply; in particular, antenna must not be placed on front wall or front roof-slope of the dwelling.)

Walls/Fences/Gates   Provision within or bounding, the curtilage of the dwelling of a gate, gateway, railing or wooden fence or wall. (Works exemption, P1/Class 5 – dimension and finish conditions apply.)

Landscaping and Hard-surfacing   Carrying out landscaping works within the curtilage of the dwelling or laying of hard surfaces for the incidental enjoyment of the dwelling. (Works exemption, P1/Class 6 – the level of ground must not be raised or lowered by more than 1 metre.)

Porches   Provision of a porch outside any external door of the dwelling. (Works exemption, P1/Class 7 – location and dimension restrictions apply.)

Exterior painting   The painting of the external part of any building or structure. (Works exemption, P1/Class 11 – restriction placed on the creation of murals: this exemption should be read in conjunction with section 4(1)(g) of the 1963 Act as it is likely that exterior painting comes within the term "other alteration".)

Change to use as single dwelling   Change of use as two or more dwellings to use as a single dwelling where the structure was previously used as one dwelling. (Use exemption, P1/Class 13(e) – no restrictions.)

Change to use as caring residence   Change of use from use as dwelling to use as a residence for disabled persons. (Use exemption, P1/Class 13(f) – restriction on number of residents.)

Caravans and boats   Keeping a caravan or boat within the curtilage of the dwelling. (Use exemption, P1/Class 18 – conditions relating to duration and number apply.)

Domestic well   The sinking of a well or other works necessary for the provision of a domestic water supply. (Works exemption, P1/Class 40 – no restriction and works not required to be carried out within the curtilage of the dwelling.)

Service connections   The connection of services to any premises including the breaking open of any street of other land for such purpose. (Works exemption, P1/Class 43 – no restrictions but note, planning entitlements cannot affect the private land interests of third parties.) and

Demolition of structures   The demolition of any structure other than a habitable house (excepting such part of a habitable house as is demolished in connection with the provision of an extension or porch) or of a building which abuts on another building in separate ownership. (Works exemption, P1/Class 45 – no limitations.)

The installation of a septic tank is a notable absentee from the above list. The relevance of building law should not be overlooked when exempted development is proposed but, equally, it may be noted that article 6 of the Building Regulations 1991 (S.I. No. 306 of 1991) does exempt many structural curtilage developments from the requirements of the Building Control Act 1990.

5.2   The Farmyard and Farmland

5.2(i)   Section 4   *Exemptions* The exemption for the *maintenance, improvement or other alteration of a structure* (section 4(1)(g) of the 1963 Act, as discussed above) applies equally to any structure situated in the farmyard; it is unlikely that the "inconsistent appearance" restriction would ever be an issue in such cases.

As regards the farmland, there are two important exemptions contained in section 4(1) of the Local Government (Planning and Development) Act 1963. The first such exemption is that which permits development consisting of *the use of any land or buildings for the purposes of agriculture or forestry* (section 4(1)(a) of the 1963 Act). "Works" (as distinct from "use") are not covered by this particular exemption. The definition of "agriculture" and "agricultural" should be referred to when applying this exemption.

The introduction of new environmental legislation has seen a clawback in the extent to which the exemption under section 4(1)(a) can be claimed. The exemption will not apply in respect of three types of agricultural and forestry land use which now require the submission of a planning application and an environmental impact statement (see article 13 of the Local Government (Planning and Development) Regulations 1994). These developments are:

1. use of uncultivated land or semi-natural areas for intensive agricultural purposes (over 100 hectares);

2. initial afforestation (over 200 hectares), or the replacement of broad leaf high forest by conifer species (over 10 hectares); and

3. peat extraction which would involve a new or extended area of 50 hectares or more.

Land reclamation works, other than the fencing of land used by the public within the preceding 10 years, are also exempt from the requirement of planning permission (section 4(1)(j) of the 1963 Act). The works envisaged by this exemption are those referred to at section 1 of the Land Reclamation Act 1949, namely: field drainage, land reclamation, the construction and improvement of watercourses, the removal of unnecessary fences, the construction of new fences and the improvement of existing ones, the improvement of hill grazing, the reclamation of estuarine marsh land and of callows, and any operations ancillary to the foregoing. The case of *Tralee Urban District Council v. Stack* (unreported, High Court, Barrington J., January 13, 1984) suggests that section 4(1)(i) can only be claimed by the Minister for Agriculture pursuant to his powers under the 1949 Act. The point is now of little relevance as a private developer can claim an almost identical exemption under the Planning Regulations of 1994 (see Class 9, Part III of the Third Schedule).

5.2(ii) Planning Regulation Exemptions   Parts I, II and III of the Second Schedule to the 1994 Regulations offer a number of exemptions to the farmer who wishes to develop the farmyard and surrounding land. These exemptions are subject to the same restrictions as apply in the case of farmhouses but there are other restrictions which are appropriate to mention in the particular context of farmyards and farmland. Thus the relevant exemptions will also be withheld if the proposed works or use would:

– involve the provision or widening of a means of access to a public road whose width exceeds 4 metres;

– endanger public safety by reason of traffic hazard or obstruction of road users;

– involve the carrying out of non-service related works under a public road;

– affect listed features of archaeological, geological or historical interest perserved in the development plan; or

– involve the enclosure of land habitually used by the public during the preceding 10 years for recreational purposes or as a means of access to a place of natural beauty or recreational utility.

The main "rural" exemptions of Part III, in paraphrased form, are:

Camping   Temporary use of land for placing or tents, caravans or the mooring of vessels for the purpose of camping. (Use exemption, PIII/C1; location and time restrictions apply.)

Drainage   Works relating to the construction or maintenance of certain drainage devices, the improvement and cleaning of watercourses and the making or repairing of embankments in connection with any such development: (Works exemption, PIII/C3, no limitations.)

Walls/Fences   The construction or erection of any wall or fence. (Works exemption, PIII/C4, dimension limitations apply; see also P1/C10.)

Structures to house animals   The provision of a roofed structure for the housing of farm animals not exceeding 300 square metres (whether new or by extension) and any ancillary provison for effluent storage. (Works exemption, PIII/C6, use, location and dimension and quality of structures regulated.)

Other structures associated with the keeping of animals   The provision of roofless cubicles, open loose yards, self-feed silo or silage areas, feeding aprons, assembly yards, milking parlours, sheep dipping units, effluent storage facililies or structures for the making or storage of silage, or any other structure of a similar character or description, having an aggregate floor area not exceeding 300 square metres, and any ancillary provision for effluent storage. (Works exemption, PIII/C7, regulated use, location, dimensions and quality of structures.)

Other farming structures   Works consisting of the provision of any store, barn, shed, glass-house or other structure (not being of a type specified in the two previous exemptions) and having a floor area not exceeding 300 square metres. (Works exemption, PIII/C8; restricted to agricultural and foresty use (excluding the housing of animals or the storing of effluent) with limitations on location and dimensions.)

Land reclamation   Land reclamation works on agricultural or forestry land. (Works exemption, PIII/C9, see section 4(1)(j) of the 1963 Act above.)

Housing horses   The provision of a roofed structure for the housing of horses or ponies, other than horses kept for use in the farming of land, having a floor area not exceeding 100 square metres (whether new or by extension)

and any ancillary provision for effluent storage. (Works exemption, PIII/C10; use, location, quality and dimension rules apply.)

Housing greyhounds   The provision of a roofed structure for housing greyhounds, having floor area not exceeding 50 square metres (whether new or by extension) and any ancillary provision for effluent storage. (Works exemption, PIII/C11; use, location, dimension and quality rules apply.)

Hard-surfaces (for purposes of keeping horses and greyhounds only) The provision of a roofless hard-surfaced yard, or of a roofless hard-surfaced enclosed area, having an area not exceeding 100 square metres (whether new or by extension) and any ancillary provision for effluent storage. (Works exemption, PIII/C12; use, location, dimension and quality restrictions apply.)

Exemptions of a more general nature can be found in various parts of Parts I and II of the Second Schedule to the Regulations and these, again in paraphrase, are:

Gates   The provision or repair of any gate or gateway. (Works exemption, P1/C8, height restriction.)

Walls/Fences   The provision or repair of any fence or wall. (Works exemption, P1/C10, restrictions on dimensions and finish.)

Exterior painting   The painting of the external part of any building or structure. (Works exemption, P1/C11, restriction placed on the creation of murals.)

Private routes   The repair or improvement of any private street, road or way and the construction of any private footpath or paving. (Works exemption, P1/C12, restrictions on dimensions of footpath or paving.)

Sports field   The laying out and use of land for athletics or certain sports where no charge is made for public admission to the land. (Works and use exemption, P1/C31.)

Local events   Use of land for any local event of a religious, cultural, educational, political, social, recreational or sporting character including the placing of temporary moveable structures (eg, tents and vans) or objects in connection therewith. (Use exemption, P1/C33, duration and reinstatement conditions apply; advertisements may be erected to publicise such an event (see below).)

Domestic wells   The sinking of a well or other works necessary for the provision of a domestic water supply. (Works exemption, P1/C40, no restrictions.)

Exploratory excavation   Drilling or excavating for the purpose of surveying land or examining the depth and nature of the subsoil. (Works exemption, P1/C41, mineral prospecting excluded.)

Demolition of structures The demolition of a building or other structure. (Works exemption, P1/C44, restrictions apply.)

Advertisements

- Any advertisement relating to the sale of goods or livestock on land where such land is not normally used for such a purpose. (Works and use exemption, PII/C10, restrictions apply.)

- Any advertisement for the purpose of identification, direction, or warning with repsect to land or structures on which they are exhibited. (Works and use exemption, PII/C13, no limitations.)

- Any advertisement erected to publicise a local event. (Works and use exemption, PII/C16, restrictions apply);

- Any advertisment relating to the demonstration of agricultural methods or processes on the land on which the advertisement is exhibited (Works and use exemption, PII/C18, restrictions apply).

As indicated above, building law requirements should not be overlooked when structural development is proposed. Many agricultural structures are, however, exempt from those requirements by virtue of article 6 of the Building Regulations 1991.

6. Established Uses and Structures

Development not coming within the exempted development provisions of the Local Government (Planning and Development) Act 1963 or the Local Government (Planning and Development) Regulations 1994 may not necessarily require planning permission. If the development consists of a use which was commenced prior to the appointed day (October 1, 1964) and never permanently abandoned, a present day exercise of such use does not require a planning permission (section 24 of the 1963 Act). Equally, an unauthorised structure which existed immediately before the appointed day does not require a planning permission or, more accurately, a permission for its retention (section 24 of the 1963 Act). The former amnesty is of particular relevance in the context of rural quarries which serve local demands on an ad hoc basis. So long as periodic extractions continue, the extracted product does not change, and the level of extraction does not intensify, planning permission will not be required.

7.   Environmental Impact Statements

The preparation of a planning application is a relatively straightforward obstacle to overcome in cases where non-exempted development is intended. Occasionally, and more commonly in recent years, an environmental impact statement (E.I.S.) will have to be prepared and submitted with the planning application. It will be recalled from chapter 3 above, the instances in which an E.I.S. will be required. Amongt these is the "threshold" category where an E.I.S. will be required if the prescribed thresholds would be exceeded. There are also the cases where, even though the thresholds would not be exceeded, an E.I.S. would be required either because an integrated pollution licence is required for an activity which is listed under the Environmental Protection Agency Act 1992, or, because the planning authority, in its discretion, considers that an E.I.S. is necessary having regard to the likely impacts of the proposed development on the environment (see articles 24 and 26 of the Local Government (Planning and Development) Regulations 1994.

"Agriculture" constitutes a separate list of "threshold" cases under Part II of the First Schedule to the European Communities (Environmental Impact Statement) Regulations 1989 (S.I. No. 349 of 1989). An exact knowledge of the list is not required in the present context so, in broad terms, the list is:

- use of uncultivated land or semi-natural areas for intensive agricultural purposes (over 100 hectares);

- water-management projects for agriculture (limited by reference to catchment area or wetlands affected);

- initial afforestation (limited by reference to hectares to be affected);

- land reclamation for the purpose of conversion to another type of land use (hectare threshold prescribed);

- poultry-rearing installations (limited by reference to number of fowls);

- pig-rearing installations (limited by reference to number of swine);

- salmonid-breeding installations (various thresholds apply according to type of installation being proposed);

- reclamation of land from the sea (hectare threshold applies.)

Two further type of "threshold" development that are relevant to farmers is where peat extraction is being proposed for an area of more than 50 hectares and where there is a proposed extraction of stone, gravel, sand or clay where the area involved would exceed 5 hectares (see the European Communities (Environmental Impact Assessment) Regulations 1989, First Schedule, Part II, "Extractive Industry").

The circumstances in which an integrated pollution licence will be required are beyond the scope of this chapter. However, by way of general information, such licences are generally required in order to ensure that significant pollution is not caused to the environment. To this end emissions from a listed activity must comply with specified air and water quality standards, relevant standards under other enactmens, and noise regulations. Of the listed activities that directly concern agricultural matters, only pig and poultry installations and the extraction of peat (in the course of business) are mentioned (see First Schedule to the Environmental Protection Agency Act 1992 under the headings "Minerals and Other Materials" and "Intensive Agriculture").

If an E.I.S. is required because a threshold is exceeded or because an I.P.C. licence is necessary, all the exemptions conferred by Parts I, II, and III of the Planning Regulations of 1994 will be withdrawn (see article 10(1)(c) of the Local Government (Planning and Development) Regulations 1994).

8. Agricultural Wastes

An issue of increasing importance to farmers is the disposal of agricultural wastes and effluents. The matter is esssentially one of environmental law. Proposed works that involve the storage of agricultural effluents are exempted in conjunction with the various farm development exemptions to be found at Part III of the Second Schedule to the 1994 Planning Regulations (see above). It is normally a condition of the exemption that effluent storage works be of such a standard as to be adequate to serve the proposed development and to avoid water pollution.

Under the Water Pollution Acts 1977 and 1990 (Local Government (Water Pollution) Act 1977 and Local Government (Water Pollution) (Amendment) Act 1990), it is an offence to cause or to permit any polluting matter to enter waters (section 3). The definitions contained in the legislation are wide and would include cases where agricultural effluents (*e.g.* slurry or fertilizer) are permitted to seep or run-off into streams, marsh areas, aquifers, etc. The civil enforcement procedures are weighted in favour of making the polluter pay and there is a statutory action for damages available to persons whose person or property is affected by the pollution (section 20 of the 1990 Act). Whilst the water pollution legislation has further relevance to agriculture in particular instances, perhaps the most notable provision is section 21 which permits a local authority to make bye-laws for the regulation or prohibition in its functional area of listed agricultural activities.

The Air Pollution Act 1987, is widely enough defined to provide remedies against agricultural odours which impair or interfere with amenities or with the environment (see sections 24 and 28A).

The licensing regime introduced by the Environmental Protection Agency

Act 1992, has already been mentioned in the context of E.I.S. requirments. The 1992 Act will gradually replace the separate licensing regimes that currently exist under other issue-specific enactments such as the Water Pollution Acts 1977 and 1990.

9.   Other Uses for Agricultural Land

The use of rural land for purposes of agricultural is the main but not the only use to which such land can be put. More and more such land is being used for public enjoyment, new roads and services, and halting sites.

9.1   Public Enjoyment

The planning authority has a variety of powers at its disposal to preserve or promote public interests in the countryside.

9.1(i) Special Amenity Orders   Under section 42 of Local Government (Planning and Development) Act 1963, the planning authority can declare an area to be of special amenity by reason of its outstanding natural beauty, its special recreational value or becuase there is a need for nature conservation. Such an order may identify the objectives of the planning authority in relation to the preservation or enhancement of the character or special features of the area including objectives for the prevention or limitation of development in the area. The proposed order must be offered for public comment before it is finally confirmed by the Minister.

The effects of such an order may not be apparent to a landowner until he or she proposes to develop land. A special amenity order will seriously lessen the categories of exempted development that are available under Parts I, II and III of the Regulations (see article 10(1)(b) of the 1994 Planning Regulations). Any planning permission that is sought will be considered having due regard, not only to the proper planning and development of the area but also, to such an amenity order. Further, if the permission is refused because of the location of the development in a special amenity area, compensation cannot be claimed under the provisions of the Local Government (Planning and Development) Act 1990 (see Second Schedule).

9.1(ii) Removal or alteration of a hedge   The planning authority has power to serve a notice directing an owner and occupier of land to remove or alter any hedge (section 44 of the 1963 Act). An appeal lies to the Board against the notice. Out of pocket expenses (only) will be paid to cover the costs of complying with the notice.

9.1(iii) Tree Preservation Orders (section 45 of the 1963 Act) Any tree, group of trees or woodlands may become the subject of a tree preservation order as the planning authority considers expedient. The purpose of such an order is to impose the requirement of planning permission in respect of the felling or destruction of preserved trees (dead trees or trees that are causing a nuisance may be felled without prior consent). The notice is served on the owner or occupier of the lands and on any other person then entitled to work the trees to which the order relates. There is a right of appeal to the Board. Compensation is only payable in respect of certain decisions that are made pursuant to the consent requirement of the order. It is a summary offence to breach a tree preservation order.

9.1(iv) Public Rights of Way As indicated above, exemptions conferred by Parts I, II and III of the Regulations will be withheld if such development:

(a) would consist of the fencing or enclosure of any land habitually open to or used by the public during the 10 years preceding such fencing or enclosure for recreational purposes or as means or access to any seashore, mountain, lakeshore, riverbank or other place of natural beauty or recreational utility; or

(b) obstruct any public right of way.

The planning authority also has powers to make an agreement with any person for the creation of a public right of way (section 47 of the 1963 Act). If this tactic proves unsuccessful, section 48 of the 1963 Act permits the authority to compel the creation of a public right of way subject, of course, to the payment of compensation.

9.2 New Roads and Services

9.2(i) Roads The acquisition of land for the building of new roads is a matter relating to the law of compulsory acquisition. The role of planning in the building of new roads is irregular as a local authority does not, as a rule, need planning permission to execute its own developments. There is provision for the submission of an E.I.S. where certain types of road are concerned, *e.g.*, motorways, busways and roads of four lanes of more (see section 50 of the Roads Act 1993, and the Roads Regulations 1994 (S.I. No. 119 of 1994)). Such an E.I.S. must be offered up for public comment before it can be adjudicated upon by the Minister for the Environment.

If this E.I.S. procedure does not apply, a customised planning process will take its place in cases where certain minor road development is proposed (see Part X, article 130(1)(b), of the Local Government (Planning and Development) Regulations 1994). This planning procedure involves offering the public an opportunity to submit its views on the proposed development, the preparation of a special report on the proposed development, and the submission of the report to the elected members of the local authority for approval.

9.2(ii) Services The planning authority may, with the consent of the owner and of the occupier of land erect or construct cables, wires and pipelines (other than water pipes, sewers and drains) and any apparatus incidental thereto on any land (section 85 of the 1963 Act). The power extends to ancillary works and the placement of appropriate signage. The consent referred to must not be unreasonably withheld. If it is, An Bord Pleanála can, on an appeal by the planning authority, bye-pass the need for consent. Compensation can be claimed in any event under section 24 of Local Government (Planning and Development) Act 1990. It might be noted that the 1994 Planning Regulations confer a number of exemptions on statutory undertakers (*e.g.* E.S.B., An Post, etc.) in relation to the laying or erection of pipes and cables (see Classes 21 to 29, Part I, Second Schedule).

9.3 Halting Sites

In recent decisions, the courts have indicated that local authorities (in their capacity as housing authorities) are under an obligation to provide halting sites in order to meet the housing needs of travellers. Local opposition to halting sites is usually fierce, so most local authorities resort to a discreet purchase of a field in a quasi-rural area which is then prepared for use as a halting site. It will be remembered that the local authority does not need planning permission to carry out its own developments and in the case of halting sites, not even the special planning procedure set out in Part X of the 1994 Planning Regulations applies. A halting site proposal does not legally require and would not normally warrant the preparation of an E.I.S. The possible challenges that can be made to such a proposal are relatively few. One popular port of call is the development plan. If there has been a material contravention of the development plan in the matter of halting sites and the proper amendment procedures have not been followed by the planning authority, its actions can be judicially reviewed (see section 39 of the 1963 Act).

Chapter 5

BANKING

Edward S. Walsh

Introduction

This chapter is intended to deal with the principal features which arise in the relationship of banker and customer in circumstances where persons engaged in trade will operate at least a current account to which monies will be lodged and from which monies will be paid out in respect of purchases, goods and/or services supplied, or for other business. The vast majority of customers also have borrowing facilities. The purpose of the chapter is to identify the principal considerations which operate in each of the particular set of circumstances and to ensure that the reader is conscious of the nature, extent and consequences which attach.

Banks

Section 7(1) of the Central Bank Act 1971 provides that:

> "[S]ubject to the provisions of this Act, a person other than the Bank (Central Bank of Ireland) shall not on his own behalf or on behalf of any other person in or outside the State carry on banking business or hold himself out or represent himself as a banker or as carrying on banking business unless—
>
> (a) he is the holder of a licence and
> (b) he maintains a deposit in the Bank of an amount determined in accordance with Section 13 of this Act".

Under subsection (4) of section 7, this section does not apply in relation to the Agricultural Credit Corporation, the Industrial Credit Company, the Post Office Savings Bank, the Trustee Savings Bank certified under the Trustee Savings Banks Acts 1863 to 1965, a building society, an industrial and provident society, a friendly society, a credit union, an investment trust company, or the manager under a unit trust scheme in respect of the carrying of the business of the scheme.

The Central Bank Act 1971 provides for the licensing and supervision of banks by the Central Bank of Ireland.

Banks and Customers

A person is deemed to be a "customer" of a bank where that person conducts a transaction. It is not necessary that the person conduct banking services on a regular basis, provided that the nature of the service is not simply a casual service.

Consequently, in *Great Western Railway Co. v. London and County Banking Co. Ltd* [1901] A.C. 414, it was held that a rate collector who habitually cashed cheques at the counter of the defendant bank with whom the rural authority maintained its account and who in all such cases retained part of the amount and requested that the balance be credited to the authority's account was not a customer in circumstances where he did not maintain an account with the bank. The issue arose in circumstances where the rate collector in question cashed a cheque which he obtained from the rate payers by fraud whereupon the bank was sued by the rate payer in question for conversion. The question arose as to whether or not the cheque had been collected by the bank for a customer. The court was of the view that although the bank had regularly cashed cheques at the rate collector's request for a number of years, he could not be considered a customer in the circumstances since he maintained no account with the bank.

In contrast, in the case of *Commissioners of Taxation v. English, Scottish and Australian Bank Ltd* [1920] A.C. 683, a cheque made payable to the Commissioners of Taxation was taken from their premises and paid by the thief into an account opened by him with the defendant bank. One of the questions which was raised was whether the thief had become that bank's customer by reason of the single transaction involved.

The judge in the case, Lord Dunedin, stated in the course of his judgment:

> "The word 'customer' signifies the relationship in which duration is not of the essence. A person whose money has been accepted by a Bank on the footing that they undertake to honour cheques up to the amount standing to his credit is . . . a customer of the Bank . . . irrespective of whether his connection is of short or long standing. The contrast is not between an habitué and a newcomer but between a person for whom the Bank performs a casual service such as for instance cashing a cheque for a person introduced by one of their customers for a person who has an account of his own at the Bank."

On the basis of the decisions in *Great Western Railway Co. v. London and County Banking Co. Ltd* and *Commissioners of Taxation v. English, Scottish and Australian Bank Ltd*, it would appear that a person becomes a customer of a bank when he opens an account and that it is irrelevant whether the account is overdrawn, or whether it is a current account or an account of some other kind, such as a savings or deposit account.

Contractual Relationship between Bank and Customer

The relationship between bank and customer is contractual in nature. The precise terms of the contract depend upon the precise nature of the relationship. Where the customer operates a current account, he is entitled to be repaid the money credited to the current account without interest and on demand. Whilst the account remains in credit, or within an authorised limit if an overdraft facility has been granted, the customer has a right to draw on the funds, whether by means of cheques and/or money transfers.

Where the customer is the holder of a fixed deposit account or a savings account, the amount and any interest which has accrued is repayable to the customer either on a determined date or at call. Pending demand for payment, the bank is entitled to use those monies together with all other monies held on deposit.

The essence of the contract of bank and customer is the bank's right to use the money for its own purposes and it in return undertakes to repay an amount equal to that paid in with or without interest, either at call or at a fixed time.

The contractual nature of the relationship is best illustrated by the decision in *Foley v. Hill* (1848) 2 H.L.C. 28. In that case, the customer paid an amount of money to the credit of an account opened with his bank on the understanding that it would earn interest at the rate of 3 per cent per annum. As no interest was credited against the bank for approximately six years, the customer instituted an action for an account in the Court of Chancery. He alleged that he was entitled to the remedy sought either as a beneficiary of a trust or as the banker's principal. He further argued that as the relationship was of a fiduciary nature, his claim was not barred by the Statute of Limitations then in force. The court held that the customer was not entitled to an account and that his correct course was to institute a common law action in debt for the amount due. In the course of his judgment, Lord Cottenham said:

> The money paid into the bankers is money known by the principal to be placed there for the purpose of being under the control of the banker; it is then the banker's money; he is known to deal with it as his own; he makes what profit he can which profit he retains to himself . . . ".

The learned Judge went on to add that it was the bank's duty to repay to the principal when demanded a sum equivalent to that paid into his hands.

The obligation on the part of the bank to make repayment arose only on foot of a demand.

Similarly in the case of *Joachimson v. Swiss Bank Corporation* [1921] 3 K.B. 110, a partnership, whose members comprised English and German nationals, maintained an account with the defendant bank. When the First World War broke out, the account had a credit balance of £2,312. The partnership became at that time an alien enemy so that operation of the account was prohibited. At the end of the war, the English partners sought to wind up the affairs of the partnership and so brought an action claiming in the partnership's name the repayment of the amount involved. As no demand for payment was made before the proceedings, it was held by the Court of Appeal that the action was premature.

However, in the course of delivering judgment, Lord Justice Atkin in describing the contract as between the bank and customers said:

> "The Bank undertakes to receive money and to collect bills for its customer's account. The proceeds so received are not to be held in trust for the customer but the Bank borrows the proceeds and undertakes to repay them. The promise to repay is to repay at the branch of the Bank where the account is kept and during banking hours. It includes a promise to repay any part of the amount due against the written order of the customer addressed to the Bank at the branch and as such written orders may be oustanding in the ordinary course of business for two or three days it is a term of the contract that the Bank will not cease to do business with the customer except upon reasonable notice. The customer on his part undertakes to exercise reasonable care in executing his written orders so as not to mislead the Bank or to facilitate forgery."

The relationship of debtor and creditor which arises in the instance of a current account is augmented by that of agent and principal where the bank undertakes to carry out orders for the payment of money as issued by the customer and to collect effects due to him.

As the customer's agent, the bank is required to adhere strictly to its mandate.

A bank may assume additional duties of care where it seeks to advise a customer on financial matters or where it accepts valuables for safe custody or where it investigates on behalf of a customer the standing of third parties, such as potential business contacts.

By way of corollary, the customer in turn owes his bank a general duty to issue clear and unambiguous instructions and to ensure that the orders as issued are not issued in such a manner that will facilitate their falsification.

Bank as Fiduciary . Apart from these general duties of care, special circumstances may constitute the bank a fiduciary (a fiduciary being a person or body who holds a position of trust in relation to another and who must act for that other's benefit) in which instance the bank then becomes subject to the additional duties of care and to a duty of full disclosure. These obligations will go far beyond the bank's general duty which may broadly be described as a requirement to take care in the execution of its mandate. As a fiduciary, the bank may have to question the validity of an instruction given to it by a person who is the representative of a customer. The bank may be obliged to acquaint the customer with extraneous circumstances relevant to specific business transactions.

This is demonstrated by the case of *Lloyds Bank Ltd v. Bundy* [1975] Q.B.

326. In that case, the bank obtained from one of its customers a guarantee covered by a charge over land to secure an overdraft granted to that customer's son. The father was advanced in age and naive in business matters and the property charged by him was his home and only valuable asset. The bank manager did not disclose to him the extent of the financial problems faced by the son and failed to suggest that the father seek independent legal advice before the execution of the guarantee in question. The transaction was advantageous from the bank's point of view as an earlier charge executed by the father did not adequately secure the overdraft incurred by the son at the time of the new arrangement.

The Court of Appeal held the guarantee void as the bank had not discharged the fiduciary duty of care owed to the customer.

It was accepted by Sir Eric Sachs, one of the Lord Justices of Appeal, that such a fiduciary duty did not normally exist where a customer agreed to guarantee the debts of a third party to his bank but it was considered that in the present case the guarantor, who was a customer of long standing, had placed reliance on the bank's advice and the failure to disclose the full facts was akin to the exercise of undue influence.

His Lordship described the situation in which a fiduciary relationship would be created as follows:

> "Whilst disclaiming any intention of seeking to catalogue the elements of such a special relationship it is perhaps of little assistance to note some of those which have in the past frequently been found to exist where the Court has been led to decide that this relationship existed between adults of sound mind. Such cases tend to arise where someone relies on the guidance or advice of another where the other is aware of that reliance and where the person upon whom such reliance is placed obtains or may well obtain a benefit from the transaction or of some other interest in it being concluded. In addition, there must of course be shown to exist a vital element . . . referred to as confidentiality."

The fiduciary duty of care was subsequently considered in England in the case of *National Westminster Bank plc v. Morgan* [1985] A.C. 686. In that case, the bank was asked to approve a refinancing arrangement for a customer whose improvident business ventures had led to his defaulting in payments under an existing mortgage granted to a building society over the family home owned jointly by the customer and his wife. As part of the proposed scheme inititated in order to preclude the sale of the home by the building society, the bank required a charge over the same property. To this end, the branch manager called on the couple and asked the wife to execute the necessary documents. Although the wife, who was also a customer of the bank, expressed her unwillingness to execute a charge covering the husband's business ventures, the branch manager did not explain to her the wide ranging nature of the security, reassuring her erroneously, though in good faith, that the charge only secured the amount advanced to refinance the original mortgage. The branch manager failed to advise the wife to seek independent legal advice. Upon the husband's demise, it turned out that he had no business liabilities but the bank sought to sell the property in order to recover the balance outstanding under the refinancing arrangement.

The House of Lords, in reversing the earlier decision of the Court of Appeal, which had ordered that the mortgage be set aside, held that the bank in the particular circumstances had not committed a breach of their duty of care or of a fiduciary duty owed to the wife.

Specifically, it was found that the relationship between the parties had remained that of banker and customer and that the branch manager had not exercised undue influence to induce the wife to execute the charge.

Lord Scarman was compelled to reach this conclusion on three grounds:

1. The bank had not derived any hidden or undue benefit from the transaction. The object of the arrangement was to save the customers from having their house sold by the Building Society, the wife being just as anxious as the husband to retain her home.

2. The branch manager's statement was incorrect technically, rather than in substance. Although the charge was formally wide enough to secure the husband's business ventures, the bank had no intention of utilising it in this manner and indeed sought to levy execution solely in respect of the refinancing agreement.

3. The wife understood the general nature of the charge and was aware that unless she executed the house would be sold by the building society. In such circumstances, the mere inequality between the bargaining power of the bank and of the wife was immaterial and it was considered that there was not a need in modern law to establish a general principle of relief against inequality in the bargaining power of parties to a contract.

In general, there is no obligation on the part of a bank to advise a person to seek independent legal advice in relation to the nature, effect or consequences of a transaction proposed to be entered into. However, circumstances may arise where, because of the fiduciary duty owed by a bank to a particular person, that person ought to beadvised as to the desirability of independent legal advice.

This is best illustrated in the case of *Bank of Ireland v. Michael Joseph Smyth and by order Una Smyth* [1996] I.C.L.C. 1. In that case, the husband, who was the first named defendant, had on May 25, 1978, executed an indenture of charge in favour of the bank to secure all borrowings. This mortgage was created over farmlands on which the family home was situate. The wife, who was the second named defendant, having been joined under order of the court to the proceedings, had signed a form of consent endorsed on the said charge, whereby she consented for the purpose of the Family Home Protection Act 1976 to the charge.

Under section 3 of the Familty Home Protection Act 1976 it is provided that if one spouse consents to the transfer or creation of any interest in favour of a third party in a family home, this consent shall be void unless the prior consent in writing is obtained from the other spouse.

The bank subsequently issued proceedings seeking an order for possession of the lands, on the basis that there were substantial sums due and owing by the first named defendant.

In the High Court, it was found that whilst there was a document which purported to be a consent in writing, it was held that this was not in fact a sufficient consent within the meaning of the 1976 Act. It was claimed by the first named defendant that it had not been explained to the wife that she would lose her home if the requisite payments were not made nor had she been advised to seek independent legal advice. It was accepted by the bank that the wife had believed that the charge did not affect the family home but it was contended that this was a unilateral mistake on her behalf and it was submitted that the bank could not reasonably have been expected to be aware of what was in the mind of the second named defendant.

It was further contended on behalf of the bank that there was no duty upon it at common law or in equity or under the provisions of the Family Home Protection Act 1976 to explain to the second named defendant (the wife), the nature of the charge to which she was giving her consent or the consequences it could have for her.

It was contended on the wife's behalf that before her consent could be valid under the Family Home Protection Act 1976, it had to be established that she had fully and freely consented to what she was doing and that since the bank had failed to establish this they should not be entitled to rely upon the consent.

The Supreme Court in dismissing the appeal by the Bank of Ireland held that the onus of proving whether the consent in question was sufficient lay on the bank. The purpose of section 3 of the Family Home Protection Act 1976 was to enable a spouse to protect the family home, not simply for his or her own benefit, but also for the benefit of any children. In giving one's consent it meant that one was approving of something, accordingly a precondition was that one should have knowledge of what one was approving. The consent in consequence must be a fully informed consent.

On the evidence, the Supreme Court was satisfied that the second named defendant had not known to what she was consenting and in particular had not been aware that the charge would affect the family home, and in consequence it was found that her consent was invalid.

The validity of the consent depended solely upon whether the second named defendant as spouse had full knowledge of what she was doing and it was in consequence immaterial whether or not the bank were aware as to the lack of knowledge.

The court further held that as a matter of law, the bank were not under any duty to the spouse to explain the charge fully to her or indeed to suggest that she should get independent legal advice. However, if the bank were concerned to ensure that they received a good title to the land which was the subject of the charge, these steps should have been taken, otherwise it could not be established that there was a sufficient consent and the onus of establishing the sufficiency of the consent rested upon the person who wished to rely upon the consent.

Confidentiality

Because the relationship of bank and customer has elements of agency, it therefore also includes an obligation of confidentiality as between the bank and a customer.

The duty of confidentiality or secrecy was described by Lord Justice Diplock in *Parry Jones v. Law Society* [1969] 1 Ch. 1 as:

> "Such a duty (of secrecy) exists not only between Solicitor and client but for example between banker and customer, doctor and patient and accountant and client. Such a duty of confidence is subject to and overriden by a duty to the party to their contract to comply with the law of the land. If it is the duty of such a party to a contract . . . to disclose in defined circumstances confidential information then he must do so and any express contract to the contrary would be illegal and void."

The duty of confidentiality was considered by the Court of Appeal in the case of *Tournier v. National Provincial and Union Bank of England* [1924] 1 K.B. 461. There, the plaintiff's account which was with the defendant bank, was heavily overdrawn, failed to meet the repayment demands made by the branch manager. On one occasion, the branch manager noticed that a cheque drawn to the plaintiff's order by another customer was collected through the account of a bookmaker. The branch manager thereupon rang up the plaintiff's employers, ostensibly to ascertain the plaintiff's private address but during the conversation he disclosed that the plaintiff's account was overdrawn and that he had dealings with bookmakers. As a result of this conversation, the plaintiff's contract was not renewed by the employers upon its expiration. The Court of Appeal held that the bank was guilty of a breach of a duty of secrecy and awarded damages against it.

Lord Justice Atkin pointed out that the information which the bank was bound to treat as confidential was not restricted to facts that it learned from the state of the customer's account. Furthermore, the bank's duty remained intact even after the account had been closed or ceased to be active. The bank's duty to maintain secrecy encompassed "information obtained from other sources than the customer's actual account if the occasion upon which the information was obtained arose out of the banking relations of the bank and its customers". Since that had happened in the instant case, the information received by the bank manager was based on a cheque made payable to one of the bank's customers and drawn by another customer, liability attached.

The Court of Appeal, however, accepted that there was a need to recognise certain exceptions to the bank's duty of secrecy which were described by Lord Justice Bankes as:

> "On principle . . . the qualifications can be classified under four heads:
>
> (a) where disclosure is under compulsion of law;
> (b) where there is a duty to the public to disclose;
> (c) where the interests of the bank require disclosure;
> (d) where the disclosure is made by the express or implied consent of the customer."

A breach of the duty of confidentiality will in the normal course entitle a person to maintain an action against the bank for damages provided it can be shown that that person has suffered loss because of the breach of confidentiality.

Operating of an Account

Current Account

A current account is the more common account operated by a customer of a bank and is used for regular financial transactions, such as the lodgment of monies to the account, whether through a lodgment made directly by a customer or by means of a transfer, whether by standing order or by direct debit, by a debtor of such customer. In turn the account will be used by the customer in the normal course for the making of payments whether by standing order, direct debit, money transfer order or by the drawing of a cheque on the account.

Where instructions to make a payment are furnished to a bank, it must comply with the instructions. However, the bank is not obliged to honour a cheque or to meet some other demand for the making of a payment if the customer's balance is inadequate unless the bank has agreed to grant the customer an overdraft and the amount of the cheque does not exceed the prescribed ceiling. The balance of a current account is calculated on the basis of the amount actually standing to its credit at the time when the customer's demand is made. The bank has a reasonable time for crediting the amount paid to the credit of a customer's account. If the funds remitted by the customer are drawn upon before the bank has had reasonable time to credit them to the account, the bank is not liable if it dishonours a cheque drawn by the customer. Where a customer instructs the bank to collect cheques payable to him, he is not entitled to draw on them until the items have been cleared.

It has been suggested that the very crediting of an account is evidence of the bank's readiness to permit the customer to draw against the balance as shown. If there has been usage under which the drawing against uncleared proceeds has been permitted, an issue may arise as to whether or not the bank should be held liable if it refuses to meet a cheque in such circumstances. It is for precisely that reason that the standard lodgment record is headed "subject to verification" and is endorsed with the legend:

> "cheques, etc. are accepted subject to examination and verification and are transmitted for collection at customer's risk. Though credited to account when paid in they should not be drawn against until cleared".

The duty of a bank to honour the customer's cheque requires that the demand must be made at the branch with which the account is maintained. In consequence, the customer is not entitled to demand payment at another branch. Further, cheques should be paid only if presented during ordinary business hours but a bank does not commit a breach of its mandate by paying the cheques shortly after closure time.

Finally, as a matter of practice, banks dishonour cheques that have been outstanding for a long period of time, usually if presented after a lapse of more than six months from the date of issue. Likewise, it is a practice not to pay an undated cheque.

Creditor and Debtor

An important feature of the current account is that the role of bank and of the customer can be reversed in given situations. If the account is overdrawn, the bank becomes the creditor and the customer the debtor.

Where a bank fails to make payment on foot of a cheque, whether in error or otherwise, and where the account is in credit or alternatively is within the authorised overdraft, the bank commits a breach of contract.

"Refer to Drawer"

Separate and apart from this, where a cheque is dishonoured, an issue may arise as to whether or not an action for defamation will lie where a cheque is returned marked with the words "Refer to Drawer".

The authorities on this area are less than clear. In *Pyke v. Hibernian Bank* [1950] I.R. 195, three of the plaintiff's cheques drawn by him within permitted overdraft limits were returned to payees by the bank marked: "Refer to Drawer – Present Again" and "Return to Drawer". Although the plaintiff pleaded innuendoes, the trial judge withdrew any question of innuendo from the jury and awarded £400 for libel, in addition to which he awarded £1 for breach of contract. On appeal to the Supreme Court, a four-man court split and the High Court decision stood. On the plain meaning of the words, Mr Justice O'Byrne (with whom Mr Justice Geoghegan agreed) said:

> "It seems to me that one or other of two alternative views at once emerges: either (a) that there are no funds to meet the cheque or (b) that the order for payment containing the cheque has been countermanded since the cheque was given to the payee and presumably consideration was obtained therefor. Either of those views seems to me to be reasonably capable of a defamatory meaning quoad

the drawer of the cheque as implying (a) that he is insolvent or (b) that he is guilty of want of good faith towards the payee of the cheque."

Chief Justice Maguire, was of the opinion that the words "Refer to Drawer" were not capable of defamatory meaning in the absence of innuendo, whilst Mr Justice Black preferred to find for the defendant on the ground that the occasion was privileged even though the occasion for the communication was brought about by the bank's own mistake.

Prior to that, in the case of *Flynn v. Hibernian Bank Ltd* [1938] Ir. Jur. Rep. 34, an action was brought by a customer against his former bankers for damages for breach of duty, breach of contract, libel and slander. The plaintiff in his statement of claim alleged that the defendants had wrongfully prevented him:

1. from realising the surrender value of and obtaining certain bonuses on an insurance policy held by them as security for his overdraft; and

2. from dealing with certain other securities similarly held by them thereby maintaining the overdraft at a higher figure and for a longer period than was necessary.

And in addition that the defendants' agent had:

3. falsely and maliciously written; and

4. published words suggested that bankruptcy proceedings might be issued against the plaintiff.

It was held on an application by the defendants to strike out such pleadings that 1 and 2 should be struck out because they did not state clearly and precisely any cause of action but that 3 and 4 should not be so struck out since they disclosed a cause of action upon which the court was unable to say that the plaintiff could not possibly succeed, the words imputed to the defendants' agent being such as the trial judge sitting with the jury would find it difficult to rule as incapable of bearing a defamatory meaning.

Subsequently, in the case of *Grealey v. Bank of Nova Scotia*, an unreported decision of April 11, 1975, the Supreme Court was concerned with an appeal from an order of the High Court which had been made in favour of a plaintiff whose cheques had been marked by the bank "Refer to Drawer". The only ground of appeal being that there was no evidence of malice on the part of the bank which would destroy a privileged occasion, as it had been conceded on behalf of the appellant that the words were in fact libellous.

As matters stand, it would appear that the words "Refer to Drawer" are capable of bearing a defamatory meaning and in general if a cheque is wrongfully returned separate and apart from the wrongful return constituting a breach of contract if there is a "sufficient" publication then the bank may be open to a claim for damages for defamation consequent upon the marking of the cheque "Refer to Drawer". Publication is required for a libel action to succeed.

Combination of Accounts

In many cases, the customer may, as a matter of convenience or for other purposes, maintain more than one account with his bank. Thus, a customer may use one account for strictly personal purposes and another one for his business. A situation may arise where a bank may wish to treat all the accounts maintained by a given customer as if they were one, *e.g.* where the customer is unable or unwilling to pay an overdraft incurred in one account although another account is in credit. Alternatively, a bank may wish to combine accounts where a customer draws a cheque for an amount exceeding the balance standing to the credit of the specific account involved but the deficiency can be met out of funds deposited in another account.

Obviously the customer is entitled to agree specific terms which will govern the operation of any given account.

In general, it will appear that in certain given situations a bank is entitled to combine the accounts of a customer even if those accounts are maintained at different branches, but in each instance the entitlement depends upon the specific circumstances relating to the accounts.

In *Greenwood Teale v William Williams Brown & Co.* (1894) 11 T.L.R. 56 the senior partner of a firm of solicitors opened three accounts: an office account, a deposit account and a private account. The bank was initially told that clients' money would be paid to the credit of the deposit account. This account was subsequently closed and thereafter both the firm's money and clients' funds were credited to the office account. As the private account was overdrawn for an amount far exceeding the credit in the office account, the bank combined the two accounts. Holding that the bank had acted properly, Mr Justice Wright said that a bank had the right to combine a customer's separate accounts subject to three exceptions:

1. The right to combine could be abrogated by special agreement.

2. It would be inapplicable where a special item of property was remitted to the bank and appropriated for a given purpose.

3. A bank could not combine a customer's private account with one known to the bank to be a trust account or to be utilised for operations conducted by the customer as trustee but the bank's knowledge in such circumstances had to be express and the mere fact that an account was described as an office account was immaterial, as usually funds utilised by a firm through its office account were not trust property.

So also, in the case of *Garnett v. M'Kewan* [1872] L.R. 8 Ex. 10 a customer's account with the bank at a particular branch was overdrawn; when he failed to discharge his liability his account was frozen. Subsequently, the customer opened an account with the same bank but at a different branch in order to facilitate the collection of cheques payable to him. The bank set off the credit balance in the account with the latter branch against the overdraft in the account of the former branch. As it did not give notice to the customer, he continued to draw cheques on the latter account and these were dishonoured by the bank. He in turn sued the bank for breach of contract and for defamation but in entering judgment for the bank the Court of Exchequer held that although there might be many accounts opened in a customer's name, there was only one contract between him and the bank. The bank was entitled to combine these accounts for its own purposes unless there was an agreement to keep them separate.

It has been suggested by the courts and by Chief Baron Kelly in the *Garnett* case (see above) that whilst it may be proper or considerate for a bank to give notice of its intention to combine accounts in order to effect a set off, there is no legal obligation in fact on a banker to so do, unless there is an agreement to the contrary or, alternatively, there has been a course of dealings as between the parties.

The position was subsequently considered by the House of Lords in the case of *National Westminster Bank Ltd v. Halesowen Presswork and Assemblies Ltd* [1972] A.C. 785. In that case, the plaintiffs maintained a current account with the defendant bank. In April 1960 when the account showed a substantial debit balance, account no. 2 was opened for the plaintiffs' trading operations. The bank agreed that in the absence of a material change of circumstances, account no. 1 would remain frozen for a period of four months. On May 20, the plaintiffs convened a meeting of their creditors. The defendants, who received a notice of the meeting, resolved to leave the arrangement of April in effect. On June 12, the plaintiffs passed a resolution to wind up voluntarily. On June 19 the bank informed the liquidator that it had determined to set off the credit balance in account no. 2 against the debit balance in frozen no. 1 account to which the liquidator objected.

Mr Justice Roskill gave judgment for the bank in the High Court but the decision was reversed by the Court of Appeal. The decision of the Court of Appeal was then appealed to the House of Lords. The House of Lords restored Mr Justice Roskill's decision.

In the course of the case, an issue arose as to whether or not the bank was required to give prior notice. Their Lordships, however, were unanimous in the view that the words of the agreement indicated that it was automatically avoided when the company decided to wind up and notice by the bank of its decision to combine the accounts was therefore not required.

It is clear, however, that the view of the court was that in the absence of clear language to such an effect, notice would *probably* be required. In particular, Viscount Dilhorne said that if a bank had made its decision to combine the accounts in the wake of the customer's decision to convene a meeting of creditors, the bank would have had to give reasonable notice, whereas Lord Cross of Chelsea said that ordinarily a bank would in the very least have to honour cheques drawn by the customer up to the time he was given notice of the combination of his accounts.

The authorities suggest that a bank is not under an obligation to combine the accounts in the customer's interests, *i.e.* in a situation where there are inadequate funds in an account against which a cheque is drawn but adequate funds exist in another account within the same branch. However, if a bank in such a situation in fact combines accounts, it appears that no claim can arise from the bank having so done. This view derives support from the fundamental principle that where a principal gives an agent an ambiguous instruction, the agent is entitled to reimbursement as long as he gives the instructions a reasonable construction which he believes to accord with the principal's genuine intention. Where a person draws a cheque in circumstances where there are insufficient funds, he may be taken to request that the amount is to be paid out of *any* funds deposited with the bank and consequently by effecting a set off between the balances of different accounts, in order to allow the cheque to be paid the bank obeys the spirit of the instruction.

The Closing of a Current Account

Where a customer elects to close an account and draws out the outstanding funds, the bank is not under an obligation to pay cheques presented to it thereafter. A customer is entitled to terminate the relationship at any time.

Where the bank, however, wishes to sever the relationship, the position is different. The reason for this is that the customer may have asked his debtors to pay amounts due to him directly to the credit of the account and in consequence the customer might well face embarrassment if cheques or other effects were returned to the drawers accompanied by a notice stating that the account had been closed.

In the case of *Prosperity Ltd v. Lloyds Bank Ltd* (1923) 39 T.L.R. 372, a course of business was established between the bank and its customer, an insurer. People were required to pay premiums due to the customer directly to the credit of his account. The bank gave the customer one month's notice before closing the account. Mr Justice McCardie said that the account could be closed only upon the giving of reasonable notice. In view of the course of dealings between the customer and his client, one month's notice was considered inadequate. The court, however, refused to grant a mandatory injunction ordering the bank to re-open the account, such an order would constitute an injunction that the bank perform personal services. It was considered that damages would constitute an adequate remedy and the award being subject to the customer's proof of loss.

The contract of banker and customer, being of a personal nature, terminates automatically where the customer dies or becomes bankrupt or, in the case of a partnership, where it is dissolved. The same applies where a corporation enters into liquidation.

Overdraft

An overdraft is a facility provided by a bank which enables a customer to draw as against a current account even in the absence of specific funds to the account up to a specified limit and provided that any drawings made by the customer are within that limit, the bank is obliged to honour all of such drawings.

The authorised overdraft limit is the maximum amount against which the customer is entitled to overdraw the account at any given time.

In theory, the overdraft is intended for short term borrowing requirements, but more often than not it may form an essential part of the borrowing requirement of the customer.

In the normal course, the overdraft will require to be renewed from time to time in that the bank would normally specify that the overdraft shall operate only for a given period.

The bank is not, in the normal course, obliged to automatically renew an overdraft and indeed a bank may reserve unto itself the right to withdraw an overdraft and the normal letter of sanction will include a specific proviso to the effect that the overdraft is repayable on demand. All borrowings as against an overdraft are liable to interest at the then current rate which obviously will depend upon the agreement struck between the bank and its customer. The rate in the normal course is a varying rate and interest is calculated on the daily balance and applied to the account quarterly.

From a legal point of view, the overdraft is a loan granted by the bank to the customer. Where the customer draws a cheque without having the balance required for meeting it, this act is construed as a request for an overdraft. An undertaking by the bank to grant an overdraft is binding on it. Consequently, in the case of *Fleming v. Bank of New Zealand* [1900] A.C. 577, where the customer gave his bank a document of title as the security for an advance which he was promised, the bank was held bound to stand by its commitment, the giving of the security being adequate consideration for the bank's undertaking.

The bank does not owe its customer a duty of care to advise on the soundness of a transaction for which he requires an overdraft though invariably a bank will assess the nature of the transaction with a view to determining whether or not the provision of facilities based upon such proposal constitutes a prudent proposal. The consideration of such a proposal is for the bank's interest and is not made by it as the customer's financial adviser.

In *Williams and Glyn's Bank v. Barnes* [1980] COM. L.R. 205, the bank granted its customer an overdraft in order to enable the customer to finance some transactions of a company which he controlled and which was facing insolvency problems. When the company's affairs deteriorated further, the bank demanded the repayment of the money outstanding under the overdraft.

Two issues arose: first, whether or not the bank was entitled to demand the immediate repayment and, secondly, whether or not the bank should have warned its customer that the transaction involved was unsound. In rejecting the latter argument, Mr Justice Gibson said:

> "No duty in law arises upon the Bank either to consider the prudence of the lending from the customer's point of view or to advise with reference to it. Such a duty could arise only by contract express or implied whereupon the principle of the assumption of responsibility and reliance stated in Hedley Byrne or in cases of fiduciary duty. The same answer is to be given to the question even if the Bank knows that the borrowing and application of the loan as intended by the customer are imprudent."

Withdrawal of an Overdraft

Whether an overdraft can be withdrawn depends upon the precise terms. The normal letter of sanction will specify that the overdraft is repayable on demand. In the absence of this being specified, it would appear that the customer should be given reasonable notice before it is withdrawn as suggested by Mr Justice Goff in *Cripps (R.A.) v. Wickenden* [1973] 1 W.L.R. 944.

Similarly, in the case of *Rouse v. Bradford Banking Company* [1894] A.C. 586, a partnership was reorganised. The new partnership was allowed to increase an existing overdraft granted to the original firm. The question was whether a surety was discharged on the ground that the bank had given time to the partnership – the debtor – without his consent. The argument was that the increase of the overdraft ceiling coupled with the mention of a new date effectively gave the partnership the right to expect to have the overdraft available for the period involved. The House of Lords rejected this argument. The Lord Chancellor, Lord Herschell, stated:

> "It may be that an overdraft does not prevent the Bank who have agreed to give it from at any time giving notice that it is no longer to continue and that they must be paid their money. This I think at least it does; if they have agreed to give an overdraft they cannot refuse to honour cheques or drafts within the limit of that overdraft which have been drawn or put into circulation before any notice that the person to whom they have agreed to give the overdraft that the limit is to be withdrawn."

This aspect was also considered in more recent times by Judge Matthew Deery sitting at Donegal Circuit Court on December 14, 1995, in the case of *Toland v. A.I.B. plc* (Irish Law Log Weekly, No. 2/96, p.17). In that case, the plaintiff had an overdraft facility with the defendant bank of £15,000. This limit was subject to annual review but on occasion there was an unauthorised accommodation in excess of the limit. By letter dated January 8, the defendant indicated that the account was overdrawn and suggested that no further cheques be drawn on the account. The plaintiff did not contact the bank.

The defendant continued to meet any cheques drawn. By letter dated January 30 which was hand delivered to the plaintiff's mother with whom the plaintiff lived, a specific request was made not to draw any further cheques. The following Monday the plaintiff called to the bank and was asked to call back before the end of the week. He did not return. On Friday, a cheque dated January 31 in the sum of £90 was refused by the bank. The plaintiff submitted that the defendant bank had unlawfully withdrawn his overdraft facility and claimed damages for breach of contract and defamation in refusing to cash the cheque. The bank argued that it had to adopt some cut-off point and that the letter of January 30, which had been delivered by hand, was an adequate way of terminating the overdraft entitlement. Consequently it was contended that defamation did not arise. The plaintiff maintained in evidence that he had not received the letter prior to the visit to the bank.

The court held that it was satisfied the plaintiff had indeed received the letter of January 30 and in such circumstances it was considered that the entitlement had been lawfully terminated on foot of that letter and in those circumstances the claim of the plaintiff failed.

Bank Loans

A bank acting in the course of its business will make available monies by way of a loan to a customer. Provision of a loan is a matter of contract which is subject to the usual requirements of contract law and it is to the specific terms of the contract that one must look with a view to ascertaining the nature of the terms and conditions attaching to the provision of a loan facility.

In the normal course, the loan will be for a fixed period but subject to a specified repayment schedule in respect of which there will be provision that in the event of default in any one or more instalments that the entire sum shall immediately fall due and owing.

Consequently, if a loan is advanced for a specific period of time, in the absence of an express term to the contrary, the bank cannot seek to withdraw the loan during the currency of the loan unless it can establish that in some form or manner there has been a specific default in the loan agreement.

In the case of *Northern Bank Ltd v. Desmond O'Hara*, unreported, Boyle Circuit Court, the bank sought to maintain a claim as against the customer for repayment of a stocking term loan which had been specified to operate for a period of 12 months. Proceedings were commenced within the 12-month period in circumstances where the manager of the plaintiff at its branch at Carrick-on-Shannon ascertained that the defendant was operating a current account with a rival bank. As the loan facility was for 12 months certain with no obligation to make repayments in the intervening period of time. In such a situation, his Honour, Judge Kevin O'Higgins, dismissed the claim of the bank on the basis that it was premature and there had been no actual breach of contract on the part of the borrower.

In the normal course, the loan agreement will specify the specific security, the interest, the repayments and include a proviso that the entire amount advanced will become repayable in certain specified circumstances such as in the event of default or bankruptcy or in the case of a corporate borrower in the event of the appointment of a receiver or the winding up of the company.

General

Money lent by an unlicensed lender cannot be recovered from the borrower because to compel recovery is in effect to constitute the enforcement of an unlawful contract. If a person wishes to engage in the business of moneylending and if that person is not a bank holding a current banking licence and unless exempt from the provisions of the Money Lenders Acts 1900 to 1989, that person must be licensed in accordance with those Acts. The Acts do not apply to licensed banks, registered trustee savings banks, registered building societies, industrial and provident societies which have been exempted by order of the Minister, registered friendly societies, credit unions or any body incorporated or empowered by special Act of Parliament to lend money or any person or body bona fide carrying on the business of insurance or any company which is certified to conduct financial trading operations in the Custom House Docks area, or any other body exempt from the Acts by Ministerial order.

A once off loan by a foreign finance company to an Irish borrower will not fall foul of the provisions of the Money Lenders Acts 1900 to 1989. Consequently, in *Cripps Warburg Ltd v. Cologne Investments Ltd* [1980] I.R. 321 the defendant who was a Dublin-based property development company obtained a very large loan from a London merchant bank which was secured by a mortgage on land in Ireland. It was established in evidence that the bank had no office or agent in the State and that around the time when the bank made the loan there was no other loan to persons in the State and further, it was involved in only two other transactions with Irish-based persons, neither of which involved making loans. The agreement to make the loan in question had been concluded in England but in such circumstances, Mr Justice D'Arcy held that:

> "The one isolated loan . . . did not constitute them money lenders for the purposes of the Act of 1900 . . .".

By contrast, in *London Finance and Discount Ltd v. Butler Ltd* [1929] I.R. 90, there the plaintiff, a company based in Northern Ireland, lent money to the defendant who resided in Dublin. The plaintiff's modus operandi was to place advertisements in Dublin newspapers for its loan facilities. Persons would then write to its Dublin office, sending all the requisite details of their situation and the plaintiff's agent would then come to Dublin, hand over the money to the borrower and take whatever security had been agreed upon. It was held that this constituted carrying on a money lending business in the State and since the plaintiff did not have an Irish money lender's licence, it could not recover the loan. The mere fact that the plaintiff was duly licensed in Northern Ireland was not sufficient.

Security

Where a bank or lending institution advances monies, it will be concerned to ensure that the monies are properly secured. The most usual type of security is by way of a mortgage against real property.

A mortgage of land (otherwise known as real property) would be either through a legal mortgage which is the more formal arrangement or by a equitable mortgage which tends to be more popular in rural Ireland, being of a less formal nature, and usually more private since there is no actual registration of a mortgage against the title to the property.

The usual mortgage is the legal mortgage which consists of a formal indenture of mortgage on foot of which the owner of the land or of a legal interest in the land transfers his interest in the lands to the mortgagee who is the bank or finance company and under the indenture of mortgage the mortgagee undertakes to transfer the property back to the mortgager as and when the obligation for which security has been given has been performed, *e.g.* as and when in the normal course the loan has been repaid.

Under the indenture mortgage it will in the normal course be a covenant that the mortgager (*i.e.* the borrower) is entitled to remain in possession, subject to the making of repayments of a specific sum on specified dates, more usually by way of monthly instalments.

The mortgager is deemed to enjoy an "equity of redemption", *i.e.* as and when the mortgagee has been repaid all monies which have been advanced by such mortgagee, the mortgagee is obliged to retransfer the land to the mortgager.

In the event of default, the mortgagee is entitled to receive possession and to effect a sale of the mortgaged property. In the event of possession not being delivered up voluntarily, proceedings can be maintained against the mortgager for an order for possession. Upon a sale of the mortgaged property, the proceeds are applied in the first instance to discharging the costs of the sale, thereafter the costs of the proceedings, thereafter the monies outstanding on foot of the mortgage and in the event of a balance arising and in the event of no other person having a claim as against the property, the proceeds are held in favour of the original mortgager.

Because the legal mortgage involves as a matter of necessity the execution of a formal indenture of mortgage, that mortgage will of course require to be registered whether in the land registry in the case of registered land, or in the Registry of Deeds in the case of unregistered land, and of course the fact of such registration becomes a matter of public record.

Equitable Mortgage

The equitable mortgage is created by a debtor, either depositing title deeds to the property in question with the creditor to be held by the creditor as security in respect of advances made and in the event of default, the creditor is entitled to maintain proceedings to have the equitable mortgage declared well charged with the outstanding liability.

The fact of an equitable mortgage is unaccompanied by any written documentation in the normal course and the mere deposit of the title deeds, whether or not accompanied by any other act is deemed sufficient, though in the normal course the borrower will require to specifically confirm verbally that the title deeds are being deposited to be held by way of an equitable mortgage in respect of all liabilities, whether present or future, and whether sole or joint, with another or others.

In the case of *Russell v. Russell* (1783) 1 Bro.C.C. 269, it was held that a deposit of title deeds of itself can consitute evidence of any agreement to create a mortgage as well as a sufficient act of part performance to satisfy the requirements of the Statute of Frauds. The advance of funds coupled with a deposit of title deeds with the intention of creating a security entitles equity to infer that a contract to grant a mortgage exists.

Not every deposit of title deeds with a creditor will of necessity create an equitable mortgage if the intention is otherwise, such as where the title deeds are deposited merely for safe custody or as a pledge.

Neither is it necessary to deposit the entire title deeds, it being sufficient merely to deposit such as constitute material evidence of title and indicate an intention to create a mortgage.

Apart from the deposit of title deeds, where a person agrees to enter into a mortgage but has not so done, it remains a fundamental principle of law that equity looks on that as done which ought to be done and consequently the courts will hold the person who has agreed to give a legal mortgage to that agreement and the property in question is then deemed to be subject to an equitable mortgage.

Consequently, in the case of *In re Hurley* [1894] 1 I.R. 488, it was held that where a debtor who had since deceased had written a letter to his banker stating:

> "In case I fail to pay you any promissory note or bill of exchange of mine when due I agree to execute to you a mortgage on all my houses and lands and all future interest in houses or lands I may acquire to secure to you the payment of all sums of money you may advance to me on my promissory note or bills of exchange or otherwise with interest . . . and without prejudice to your right to sue me for all such monies and interests."

Such letter was deemed sufficient to create an equitable mortgage.

An equitable charge arises where an owner of property appropriates it as security for a debt so as to give to the creditor an equitable charge on the property. Such a charge may be created by written agreement or by Will although no special words are necessary so long as the intention is clear.

In the case of either an equitable mortgage or an equitable charge in the event of default, proceedings will be brought seeking a declaration that either an equitable mortgage or an equitable charge has arisen and that it stands well charged against the property in respect of which the mortgage or charge arose seeking an order for sale.

Family Home Protection Act 1976

As has been seen earlier in this chapter, if the property in respect of which it is intended to create a charge or interest comprises the family home, then it is necessary to have the prior consent in writing of the other spouse, otherwise the purported conveyance shall be void.

One of the issues which was raised in the case of *Bank of Ireland v. Smyth* (see above) was as to whether or not the Court should have made an order for possession of the land excluding the family home, the Bank of Ireland as appellant arguing that section 3 of the Family Home Protection Act 1976 made the charge void in respect of the interest in the family home only, and if the consent were held to be invalid an order for possession should nonetheless be made of the land excluding the family home.

The Supreme Court did not make any finding on this issue in circumstances, as the matter had not been raised initially in the High Court nor had there been any finding of fact within the High Court as to what constituted the boundaries of the family home.

The decision of the Supreme Court was delivered on November 5, 1995. Coincidentally, Ms Justice Laffoy was also faced with this issue in an unrelated matter in *Allied Irish Banks plc v. O'Neill and Kidd* [1996] I.C.L.C. 36. In that case, the plaintiff had sought a declaration that the sum of £50,303.94 together with further interest at the court rate was well charged on the second named defendant's interest in lands comprising some 63 acres. In 1992, the second named defendant had desposited the land certificate in respect of those lands with the plaintiff as security for her debts. The family home of both defendants was situate on the lands. The first named defendant had not given his prior consent to the creation of the equitable mortgage. The plaintiff conceded that as a result the deposit of the land certificate did not create an equitable mortgage on the defendants' family home within the meaning of the 1976 Act, but contended that the deposit did create a valid equitable mortgage over so much of the lands as did not constitute the family home of the defendants.

Ms Justice Laffoy declared the deposit of the land certificate had created an equitable mortgage over so much of the lands as did not constitute the family home of the defendants. She considered that under section 3(1) of the 1976 Act, a conveyance of property which included a "family home" was rendered void only insofar as it affected the "family home" as defined in the Act. The consequences of limiting the invalidating effect of section 3(1) of the 1976 Act was that the title of the family home remained in the disponer but the title to the balance of the property vested in the disponee. The court was required therefore to make a finding of fact as to the extent of the family home portion of the land. In that case, the court indicated that it would adjourn for further consideration and submission at a later date as to where the dividing line should be drawn between the family home as defined and the balance of the lands.

Guarantee

A contract of guarantee arises where a person known as the surety or guarantor assumes a secondary liability to answer for a debtor in respect of the obligations of the debtor who is primarily liable. A contract of guarantee is distinguishable from a contract of indemnity where the surety as such assumes a primary liability, either alone or jointly with the principal debtor. Under section 2 of the Statute of Frauds (Ireland) 1695:

> "No action shall be brought . . . whereby to charge the defendant upon any special promise to answer for the debt, default or miscarriage of another person . . . unless the agreement upon which such action shall be brought or some memorandum or note thereof shall be in writing and signed by the parties to be charged therewith or some other person thereunto by him lawfully authorised."

A more usual type of guarantee is where the bank requires a person (whether a customer or not) to guarantee the liabilities of a customer in respect of the provision of certain facilities, whether already granted or to be granted, for which the guarantor (*i.e.* the surety) is liable in the normal course up to a specified sum. In order to be valid, the contract of guarantee must be specifically in writing and signed by the guarantor.

While the surety may be proceeded against without demand against him, nonetheless the usual form of guarantee requires that there be a demand and it is only as and when the demand is made and upon default on foot of the demand that proceedings will lie. It is not however necessary for the bank to first proceed as against the principal debtor unless the contract lays down conditions precedent to the surety's liability.

There is no requirement for independent legal advice other than in specific situations where the bank who require the function of a contract of guarantee may be under a fiduciary duty of care to the person from whom the guarantee is sought.

A contract of suretyship, like any other contract, is voidable by the surety on the grounds of fraud or misrepresentation or undue influence and it is no bar to recission that the creditor has acted on the contract by granting credit to the principal debtor. However, if the contract is to be voidable on such grounds, it is necessary that the creditor (and not merely the principal debtor) be a party to the fraud or misrepresentation or undue influence, or at least have notice of it.

A contract of suretyship is not a contract *uberrimae fidei* (of utmost good faith) and does not therefore require full disclosure of all material facts to the surety. However, if there has been partial disclosure of the facts only and in such a manner as to be tantamount to a misrepresentation then and in those circumstances recission may lie.

In consequence, it has been held that a surety should not be liable on a fidelity bond where an employer has failed to disclose previous misconduct by the employee which was known to him but not to the surety. On the other hand, it has been held that there is no duty on the part of a banker to disclose to a surety the fact that the principal debtor's husband is an undischarged bankrupt and has authority to draw on her account (*Cooper v. National Provincial Bank* [1946] K.B. 1).

Where a surety undertakes to meet a liability which is void against the principal debtor if the contract is by way of guarantee as distinct from an indemnity, then liability will not attach to the guarantor since there is no default on the part of the borrower who is the primary debtor. This type of situation would arise in the case of borrowings by a minor.

It is important to note that a guarantee even of a past debt or transaction would be valid if the creditor promises to forbear from suing or to give time to the principal debtor or if he actually does so at the request of the surety. The mere fact of forbearance, however, is not enough in that there must be an actual promise to do so or the forbearance must be at the request (whether express or implied) of the surety.

In the absence of agreement to the contrary, in the case of a continuing guarantee to secure the balance of a running account at a bank, a surety may at any moment revoke his guarantee in respect of future advances.

A surety under contract of guarantee will be discharged from further liability upon the performance by the principal debtor of his obligations. Partial performance by the debtor such as part payment of the debt guaranteed will discharge the surety only insofar as it may reduce the ultimate liability.

In the event of a variation in the terms of an agreement between the creditor and the debtor which prejudices the surety, then in the absence of consent from the surety, the surety will be discharged from liability in the absence of provision to the contrary.

The law in relation to guarantees is quite complicated and it is not within the remit of a work such as this to deal with the specific legal considerations which may arise in any given number of instances but rather to give a brief outline of the principal characteristics of a contract of guarantee.

The important point which should be noted is that where a person enters into a contract of guarantee, that person undertakes a liability to meet up to a specified sum the liabilities of the principal debtor and in accordance with the terms of the contract of guarantee as entered into and which obligation may well expose the guarantor to a liability for which the guarantor receives no real benefit and in consequence any prudent person should be extremely careful in determining whether or not to commit himself to such guarantee and should, as a matter of course, make all necessary inquiries in relation to the nature, purpose and effect of the guarantee prior to entering the transaction.

Judgment Mortgage

In the latter part of this chapter, we have dealt with the provision of security in respect of borrowings on a voluntary basis. However, where a person borrows money and if that person defaults, obviously the borrower is liable to be sued and a judgment obtained against him for the original sum, together with interest or costs as the case may be. Once judgment has been obtained, the judgment creditor has a variety of steps which may be pursued with a view to enforcement but one of the more effective remedies available to a judgment creditor, where the judgment debtor is the holder of an interest in land, is to proceed with the registration of a judgment mortgage under the provisions of section 6 of the Judgment Mortgage (Ireland) Act 1850. Section 6 provides that a judgment may be registered as a mortgage against the judgment debtor who:

> "is seised or possessed at law or in equity of any lands, tenements or hereditaments of any nature or tenure or has any disposing power over any such lands, tenements or hereditaments which he may without the assent of any other person exercise for his own benefit . . .".

The section covers a wide range of legal and equitable estates and interests in land and even includes certain powers of appointment.

Under section 6 of the 1850 Act, registration of a judgment as a mortgage on the land of the judgment debtor is to be accomplished by filing a sworn statement known as an affidavit in the court where judgment was obtained, containing details of the judgment. Then a copy of this is required to be registered in the registry of deeds or in the event of the land being registered in the Land Registry.

The affidavit setting forth details of the judgment must be specific though a mere technical error will not of necessity invalidate the judgment mortgage.

Insofar as unregistered land is concerned, the general rule is that the judgment mortgage registered in the registry of deeds takes effect subject to all equities affecting the land at the date of registration so that a prior unregistered deed should still have priority.

It has been held in Ireland that "a subsequent registered deed carries a judgment mortgage on its back", a subsequent registered deed made for a value secures priority for the judgment mortgage over a prior unregistered deed, though only where an issue of priority arises as between the prior unregistered deeds and the subsequent registered ones.

So far as subsequent registered mortgages or charges are concerned, the judgment mortgage has in general the same priority accorded to it as other registered instruments.

In the case of registered land, section 71(4) of the Registration of Title Act 1964 provides that the charge in the interest of the judgment debtor is subject to existed registered burdens and burdens affecting the interest without registration and "all unregistered rights subject to which the judgment debtor held that interest at the time of registration of the affidavit".

It has been held that a purchaser from the registered owner of the lands has such an "unregistered right" under the contract for sale, *i.e.* before the execution of the transfer or payment of the purchase money and therefore such purchaser takes free of a post-contract judgment mortgage registered against the vendor (*Tempany v. Hynes* [1976] I.R. 101).

Where a judgment mortgage has been registered, in the event of a failure on the part of a judgment debtor to discharge the monies due and owing, the judgment creditor is entitled to maintain proceedings seeking a declaration that the judgment mortgage is well charged and which proceedings will involve an application for ancillary relief including an order directing a sale of the lands in the event of a failure to discharge the outstanding liability as ascertained.

CHAPTER 6

CONTRACT

Simon McDonald, Barrister-at-Law

Introduction

Commercial transactions to buy or sell goods, crops, fruit, cattle or to provide or accept a service are termed contracts. The Law of contract is the principal legal framework regulating the purchase and sale of goods and the provision and acceptance of services.

A contract is a legally binding agreement, which the parties by their offer, unqualified acceptance and exchange of consideration conclude it is intended to have legal consequences. Consideration is required for most enforceable contracts and is the value given by the parties in respect of the contract. The concept of consideration involves the imparting of a benefit or the suffering of a detriment.

The agreement indicates a meeting of minds, signifying that the parties are agreed about the same thing. The law facilitates what the parties to a contract agree by giving legal effect to that agreement.

Contractual agreements carry legal rights and obligations which the law recognises and enforces. Contractual principles govern many practical farming activities, from the purchase of livestock, seed, fertilizer and machinery to contracts of insurance and hire-purchase agreements.

Contracts may be made in writing, by word of mouth or may be implied by the conduct of the parties or by customers and trade usage or by any combination of these. When contracts are agreed verbally, it may be difficult to resolve subsequent disputes without giving evidence before a court. The Statute of Frauds (Ireland) 1695 provides that certain types of contracts, in order to be enforceable must be evidenced by a note or memorandum in writing, for instance, contracts for the sale of land or any interest in land, contracts of guarantee or contracts in consideration of marriage. If these particular contracts are not in writing, the courts are reluctant to enforce them. The Statute of Frauds as the name suggests was introduced to prevent the potential for defrauding persons in commercial transactions.

The contract itself need not be, but often is, in writing; but to be enforceable a memorandum of evidence of the contract must exist.

Evidence of a contract may consist of a number of documents *e.g.* letters. Provided there is some proof, oral or written, connecting them, the various documents taken together may evidence the contract and thus constitute the "memorandum" to satisfy the statute.

The case of *Boyle v. Lee* [1992] 1 I.R. 555 concerned a dispute over the sale of property concluded by an oral agreement evidenced by a letter which had not referred to specific terms such as the deposit payable or the closing date for the sale. Our Supreme Court reiterated that in order to satisfy the 1695 Act:

1. the actual contract must be in writing or there must be some memorandum or note of it;

2. the agreement must be one where there was an intention to create legal relations; and

3. the writing must contain all the essential terms of what had been agreed.

Capacity to Contract

In general a person has legal capacity and competency to transfer and acquire property and to that end, to enter and be bound by a contract; but for instance, a person who is insane or drunk has a diminished capacity. If a person who is temporarily insane, under the influence of drugs or drunk enters into a contract it is binding on him unless he is at the time incapable of understanding the nature of the contract and the other party knows or ought to know of his disability.

A contract made by a drunk or mentally disordered person may be ratified or adopted on recovery to a sober state and thereby become valid.

Duress/Undue Influence

Contracts must be freely entered into in order to be valid; therefore any contract prompted by improper force or pressure will undermine the agreement, entitling the party taken advantage of to withdraw or resile from it if they wish. In the classic case of *Cumming v. Ince* [1849]11 Q.B. 112, an elderly woman induced to make a settlement of her property in favour of a relative by a threat of lawful detention in a mental home was allowed to withdraw from the contract on account of coercion and the lack of consent. A defence to an allegation of duress or undue influence is to show that the other party expressed free and independent judgement (if appropriate, with the benefit of independent legal advice), and that there was full disclosure of all the relevant facts.

The Contents of a Contract

The contents of a contract set out the rights, obligations, rules or terms the parties have bound themselves to observe. The terms of a contract must be sufficiently clear and complete to produce an agreement which can be binding. Thus, the subject matter of the contract, the quantity and quality of the subject, the price and details of delivery, etc., might be required to be specified. If they are vague or there are mistakes as to essential facts no contract may exist. If there is mistake as to the identity or existence or quality of the subject-matter or mistake as to the identity of the other party, the contract may be set aside on such terms as the court sees fit. With regard to mistaking the nature of a document, the general rule is that a person is bound by the terms of any document which he signs even if he did not read or understand it. Where, however, a person signs a contract in the mistaken belief that he is signing a document of a fundamentally different nature, such a mistake will render the contract void and of no legal effect.

Prior to reaching a final agreement, statements may be uttered and representations may be made which persuade one party to make the contract, but which are not actual terms of the contract. Any statement of fact that is made in contemplation of a contract is known as a representation. Interpretation by a court of the circumstances surrounding the making of the contract will then be necessary to decide whether such terms form part of the contract or whether such statements amount to fraud or misrepresentation. A misrepresentation is an untrue statement of fact (not of opinion), made by one party to the other party to a contract, either before or at the time of making the contract, with the intention that the person to whom the statement is made shall act upon such representation and he does so act. For instance in *Schawel v. Reade* [1913] 2 I.R. 64 when the buyer was about to examine a horse, which he intended buying for stud purposes, the seller said "you need not look for anything; the horse is perfectly sound. If there was anything the matter with the horse I should tell you". Relying on this, the buyer went ahead and bought the horse which transpired to be incurably diseased. The court held that the statement was a vital term of the contract uttered at the time of sale and the buyer was entitled to rescind the contract and recover the price paid.

The person to whom the representation is made is under no obligation to check upon its truth or relevance, even if given the opportunity. In *Gahan v. Boland* (unreported, High Court, January 21, 1983) a purchaser while inspecting property, enquired of the seller, whether a projected motorway would affect the property. The seller stated that the motorway would not affect the property. Accepting this assurance, the plaintiff agreed to purchase. The motorway was in fact routed to pass through the property. The court held that the seller had innocently misrepresented the situation and the plaintiff was entitled to rescind the contract.

The courts have held that mistake as to the quality of goods goes to the root of the contract and will render the contract void. Such was the case in *Western Potato Co-Operative Ltd. v. Durnan* [1985] I.L.R.M. 5, where the parties had contracted for the sale of seed potatoes. In fact the seed was unsound and the crop failed. The court held that the mistake as to quality was so fundamental that it went to the root of the contract which had no legal effect.

Terms: Express or Implied

Whether contracts are expressed orally or in writing, or by conduct, the terms must be certain, otherwise the contract will fail. The terms of a contract define the rights and duties arising under a contract. Contracts contain several terms which may be express or implied.

Express terms are terms that the parties have agreed on. Typically, the price to be paid and the quantity of goods bought are express terms. Express terms may be reduced to writing or may have been agreed orally between the parties.

Implied terms are terms of the contract which the parties did not specifically agree on, but are implied by the court to give the contract business efficacy or are implied by the custom of a locality or a particular trade. Terms may also be implied by the Sale of Goods Act 1893 (as amended by the Sale of Goods and Supply of Services Act 1980) into contracts for the sale of goods which are for the protection of the buyer when buying as a consumer. (See below.)

The terms of a contract whether express or implied are usually classified as conditions or as warranties according to their importance.

Conditions and Warranties

A condition is a vital term (oral or written) which goes directly "to the root of the contract", or is so essential to its very nature that if it is broken the innocent party can discharge (or reject) the contract, that is, he will not be bound to do anything further under the contract and he might also be able to claim damages. A warranty is a term of a contract which is collateral or subsidiary to the main purpose of the contract. It is therefore not so vital as to effect a discharge or cancellation of the contract. A breach of warranty only entitles the innocent party to an action for damages. He cannot treat the contract as discharged.

"Let the Buyer Beware" (*Caveat Emptor*)

The purchase of goods, for instance cattle, can result in unforeseen problems even for the most cautious buyer who is unaware of latent or hidden defects. In such situations the long established legal rule "*caveat emptor*" applies, that is "let the buyer beware". This means that the buyer must accept for instance, the animal as he finds it and cannot complain afterwards should the animal prove defective in some way.

A buyer can protect himself in law by ensuring conditions or warranties are included as part of the transaction. A prudent buyer of a pedigree bull which he has informed the seller is required for breeding purposes, could make it a condition of the sale that the bull is fit for the purpose stated.

The Sale of Goods Acts 1893 to 1980 imply certain terms into contracts of sale, but only where the seller or supplier is in the business and the buyer is a private individual or purchaser. There being a disparity in skill and knowledge, consumers are protected from possible exploitation by the supplier's superior bargaining power. So, where a farmer purchases goods from a trader or someone in business, some implied terms may apply, but where he purchases from another farmer not in a business, the Acts' implied terms do not apply and the "*caveat emptor*" rule applies.

In negotiating a contract of sale with another private individual it is recommended that a buyer protect himself by requiring an express condition or warranty that the goods in question are free from defect. A subsequent breach of condition will entitle the buyer to repudiate the contract, which means he may return the goods and be entitled to the return of his money; but a breach of warranty is collateral to the main purpose of the sale and breach of it only entitles the buyer to sue the seller for the loss suffered.

In *Bank of Ireland v. Smith* [1966] I.R. 646, the High Court held that a statement in an advertisement representing that lands for sale sown with barley were undersown with permanent pasture was incorrect, although made innocently and honestly. As a result, the purchaser was entitled to recover damages for breach of warranty by reason of the fact that the relevant portion of land advertised was not in fact undersown.

A seller creates a warranty when he states that an animal, for instance, is sound. A condition is created if he states that the animal is sound and undertakes to take back the animal if it proves otherwise than sound. An animal examined by a buyer before a sale will not be subject to a warranty in favour of the buyer, as he has taken the opportunity to inspect. Warranties offer protection against defects which are not obvious.

If a buyer makes it a condition of the sale that he may return the goods which turn out to be defective within a specified time, he may return the goods within that time.

Sale of Goods and Supply of Services Acts 1893 to 1980

In addition to the 1893 Act, the Sale of Goods and Supply of Services Act 1980 sets out rules which apply when some detail of a sale of goods transaction is not covered by express agreement. This legislation implies certain conditions and warranties into contracts for the sale of goods which can give extensive protection to the buyer "dealing as a consumer". The Sale of Goods Acts imply several terms into most sales agreements.

A contract for the sale of goods is a contract whereby the seller transfers or agrees to transfer the property or ownership in goods to the buyer for a money consideration called the price.

Goods, for the purpose of these Acts include all chattels personal (*i.e.* movable, tangible articles of property) and things attached to or forming part of the land which are agreed to be severed before sale or under a contract for sale, *i.e.* crops, such as grain, and vegetables and other matter in or on the land such as timber, sand or gravel, etc. The letting of a meadow constitutes a sale of goods. Sales of land or of any interest in land such as leases or licences are excluded from the scope of these Acts.

The Sale of Goods Acts protect buyers when dealing with retailers in contracts for the sale of goods. By way of illustration, a buyer of goods, for instance cattle, is entitled to expect:

– that the seller has the right to sell the animal;

– that the animal is reasonably fit for any particular purpose which he makes known to the seller (being one who is acting in the course of business) showing that the buyer is relying on the seller's skill or judgement; and

– that the animal is not subject to any charge or incumbrance not known to the buyer.

Seller's Title

It is an implied condition that the seller has, or will have at the time when the property in the goods is to be transferred, a right to sell the goods.

If the seller delivers goods to the buyer without having the right to sell, the buyer does not obtain ownership of the goods which is the essential basis of the contract. If the buyer has then to give up the goods to the real owner he may recover the entire price from the seller, without any allowance for the use of the goods in the meantime.

Goods to Correspond with Description

In a contract for the sale of goods by description (or sample), it is an implied condition that the goods correspond with the description (or sample), so if the sale is by description (or sample), a misleading description (or sample), as a breach of condition will entitle the buyer to withdraw from the transaction. An agreement for the sale of spring wheat or of turnip seed is a sale by description so, if winter wheat or cabbage seed is supplied, the seller is in breach of the implied term.

Merchantable quality

Where goods are sold (to an individual) *in the course of business* (meaning not purchased from another private indvidual, but from a retailer), there is an implied condition that the goods will be of a reasonable standard and suitable for the purpose or purposes for which goods of that kind are commonly bought and as durable as is reasonable to expect having regard to any description applied to them, the price (if relevant), and all other relevant circumstances. The condition applies to all "goods supplied under the contract" which includes the packaging and any instructions provided for the use of the goods. This condition also applies to all sales by sample. The condition that the goods supplied under a contract of sale are of merchantable quality is excluded if:

(a) any defects are brought to the buyer's attention before the contract is made; or

(b) the buyer examines the goods before the contract is made, which examination ought to reveal any defects.

"*Caveat emptor*" is still relevant to a considerable extent in private sales or sales between individuals or sales between traders or dealers having regard to the merchantability term. Once the seller is engaged in any business whatsoever which includes any profession and most public sector activities and the sale is made as a part of that business, then the goods must be merchantable. The Sale of Goods Acts 1893 to 1980 seeks to protect the individual consumer when dealing with a business trader.

Fitness of Goods for a Disclosed Purpose

Again, where goods are sold *in the course of business*, and the buyer expressly or by implication makes known to the seller any particular purpose for which the goods are being bought, then there is an implied condition that the goods supplied under the contract are reasonably fit for that purpose, whether or not that is a purpose for which such goods are commonly supplied. There is no such implied condition of fitness of goods for a disclosed purpose where the circumstances show that:

(a) the buyer does not rely on; or

(b) it is reasonable for the buyer to rely on the skill and judgement of the seller.

Like the merchantability term, the implied fitness for their purpose term does not apply in purely private sales, where accordingly "caveat emptor" still applies to a considerable extent.

Sale by Sample

There are implied conditions in a sale of goods by sample that:

(a) the bulk corresponds with the sample in quality;

(b) the buyer has a reasonable opportunity of comparing the bulk with the sample; and

(c) the goods shall be free from any defect rendering them unmerchantable, which would not be apparent on a reasonable examination of the sample.

If there is any appreciable difference in the quality of the sample and that of the goods actually supplied, the buyer is entitled to rescind the contract.

Sale of Motor Vehicle

There is an implied warranty in a contract for the sale of motor vehicles (that is, motor cars, vans, lorries, motor bicycles and electrically propelled vehicles and mobile agricultural tractors and other machinery when operated by a driver in or on the vehicle), that the seller will make available for the specified period if any, such spare parts and "adequate aftersale service" as are stated in any offer, description or advertisement given by the seller or given by him on behalf of the manufacturer.

The legislation also implies a condition in a contract for the sale of a motor vehicle, that, at the time of delivery, the vehicle is free from any defect which would render it a danger to the public, including persons travelling in the vehicle. There is no such implied condition when in a fair and reasonable agreement, the parties agree that the vehicle is not intended for use in the condition in which it is intended to be delivered to the buyer and a certificate to that effect is signed by the seller or someone on his behalf and the buyer and given to the buyer prior to or at the time of delivery.

Exemption Clauses

Exemption clauses in contracts attempt to limit or exclude a party's liability, that would otherwise have been incurred as a result of the contract, for instance, such a clause might seek to limit liability for defective goods. Since the Sale of Goods Act 1980, such exemption clauses are generally ineffective, providing protection to the private consumer and reflecting the improved balance of power in favour of the consumer as against the retailer.

Liability of Finance Houses

It frequently happens that where goods are sold to a buyer dealing as a consumer, that buyer cannot pay the purchase price all at once. It has become common commercial practice that the buyer enter into an agreement with a finance house, a bank or other financial institution, for the repayment of money paid by the finance house to the seller in respect of the goods purchased by the buyer. The finance house is deemed to be a party to the contract and will be liable for breach of contract of sale and any misrepresentation made by the seller with respect to the goods.

Auction Sales

There are special rules contained in the Sale of Goods Act 1893 for the formation of contracts where goods are sold by way of auction. A bidder makes the offer (not the seller or auctioneer). A bid is accepted and sale by auction is complete when the auctioneer announces its completion on the fall of the hammer or other customary manner; bids may be withdrawn before this.

Each "lot" of goods in an auction is a separate contract of sale. A reserve price at an auction is the price above which the bidding must go before the goods will be sold or "knocked down". Auctions may also be conducted in accordance with stated "conditions of sale" which can differ from the rules set out here.

When land is sold by auction, an agreement comes into force when the propety is sold to the highest bidder. This agreement is witnessed by a memo- randum being signed by the successful bidder while still on the auctioneer's premises and signed by the auctioneer on behalf of the vendor.

Hire Purchase Contracts

In hire-purchase contracts goods are delivered by their owner to the hirer for his use and the hirer has an option to purchase the goods when he has completed payment of a number of payments which represent the cash price plus a charge for credit. In practice the hirer selects the goods which the seller sells to a finance house, which then enters into a hire-purchase agreement with the buyer.

Hire-purchase is governed by the Hire-Purchase Act 1946 which requires the owner to notify the hirer of the cash price of the goods before the agreement is made. This is done if the hirer is informed in writing; by having a ticket or label attached to the goods, clearly stating the cash price and by having the cash price clearly stated in any catalogue, price list or advertisement from which the goods have been selected. A hire-purchase agreement must meet particular statutory requirements, *e.g.* there must be a note or memorandum in writing of the requirement which contains the hire-purchase price, the cash price, the amount and date of each instalment, a statutory notice on the right of the hirer to terminate the agreement and on the restrictions on the owner's right to recover the goods and a copy of the note or memorandum must be delivered to or sent to the hirer within 14 days of the making of the agreement.

The hirer may put an end to the HP agreement by giving notice in writing and by paying any arrears and must in total pay one half of the HP price. Legislation provides that the owner may not enforce any right to re-possess the goods where one third of the HP price has been paid other than by court action.

Contracts of Insurance

In fire, life and other insurance contracts, the insured party must disclose all facts which might influence the judgement of the other party, ie. the insurer, as to whether or not to take the risk of insuring or to increase the premium. If, therefore, the insured omits the information required, the insurer may repudiate or reject the contract.

The person who enters into a contract of insurance must have legal ownership of the property insured or a legal interest in it. One may only insure the life of oneself, one's spouse or any other person, *e.g.* a debtor or employee, if the latter's death will cause loss to the insured. Insurance against an event in which one has a financial interest is also possible, for instance against adverse conditions, weather or otherwise causing damage to crops. Similarly, one can insure one's herd against loss incurred as a result of compulsory slaughter following "failure to pass the routine brucellosis test" as set out in the Diseases of Animals Act 1966.

In *Dillon v. McGovern* (unreported, High Court, March 16, 1993) the plaintiff herd-owner arranged insurance to cover loss to his 79 strong herd as a consequence of the possibility of some animals "failing to pass the routine brucellosis test". Subsequently 15 cattle "went down". The Department of Agriculture and Food required the slaughter of the 15 cattle which had failed the test. The insurer undertook to indemnify the owner for the loss of these 15 cattle. But because of the danger of infection, the remainder of the animals, eventhough they had not failed the test, were "deemed to be reactors", and were also required by the Department to be slaughtered. The insurance company argued that as the 64 cattle had not "failed the routine brucellosis test", they were not liable to indemnify or compensate the owner for their slaughter.

The High Court was satisfied that the owner of the herd was entitled to recover on the basis of indemnity for all 79 animals.

Contracts for the Supply of Services

The Sale of Goods and Supply of Services Act 1980 states that the following terms are implied in every contract for the supply of a service, where the supplier is acting in the course of a business including a profession and the activities of a state or local authority:

1. that the supplier has the necessary skill to render the service;
2. that he will supply the service with due skill, care and diligence;
3. that, where materials are used, they will be sound and reasonably fit for the purpose for which they are required; and
4. that, where goods are supplied under the contract, they will be of merchantable quality.

Termination of a Contract

A contract may be discharged or terminated:

- by performance of the contract, meaning that the parties have fulfilled their obligations under the contract;

- by agreement between the parties. Since both parties enter a contract by agreement, it follows that they may also release each other from their respective obligations by agreement;

- by frustration, that is, when some event occurs during the course of the contract, without the fault of either party, which alters the fundamental nature of the contract from that originally entered into. For instance, a contract may be discharged by frustration due to the destruction of the subject-matter of the contract or the non-occurrence of an event upon which the contract is dependent;

- by breach, so that if a condition in a contract is breached or broken, for instance if one of the parties fails to perform their obligations under the contract, the injured party may treat the contract as discharged and claim damages.

Constructural Remedies

On breach of contract the following remedies are available to the injured party.

Damages   Damages in contract law are concerned with what the parties agreed. Damages as compensation, seek to put the injured party into the same financial position he would have been in if the contract had been performed. A successful plainfiff will be entitled to such damages as may fairly and reasonably be considered as arising naturally from the breach of contract, or such damages as may reasonably be supposed to have been in the contemplation of both parties, at the time when they made the contract, as the probable result of the breach.

The injured party must do as much as is reasonably possible to mitigate the loss, meaning the injured party must not let matters get any worse.

Recission   Recission aims at restoring the parties to the position that existed prior to the contract. On breach of a condition of a contract, the injured party may treat the contract as at an end (or rescinded) and may refuse to perform or fulfil their part of the contract. A court may rescind a contract in order to relieve a party from further liability to perform obligations. Where an injured party treats the contract as rescinded, he must return any benefits received under the contract, like a deposit.

In *McCormick v. Collinstown Stud Ltd. and Goff's Bloodstock Sales* (*Irish Times*, September 11, 1993), the plaintiff, assured that a filly, withdrawn from auction not having made the reserve price, was fine, purchased the horse with the express intention of racing. A short time later a serious condition was diagnosed which made the horse unfit for racing. The High Court concluded that the seller had used some expression to indicate that the filly was all right and this was to be regarded as an assurance that the filly was sound in wind and limb. The seller had thereby warranted the condition of the filly in a manner that would comply with one of Goff's conditions of sale that "guarantee as to soundness . . . expressly announced at the time of sale". The defect from which the filly was suffering at the time of the sale was so serious in character as to entitle the purchaser to reject the filly and return it to the defendants when the true state of affairs regarding its condition came to light. In the circumstances, the judge ordered the recission of the agreement to purchase the horse. He awarded the plaintiff damages and costs, and ordered that the horse be returned to the original owners.

Quantum Meruit

An action to recover an amount payable for the work done or the services provided, when a contract is discharged beacuse of breach by one of the parties. A claim for "as much as he has earned" is an alternative to remedy for damages.

Specific Performance

As the name suggests, a court order that a certain task contained in a contract be performed. This remedy is only available if, in the circumstances, damages are an inadequate remedy.

Injunction

A court order to a party to perform or not to perform a certain act.

Conclusion

The importance of the law of contract is based on the notion of the preservation of the private ownership of property and to that end, a system of practical rules has evolved which facilitate the voluntary transfer of property through the performance and enforcement of contracts. As the law affects many agricultural matters including seemingly routine farming transactions, an appreciation of the law of contract has become more necessary.

CHAPTER 7

EMPLOYMENT LAW AND AGRICULTURE

Paul Greene, Barrister-at-Law

1. The Contract of Employment

The working relationship between an employer and his employees is governed by the contract of employment whereby, in return for remuneration (generally the payment of a wage) an employee agrees to render a service to the employer in the form of his labour. The contract may be in writing or be agreed orally or its terms may be implied by the conduct of the parties to the contract. The contract is governed by the principles of the law of contract established by the common law, supplemented by a comprehensive body of legislative enactments by the Oireachtas, the majority of which were passed in the last two decades or so in response to an increased desire within society that employees should enjoy certain benefits as of right rather than as a privilege bestowed by the enlightened employer.

The terms of an employment contract may be express or implied. Those terms which are expressly agreed will usually include the rate at which the employee is to be paid, the hours to be worked, whether there is an entitlement to holidays (where the employee is an agricultural worker) and what period of notice is to be provided by either the employer or the employee in the event that the employment agreement is to be terminated. The implied terms of the contract will exist by virtue of common law or under statute and, in most circumstances, will be implied into a contract in order to ensure compliance with statutory demands irrespective of the wishes of one or other of the parties to the contract to seek expressly to exclude them from a written agreement. In particular, it is noteworthy that the law prohibits terms in an employment contract which purport to exclude application of certain protective legislation, such as the Unfair Dismissals Act 1977.

Terms Implied into the Employment Contract by the Common Law

2. Duties of the Employer

In the absence of any specific provisions in the employment contract, an employer has the following implied duties towards his employees.

2.1 The Payment of Wages

An employer is obliged to pay wages as and when they fall due at the rate agreed between him and the employee. Failure on the part of the employer so to do entitles the employee to treat the contract as at an end and he may leave the employment without notice. Under the Truck Acts of the nineteenth century, attempts were made to protect the employee engaged in manual work from interference with his right to deal with his wages as he saw fit. This legislation has been replaced by the Payment of Wages Act 1991. It requires that wages be paid in legal tender and without unreasonable deductions. Under the 1991 Act where both the employer and employee agree, payment may be made otherwise than in cash, by methods such as cheque, banker's draft or postal order.

In addition, the 1991 Act requires that all deductions made by an employer be itemised by the employer on a written statement of account and that the amount of wages paid to an employee be treated as confidential by the employer. An employer may make certain deductions, *e.g.* PAYE and PRSI by virtue of his statutory authority so to do; others, *e.g.* VHI contributions may only be made with the employee's consent.

2.2 The Provision of Work

Generally an employer is not obliged to provide work to his employee as long as he continues to pay the remuneration agreed under the contract of employment. Exceptions to this principle include situations where the employee needs to work in order to provide him with a reputation which he can bring to another job or where an employee, employed to do a particular task finds that the task is abolished by the employer; this latter situation amounts to a breach of contract on the part of the employer.

3. Duties of the Employee

3.1 Availability for Work

An employee must make himself available to work for the employer at the hours and on the days agreed within the contract of employment. He may not delegate his duties to another without the consent of his employer.

3.2 Obeying Lawful Orders

An employee is obliged to carry out the reasonable orders of his employer once they are within the law and do not expose him to personal danger.

3.3 Exercising Reasonable Skill and Care

There is an implied duty on an employee to exercise all reasonable care and skill in the performance of his work. He is further obliged to behave honestly, to treat confidential information with discretion and to carry out those duties in which he claims a proficiency with due diligence.

Terms Implied into the Employment Contract by Statute

4. Statute Law

As the discussion of the Payment of Wages Act 1991 above indicates, statute has played an important role not only in introducing newly implied terms into the employment contract but has served also to supplement those implied by the common law. The focus of the Oireachtas in enacting employment legislation during the recent past has been to seek to protect the employee from the unwarranted termination of the employment contract whilst striving to place on a statutory footing commonly accepted entitlements, such as holidays and attempting to remove gender inequalities in the treatment of employees.

It is important to remember that this protective legislation applies only to employees working under a contract of service, collecting a regular wage, performing recurring tasks and under the supervision of the employer. The legislation does not extend to persons contracted to perform duties of a specific one-off nature.

5.   Minimum Notice and Terms of Employment Act 1973

This Act has two purposes:

1. it sets out the minimum periods of notice which employers and employees must provide when they choose to terminate the employment contract; and

2. it requires that an employee be given a written notice setting out the terms of his employment.

The Act applies to all persons working under a contract of employment with the exception of:

1. employees who work for an employer for less than eight hours per week (as amended by the Worker Protection (Regular Part-Time Employees) Act 1991);

2. employees who work for close relatives – in particular, it should be noted that the Act does not apply in situations where the employer and employee are close relatives working on a farm on which they reside together;

3. members of the Garda Síochána or the army; and

4. most civil servants.

In addition, to benefit from the minimum periods of notice provided under the Act, an employee must have been in his employer's continuous service for a period of at least 13 weeks.

5.1   Minimum Periods of Notice

The 1973 Act lays down minimum periods of notice to be given to an employee by their employer when their employment contract is terminated; the amount of notice required is determined by the employee's length of service. It should be noted that these periods act only as the statutory minimum and it is open to the parties to allow in the employment contract for longer notice periods.

Length of service	Minimum notice
13 weeks to 2 years	1 week
2 years to 5 years	2 weeks
5 years to 10 years	4 weeks
10 years to 15 years	6 weeks
over 15 years	8 weeks

The 1973 Act requires an employee in continuous service for more than 13 weeks to give at least one week's notice. It is open to an employee to accept wages in lieu of the statutory notice period.

5.3   Written Statement of Terms

In addition the Act stipulates that employees are entitled to a written statement of the terms of their employment; the statement should include the following:

– the date the employment commences;

– how pay is calculated;

– details of when payment is due;

– basic hours of work and overtime;

– holiday entitlement;

– pension entitlements;

– the length of notice required by each party;

– if applicable, the date on which the contract will terminate.

The statement must be provided to the employee within one month of the commencement of employment.

6.   The Unfair Dismissals Acts 1977 to 1993

This Act's purpose is to protect the employee by providing a remedy in circumstances where an unfair dismissal has occurred.

The Act applies to employees who have at least one year's continuous service with the same employer and who work a minimum of eight hours weekly; however, a significant number of persons are excluded from the Act. They are:

– employees of retiring age;

– persons employed by close relatives, in particular close relatives of an employer working and residing together on a farm;

– members of the Garda Síochána or the defence forces;

– FÁS trainees and apprentices;

– most state employees.

6.1   Dismissal

Dismissal under the 1973 Act is deemed to have occurred where:

– the employer terminates the contract with or without notice;

– the contract is for a fixed term and is not renewed;

- because of the conduct of the employer the employee terminates the employment with or without notice.

The Act presumes that a dismissal is unfair until the contrary is shown by the employer. At all times the burden of proof lies on the employer.

A dismissal will always be deemed to have been unfair and impossible to justify if it resulted wholly or mainly from any of the following:

- the employee's trade union activities or membership, either outside working hours, or inside working hours at times permitted by the employer;

- the employee's religious or political opinions;

- the employee's race, colour or sexual orientation;

- the age of the employee;

- the employee's membership of the travelling community;

- the employee's pregnancy, giving birth or breastfeeding or exercise by the employee of her rights under the Maternity Protection Act 1994;

- the employee's participation in legal proceedings against the employer;

- the exercise by an adopting parent of the right under the Adoptive Leave Act 1995 to adoptive leave;

- the unfair selection of the employee for redundancy, there being no grounds for the redundancy or because the redundancy was made in a manner inconsistent with procedures agreed between the employer and the employee.

A dismissal will be deemed fair where it has resulted wholly or mainly from one or more of the following grounds:

- the competence, capability or qualifications of the employee in the performance of work which the employee was employed by the employer to do;

- the conduct of the employee;

- the redundancy of the employee;

- the continuation of the employee's employment would cause a breach of statutory provisions;

- other substantive grounds – this ground has yet to be used to successfully justify a dismissal.

Once an employee establishes the fact of his dismissal, it is presumed to be unfair. The onus of proving that the dismissal was justifiable and, therefore, fair then lies on the employer; to do so he must show that the dismissal comes within one or more of the grounds listed above.

If the dismissal relates to an employee's trade union membership or pregnancy and involves an employee without one year's continuous service, or an employee at retiring age or an employee serving an apprenticeship, the Act will apply but without the presumption that the dismissal was unfair or that the employer must justify it.

As well as showing that the dismissal was for a fair reason, an employer is obliged to establish that his decision to dismiss was taken reasonably. To show reasonableness the employer ought to have conducted a proper investigation before dismissing the employee; the employee should have been afforded an opportunity to present his side of the case before the dismissal; the employee must have been issued with at least one warning and allowed time to ameliorate the situation before his dismissal; and the employer must be able to show that agreed disciplinary procedures were followed where such exist.

6.2 Adjudication under the Unfair Dismissals Acts

An unfair dismissal claim must be made within six months of the date of dismissal; there is no provision under the legislation for an extension of the time limit. The employer is obliged, upon the employee's request, to provide, within 14 days, a written statement explaining the grounds for the employee's dismissal. A claim may be adjudicated, under the Act, by a Rights Commissioner, the Employment Appeals Tribunal (E.A.T.) and, on appeal, by the Circuit Court.

Within six months from the date of dismissal, the employee can refer the case to a Rights Commissioner, who is appointed by the Minister for Enterprise and Employment. A copy of the application must be sent to the employer. Having heard the matter, in camera, the rights commissioner issues a recommendation which may be appealed by either party to the Employment Appeals Tribunal (E.A.T.) within six weeks.

Alternatively, the matter may be initiated before the E.A.T. by an employee, without recourse to the Rights Commissioner. The matter must be initiated before the E.A.T. if the employer objects to the Rights Commissioner dealing with the case.

The E.A.T. issues a determination on the case which may be appealed to the Circuit Court. Should an employer fail to comply with the determination within six weeks, the Minister for Enterprise and Employment may seek to enforce the determination on behalf of the employee by bringing the matter before the Circuit Court. It is also open to either the employer or the employee to appeal a determination of the E.A.T. to the Circuit Court within six weeks.

6.3 Remedies under the Unfair Dismissals Acts

Three possible remedies are open to the Rights Commissioner, E.A.T. or the Circuit Court, who will decide on the most appropriate redress in all the circumstances. The remedies are:

– *Re-instatement* This involves reinstating the employee to the position he held immediately prior to his dismissal on the same terms and conditions as he enjoyed at that time. Reinstatement is deemed to have occurred as of the date on which the employee was first dismissed.

– *Re-engagement* In this instance, an employer is obliged to employ the employee in the position he held before his dismissal or in a different position that could be deemed reasonably suitable for the employee and on such terms and conditions as are reasonable in all the circumstances.

– *Damages* Here the employer must pay such compensation to the employee as is considered to be the financial loss suffered by him and is attributable to the dismissal to a maximum amount of 104 weeks pay. Considerations which might be relevant in fixing the amount of compensation may include the steps taken by the employee to mitigate his loss, whether proper procedures were followed in carrying out the dismissal and whether the employee in any way contributed to the decision to dismiss.

Rather than use the procedure laid down in the Unfair Dismissals Acts, an employee may pursue a claim for wrongful dismissal at common law by seeking a declaration of same and damages by way of plenary summons in the High Court. Whilst this approach affords a longer period within which he may initiate his claim, it may prove a costlier process and an employee will not enjoy the statutory presumptions with respect to dismissal and fairness contained in the legislation. An employee is not entitled to use both courses of action in seeking to process his claim.

7. The Employment Equality Act 1977

The purpose of this Act is to make it unlawful to discriminate on the grounds of gender or marital status in employment recruitment, conditions of employment, training or work experience or in offering promotions. An employer is further precluded from taking action against an employee who has taken action against him for discrimination.

The legislation applies to all persons working under a contract of employment except for those occupations specifically excluded under the Act, *e.g.* members of an Garda Síochána and occupations where the gender of the prospective employee is an occupational qualification.

Direct and indirect discrimination are each prohibited.

Direct Discrimination Direct discrimination shall be deemed to have occurred in the following cases:

– where by reason of his sex, a person is treated less favourably than a person of the other sex;

– where by reason of his marital status, a person is treated less favourably than a person of the same sex.

Indirect Discrimination   This occurs where, owing to a person's sex or marital status, he is obliged to comply with a demand that is not essential to the employment where the demand is such that persons of the other sex or marital status can more readily comply with it. Examples might include a minimum height requirement for a position that could not objectively be viewed as one where the potential employee's height was a relevant factor to be considered in assessing an applicant's suitability.

The 1977 Act makes it unlawful for an employer to discriminate on the grounds of sex or marital status when advertising a position for which he wishes to recruit; in limiting interviewees for a position; or to instruct his interviewers not to consider employing persons of a particular sex or marital status. Cases have decided that it is unlawful to question an applicant at interview in a fashion that could amount to less favourable treatment even where the applicant's response does not result in him being refused the position. Such questions might include queries as to how an applicant feels he might function in a single sex employment situation.

7.1   Adjudication Procedure under the Employment Equality Act 1977

Where an allegation of discrimination is made it may be referred to the Labour Court who will appoint an Equality Officer to mediate in an attempt to compromise the dispute. Where either party disagrees with the Equality Officer's recommendations, an appeal lies, within 42 days, to the Labour Court. The Labour Court may rule whether there has been discrimination, recommend a course of settling the matter and/or order the payment of compensation to a maximum of 104 weeks' pay. The Labour Court comprises a chairman, three deputy chairmen and eight ordinary members, four of whom represent employers and four who represent workers. It is open to either party to ignore a recommendation of the Labour Court unless the parties agree in advance of the hearing to be bound by the recommendation.

An appeal, on a point of law only, lies to the High Court from a determination of the Labour Court.

7.2   The Employment Equality Agency

The Employment Equality Act 1977 also provides for the establishment of an Employment Equality Agency with the following functions:

– the elimination of discrimination in the area of employment;

– the promotion of equality of opportunity in employment between men and women generally;

— the continuing review of the operation of the Employment Equality Act 1977, and the Anti-Discrimination (Pay) Act 1974, discussed below.

8.   The Anti-Discrimination (Pay) Act 1974

This Act guarantees the right to the same rate of pay between men and women who are employed in "like work" by the same employer, or by an associated employer in the same place; place has been defined to mean the same city, town or locality. The legislation guarantees not only the same rate of pay for like work but also similar overtime and holiday entitlements.

8.1   "Like Work"

The concept of "like work" applies in one of three possible fashions. They are:

— when male and female workers each perform the same work under the same or similar conditions;

— when the work performed by one is of a similar nature to that performed by the other and any differences between the work performed rarely occur or are not of significant importance compared to the work as a whole;

— where the work performed by one is of equal value to that performed by the other in terms of the demands which it makes in relation to such matters as skill, physical and mental effort, responsibility and general working conditions.

It should be noted that the legislation does not prohibit difference in rates of pay for the same work for reasons other than a difference in sex between employees.

The 1974 Act sets out a procedure akin to that under the Employment Equality Act 1977. A complaint is initially referred to an Equality Officer of the Labour Court; a complaint may be referred by an employee, an employer, a trade union, an employer's organisation or by the Employment Equality Agency. Following an investigation the Equality Officer issues a recommendation which may be appealed by either party to the Labour Court within 42 days. Thereafter an appeal lies to the High Court on a point of law. It is an offence to fail to act on the decision of the Labour Court.

9.   The Redundancy Payments Acts 1967 To 1991

This body of legislation makes provision for lump sum payments to dismissed employees whose dismissal is due to the complete or partial shut-down of their place of employment, or due to a decrease in the employer's needs for employees of that kind or qualification. The payment of pay-related social insurance (PRSI) by employers and employees contributes to a redundancy fund which is run by the State. The fund provides a rebate to the employer to a maximum of 60 per cent of the redundancy which he has paid to the dismissed employees. Payment is made from the redundancy fund directly to the employee in circumstances where the employer is either unable or unwilling to make a redundancy payment.

All persons working under a contract of employment are covered by the Redundancy Payments Acts if they are between the ages of 16 and retirement age and if, while they were employed, they were normally expected to work for eight hours or more per week for the employer who has made them redundant. The dismissed employee must be in employment which is insurable for benefits under the Social Welfare Acts or have been in such employment in the two years prior to their redundancy.

9.1   Entitlement

Entitlement to redundancy is afforded to the employee who has been continuously employed by the same employer for two years or more after the attainment of 16 years of age and his dismissal is by reason of redundancy or he has been laid off or is on "short time" for a specified minimum period. The concept of short time is defined as a situation where because of a decrease in the employees work load, a decrease in earnings or the hours worked by him in any week are less than half of his normal weekly working hours. An employee's absence through sickness or injury for up to eighteen months, strikes and maternity leave do not constitute a break in the employee's continuous service for the purposes of the Redundancy Payments Acts.

Dismissal is presumed to have been by reason of redundancy until the contrary is shown by the employer. Should the employee have his contract of employment renewed or should he be unreasonably refused a suitable offer of alternative employment, it is unlikely that his claim for a redundancy payment will succeed.

9.2   Calculation of Payment

In calculating the amount due as a redundancy payment to a qualifying dismissed employee regard is had to his length of continuous employment, age and wage. He is entitled to a half week's pay for each year of continuous employment between the ages of 16 and 41, a full week's pay for each year of continuous employment over the age of 41 years plus the equivalent of one week's normal pay.

10.   Employment of Young Persons and Part-Time Employees

Two Acts of the Oireachtas have sought to assist young and part-time employees by, in the first place, bringing them within the ambit of other legislation designed to protect employees generally and, secondly, by setting out a regime to prevent the exploitation of persons required to enter into employment contracts at a younger age than that normally expected in society.

10.1   Workers Protection (Regular Part-Time Employees) Act 1991

The Act's purpose is to provide "regular part-time" workers, as defined, with the protection, *inter alia*, of the following legislation:

– Minimum Notice and Terms of Employment Act 1974

– Unfair Dismissals Act 1977

– Redundancy Payments Acts, 1967 to 1991

– Holidays (Employees) Act 1973

"Regular Part-Time"   *Worker* The Act defines a "regular part-time" worker as one in the continuous service of an employer under a contract of employment for a minimum period of 13 weeks. The Act further requires that the employee be ordinarily expected to work at least eight hours in any week.

The Employment Appeals Tribunal is empowered to deal with disputes that may arise in circumstances where employers seek to avoid coming within the scope of the Act by reducing an employee's hours of work to less than eight per week or by purporting to employ a person on a series of fixed term contracts of employment, each for a duration of less than 13 weeks.

The protection of the legislation enumerated above is extended to employees qualifying under this Act to the same extent as all other employees benefiting already from those statutes. Holiday entitlement for regular part-time employees is, however calculated in a manner different to that which relates to full-time employees under the Holiday (Employees) Act 1973. A regular part-time employee is now entitled to annual leave at the rate of six hours for each 100 hours he works. With respect to pay for public holidays, where the employment has ceased in the five week period immediately before the public holiday, a regular part-time employee must show that he has worked for at least four weeks of that five-week period in order to qualify for a day's pay for the public holiday.

10.4   Protection of Young Persons (Employment) Act 1977

The Act applies to workers under 18 years of age. As well as extending the protection of employment legislation to young persons it serves to regulate the minimum age for entry into employment, regulates a young person's working hours, provides for statutory rest periods for young persons and prohibits night work for young persons.

In general, a person under the age of fifteen is prohibited from entering into a contract of employment, though, in limited circumstances, a person of 14 may work provided that the work is undertaken outside of school hours and does not impinge upon his education. An employer may not employ a person under the age of eighteen without the provision of a birth certificate by the young person; a child (*i.e.* a person aged between 14 and 15) may not be employed without the provision of a written permission from the child's parent or guardian.

A child or young person's employment may only involve work of a light non-industrial nature which does not prove harmful to the health or normal development of the employee. During the school term a child may work a maximum of fourteen hours per week; the figure increases to 35 during the school holidays. A young person aged between 15 and 16 years may work a maximum of 40 hours per week and in the case of a young person aged between sixteen and eighteen, the statutory maximum is 45 hours per week.

Where an employer employs children or young persons, the Act obliges him to keep a record of the particulars of each such employee. The record should include the employee's full name, date of birth, hours of work each day, rate of pay and the total amount paid to the employee in wages. It is a statutory offence for an employer to fail to keep such a record.

11. Termination of the Contract of Employment

Much of the statutory provisions and implied common law terms discussed, above, are obviously of relevance should the termination of an employment come about in a situation of acrimony between the employer and employee and, it will be appreciated, enactments such as the Unfair Dismissals Act 1977, came about in an attempt to ensure that an employee, in particular, would not find his employment terminated by reason of what might be perceived as the arbitrary or capricious action of an employer. As well as the statutory protection afforded by such legislation a person may also find his remedy at common law.

The principal remedy is the institution of proceedings for damages for wrongful dismissal. Here a dismissed employee will seek a declaration that the termination was unlawful and claim damages for the resultant loss suffered. In such circumstances damages are, in reality, the only realistic option available to the dismissed employee; a court will be very slow to grant an order requiring the re-instatement of the employee as it will take the view that the mutual trust necessary to the employment relationship has broken down.

In measuring the appropriate damages to be awarded to the wrongfully dismissed employee, a court will have regard to the ordinary principles of the law of contract. In general damages will be measured by reference to the amount that the employee would have earned had he been given a reasonable period of notice of termination of the employment contract. An employer might, therefore, seek to cut off an employee's potential cause of action by paying him a reasonable sum (perhaps a month's wages) in lieu of a notice period. In addition, an employee seeking to litigate in this way must, as with all disputes in contract show that he made his best efforts to mitigate his loss by, for example, doing all that he could to find himself suitable alternative employment as soon as possible after the termination of the employment.

CHAPTER 8

EMPLOYERS' LIABILITY

Elizabeth Mullins, Barrister-at-Law

Self-employed people may be liable in law for injuries to anybody that works for them in the same way that employers are liable for injuries to their employees that they could have prevented. They have many duties to people that work for them but none more fundamental than their duty to their workers' health and safety. The law expects an employer to take reasonable care for his employees' safety, even if they are not full time employees. If they are under the farmer's control then he must take reasonable care. Employers are not expected to prevent the occurrence of all accidents at work nor to prevent any employees becoming ill through work. It is understood that in any normal everyday endeavour or routine an accident can occur or an illness can result. It is only if this accident or illness was caused by a negligent act or omission of the employer that the employer will be held liable for it.

At common law a self-employed person has no duty of care to himself. This still holds true to some extent in legislation but he does have a duty to his own health and safety in the same way as he has to anybody who may be affected by the way he conducts his undertaking as regards their health and safety. In the Health and Safety Regulations 1993 the provisions apply to a self-employed person as if he is an employer and his own employee. Therefore, it is necessary to go through the common law of this area with that in mind.

Common Law

An employer's duty to his employees at common law is not absolute; there is a limit to the duty of care owed to employees. However, the legislature has introduced some absolute duties which I will deal with later in this chapter. In *Hough v. Irish Base Metals Ltd* (unreported, Supreme Court, 1967) an employer was held not negligent where one of his employees was injured when jumping away from a gas fire placed near him for a joke by another employee. In that case the court found that the accident was not caused by anything the employer had done. The court held that the nature of the "larking" was such as to make it not easily detectable since it was of recent origin and infrequently engaged in. Therefore it could not reasonably be said that an employer who did not detect it had failed in his duty to provide a safe system of supervision.

Similarly in *Brady v. Beckmann Instruments (Galway) Inc.* [1984] I.L.R.M. 361 where an employee contacted dermatitis as a result of inhaling certain fumes. The Supreme Court found that while the evidence established that the employee did develop dermatitis from the level of exposure to which he was subjected, it was, on the evidence a result so unique and improbable as not to be reasonably foreseeable by his employers. Therefore the injured party's employers were found not to be negligent. As Mr Justice Henchy stated in *Bradley v. C.I.E.* [1976] I.R. 217:

> "the law does not require an employer to ensure in all circumstances the safety of his workmen. He will have discharged his duty if he does what a reasonable and prudent employer would have done in the circumstances".

While the courts impose a limit on this duty they equally hold employers to a high standard of care.

At common law it is held that if an employer employs competent workmen, gives them adequate materials and resources and maintains a safe system of work within which to do the job assigned, then he has fulfilled his obligations. However the courts do look very carefully at these criteria and the factual circumstance of every accident before deciding if the applicable standard of care has been reached.

They will consider whether the workmen employed are competent to do the specific job assigned to them, if they have had sufficient training to do the job safely and whether their colleagues are competent and not a danger to them. An employer must not ask a workman to carry out a task that he cannot do safely either due to lack of experience or lack of training. In *Doran v. Dublin Plant Hire Ltd* [1990] 1 I.R. 488 the court found that not only should an employer provide proper training and instruction but he must also ensure that all necessary instruction manuals are provided to his employees so that they may use any equipment safely. Employees must have full and complete knowledge of how to undertake their work safely.

The courts look at the equipment provided to do the assigned task and whether it is suitable for the task at hand. If any adjustments are made to the equipment for a particular job they must be made with due regard to safety. A continuing duty is owed to employees to ensure that all equipment is properly maintained and kept in good repair. This duty is personal to the employer and may not be delegated to an independent contractor. In *O'Hanlon v. E.S.B.* [1969] I.R. 75 the court found the employers negligent for not providing the necessary equipment even when they had expressly prohibited their employee from proceeding with the job without this equipment.

The method by which the job is done will be scrutinised by the courts to see if it was a safe and reasonable way of doing the job in all the circumstances. It was held in *General Cleaning Ltd. v. Christmas* [1952] 2 All E.R. 1110 that it was "the duty of an employer to give such general safety instructions as a reasonably careful employer who has considered the problems presented by the work would give his workmen". This requirement apples to everyday repetitive work and to isolated tasks. In *Patrick Caufield v. George Bell & Co. Ltd* (1959) 93 I.L.T.R. 108 the judge held that the expression a "safe system of work" has to be considered in every case, in relation to the particular circumstances of the case in hand. The word "safe" meaning as safe as reasonably possible in the circumstances.

Safety, Health and Welfare at Work Act 1989

These common law concepts may seem difficult to grasp in practical terms in seeking to limit one's liability. So to aid the self-employed employer the legislature enacted the Safety, Health and Welfare at Work Act 1989. This Act deals more particularly with an employer's duties to his employees than with the self- employed person's duties but it is useful to go through all the provisions because they apply even if only one person is employed.

Also while the Act defines "employee" as a person who has entered into or works (or if the contract of employment has terminated, worked) under a contract of employment with an employer, the 1993 Regulations widen the scope to include "fixed-term employee", as being an employee whose employment is governed by a contract of employment for a fixed term or a specified purpose. This purpose would be where the duration of the contract was limited but was, at the time of its making, incapable of a precise date of termination and applies to temporary employees.

Therefore, it is important to keep within the confines of the Act in discharging your duties to all those who work for you. Some of the provisions may only be applicable if a farm employs a number of full time workers, such as those dealing with an employee representative but it is still a good idea for the farmers to understand what the law expects so that they can decide how best to satisfy their duties.

The Safety, Health and Welfare at Work Act 1989 applies to criminal liability only and the Act cannot be used in civil litigation. However, if a farmer obeys the provisions of this Act it is likely that he will avoid civil liability as well as criminal sanctions. The 1993 Safety, Health and Welfare at Work (General Application) Regulations 1993 (S.I. No. 44 of 1993) bring many of the 1989 Act provisions into the civil jurisdiction. For the sake of simplicity I will go through the provisions of the Act and I will only mention those parts of the Regulations that vary from the Act.

The 1989 Act reduces the fundamental common law principles into a mechanism under which employers can fulfil their obligations to their employees safety. To make best use of this Act it is necessary to understand what the legislature expects of the employer.

Section 6 of the Act goes through the employers duties to his employees: "It shall be the duty of every employer to ensure, so far as reasonably practicable the safety, health and welfare at work of all his employees." The section then goes on to give instances where the employer has a specific duty to his employees:

– The employer must ensure that the place of work is as safe as reasonably practicable and without risk to his employees' health, and that as much of the access to and egress from the place of work that is under the employer's control is safe.

– The employer must provide and maintain all plant and machinery so that they are safe to use.

– If in the circumstances it is not reasonably practicable for the employer to eliminate the hazards at work then he has a duty to provide and maintain suitable protective equipment or clothing.

– Any such equipment or clothing must not involve any financial cost to the employee.

– The employer must also organise and maintain systems of work that are, so far as reasonably practicable, safe and without risk to health. To achieve this he must instruct, train and supervise his employees as is necessary.

– There must be in place adequate emergency plans and he must, where necessary employ a competent person to ensure the safety and health at work of his employees.

Section 7(2) of the 1989 Act states that it shall be the duty of every self-employed person to conduct his undertaking in such a way as to ensure, so far as reasonably practicable, that he and others who (not being his employees) may be affected are not exposed to risks to their safety and health.

Safety Statement

The 1989 Act demands that all employers prepare a safety statement which specifies the manner in which the safety, health and welfare of persons employed shall be secured at work. This statement can be used in evidence in civil and criminal proceedings so it is imperative that an adequate statement exists.

The statement identifies and assesses hazards at work and their risk to the health and safety of persons employed. It is a general statement of safety at work but section 12 of the Act does mention a number of matters the statement should specify. It should state the arrangements made and resources provided for safeguarding health and safety. It should state what co-operation is required from employees and if there are specific health and safety tasks assigned to particular employees it should list the names and job titles of these employees.

If an inspector is unhappy with the safety statement in place and feels that it is inadequate in some material respect, he may direct that the statement is revised and the employer must comply with his directions within thirty days. If the farm is run by a company then the employer is required to include in its Section 158 report the extent to which the safety statement was adhered to during the period of time covered by the said report.

Safety Representative

Under the 1989 Act, an employer must consult with his employees so as to bring about effective co-operation in developing health and safety measures. Employees may appoint a safety representative for these consultations with their employer. A safety representative may make representations to an employer on any aspect of health and safety and an employer should consider and – if necessary, act on these suggestions. Of his own accord or with his employer's approval, a safety representative may inspect the work place and if it is reasonable to assume that a risk of personal injury exists, to investigate potential hazards and complaints. While he may investigate accidents, a safety representative may not interfere with the performance of any statutory obligations. He may also meet with any inspector, and employers have a duty to inform the safety representative when a safety inspector enters a place of work. He may make representations to the inspector and receive advice from the inspector.

A safety representative must be afforded such time off as is necessary to acquire the requisite knowledge for the discharge of his duties and to fulfil the responsibilities attached to the job.

Employers Duties to Persons other than his Employees

In general if a person is found at a place of work at a time work is going on, he is deemed to be an employee for the purposes of the 1989 Act. However, an employer has duties to people other than his employees. As discussed, under section 7 of the 1989 Act a self-employed person is obliged to conduct his business in such a manner as to ensure that persons not in his employment who may be affected are not exposed to risks to their health or safety. A self-employed person must also give those people that are affected the necessary information about his undertaking as might affect their safety or health. A farmer's duty to strangers to his enterprise will be dealt with more fully and completely in chapter 9, "Occupiers Liability". Suffice to say here that the courts will look at the safety of the system of work in operation and all other attending safety measures.

In *Mullen v. Quinnsworth (trading as Crazy Prices) (No. 2)* [1991] I.L.R.M.

439 (S.C.) where a customer slipped on cooking oil in an aisle of a supermarket, the court held that the system devised to cope with spillage's had not been adequate, therefore the employer was held liable in negligence. Section 8 of the 1989 Act imposes a duty on employers to persons not directly employed, persons such as independent contractors and employees of persons employed by the employer.

Safety, Health and Welfare at Work (General Application) Regulations 1993

These Regulations are based on the duties imposed in the 1989 Act and they impose liability in civil law. One area in which the Regulations impose new duties on self-employed employers is their duties in time of emergency.

Emergency Duties

The employer must take into account the type of farm he has when planning emergency measures; also the amount of people present and the nature of the activities. He must arrange contact with the appropriate emergency services. Employees must have training in the measures to be used in an emergency, especially in the equipment to be used. Employees must also have knowledge of the dangers or risks to which they are exposed and the steps to be taken for their own protection.

In the event of an emergency, instructions must be given and action taken to enable employees to stop work and proceed to safety. Employees cannot be penalised for leaving work in these circumstances. In exceptional circumstances an employer may ask an employee to resume work; he must give a reason for this request.

Employers have duties to ensure that first-aid equipment is provided and maintained in every place where working takes place, and that it is adequate to render first-aid. They must also ensure that there are sufficiently qualified individuals to administer first-aid.

Lifting and Carrying

The law puts special emphasis in ensuring that a safe system of work exists. Generally, if there is a safe system of work then there has been compliance in the other aspects of health and welfare. In the farm industry where there is a lot of lifting and carrying, back injuries are a risk. Lifting heavy containers of foodstuffs and pieces of machinery can cause serious injuries if they are carried in an unsafe fashion. For this reason it is vital for the farmer to devise and adhere to a safe system of lifting and carrying.

Part VI of the Safety, Health and Welfare at Work (General Application) Regulations 1993 defines manual handling of loads as:

"any transporting or supporting of a load by one or more employees and including lifting, putting down, pushing, pulling, carrying or moving a load, which by reason of its characteristics or unfavourable ergonomic conditions, involves risk, particularly of back injury, to employees. In these Regulations employees include those who are employed for a fixed term or for a specific purpose and therefore this provision applies directly to farmers who may employ on an ad hoc basis."

An employer is held to have a duty to his employees to take whatever measures appropriate to avoid the necessity of manual handling of loads. If it is necessary then the workplace must be laid out in such a way, and sufficient means used, to reduce the risk involved in manual handling. Employers are expected to assess the risks and the dangers inherent in lifting and carrying and they must take care to avoid or reduce the risk, particularly of back injury to employees. In doing this he must take into account the characteristics of the working environment.

Employees must be given general indications, and where possible precise information on the weight of the load they are expected to carry and the centre of gravity of the heaviest side of a package, if it is eccentrically loaded.

When taking into account the physical effort which may present a risk the employer must look at how strenuous the effort must be; if the employee must twist himself into an awkward angle or if the load can only be held while the employee is in bad posture or if the load is likely to move or jerk suddenly.

The employer is also advised to look at the work environment and how that may increase any risk, particularly of back injury.

- Is there enough room vertically as well as in floor space to carry out the activity?

- Is the floor uneven or slippery having due regard to the employee's footwear?

- Is the place of work such a type as to require the load to be carried at an unsafe height or to be carried in a bad posture?

The employer must be alert to the dangers of an unstable floor or foot rest, or if there are variations in the level of the floor. An employer must be alert to the dangers of the temperature, humidity or ventilation in existence, being unsuitable for the handling of loads. Employers should develop a system whereby the lifting, lowering or carrying distances are minimised.

In general, an activity may present a risk, particularly of back injury if it involves over frequent or over prolonged physical effort involving the spine or if the employee isn't given sufficient bodily rest or recovery periods after the activity. An employee should be able to alter the rate of work if need be. An employee may especially be at risk if he is physically unsuited to carry out the task, if he doesn't have adequate training or appropriate knowledge to carry out the task, or if he is unsuitably dressed or if he is not wearing suitable footwear for the task.

Maximum Weights

By the Manual Labour (Maximum Weights and Transport) Regulations 1972 there are maximum weights that men and women are allowed lift. Since 1993 these maximum weights are of general application. The breakdown of these are as follows:

- an adult male should not carry a weight above 55kg (121lbs);

- an adult female should not carry a weight above 16kg (35.2lbs);

- a male between 16 and 18 years of age should not carry a weight above 16kg (35.2lbs);

- a female between 16 and 18 years of age should not carry a weight above 11kg (24.2lbs);

- a person between 14 and 16 years of age should not carry a weight above 8kg (17.6lbs).

Machinery

In farming there can be a lot of heavy machinery which can be dangerous and constitute a risk to anybody using it. The 1993 Regulations outline the duties a farmer owes in respect of the use of this machinery. He must ensure that it is suitable for the work being carried out; if it needs to be specially adapted for the particular job, care must be taken that it is adapted safely. When selecting equipment it is important to have regard to the specific working conditions and how its use may cause additional hazards to the health and safety of workers. If the machinery must be used, appropriate measures should be taken to minimise any risk. The use of dangerous machinery must be restricted to those required to use it. Any modifications or repairs must be carried out only by workers competent to do so. Information should be given on the risks attached to the use of the machinery and how to deal with any situations that may arise.

Enforcement of the 1989 Act

The National Authority for Occupational Safety and Health is the principal supervisory body set up to administer the Act. Its functions are to encourage the promotion of health and safety at work by providing information and advice on these and related matters. In particular the Authority evaluates and publishes results of research and surveys. It may have regard to any matters related to health and safety of employees and any other persons who are at risk from work activities. The Authority may appoint advisory committees as it thinks necessary to advise on these matters. The Authority may draw up and issue codes of practice which should be of practical guidance in complying with the Statute.

It is a good idea to keep up to date with any codes that are relevant to the farming industry.

Enforcing Agency and Inspectors

An enforcing agency can be appointed to enforce these duties and obligations for the Authority. This agency has a duty to furnish any reports or information relating to its functions to the Authority as required. The agency authorises a person to be an inspector who then carries a certificate of authorisation. When exercising his powers of inspection he must be able to produce this certificate or an authenticated copy with a form of personal identification.

An inspector has powers to enter, inspect and search any place he has reasonable cause to believe is used as a place of work. He may bring a garda if he believes his entry will be obstructed. He may take any other authorised person or equipment or materials required for any purpose for which power of entry is being exercised. If he has reasonable cause to believe that an offence under the Act is being committed, he is entitled to use reasonable force to gain entry, provided he has a warrant from a District Court judge.

Once he has entered the place of work an inspector may examine and enquire as is necessary to ascertain whether the employers' obligations to their employees' health and safety are being upheld. He may require the production of all relevant documentation such as the safety statement or any books, registers or notices. For the purposes of any examination the inspector can require any person whom he believes to be able to give him relevant information to answer relevant questions. This person must sign a declaration of the truth of answers given. However nobody is required to incriminate himself.

The employer must direct that the place of work is left undisturbed for as long as is reasonably necessary for the purposes of the examination. The inspector can require that any substances be handed over for analysis and if any article or substance is found which may cause a danger to health and safety it may be dismantled. It may not be destroyed unless in the circumstances this is necessary. This power must be used in the presence of the person with responsibilities for the place of work. Any articles and substances taken may be kept for as long as is necessary to examine them, they may not be tampered with as they may be used in evidence.

Improvement Plan

An inspector may serve directions in writing to anybody who is engaged in activities or intends to engage in activities when he thinks these activities may involve a risk to the safety or health of persons. This improvement direction requires a submission by the person controlling this activity of an improvement plan specifying the remedial action proposed to rectify the matters stated in the direction. If this plan is not adequate an inspector may direct that the plan be revised and resubmitted to him within a specified time.

Improvement Notice

If the inspector believes that an employer is contravening any of these provisions or has failed to submit or implement an appropriate improvement plan, he may serve on the employer an improvement notice. An improvement notice shall specify that the Inspector is of the opinion that the employer is contravening the Act by his activity and his reasons for this belief will be stated. The notice will direct that the employer remedy these alleged contraventions and the remedial measures to be taken. These measures must be taken by a date specified. This date should not be during the period within which an appeal can be brought.

Appeal An employer aggrieved by an improvement notice may appeal within 14 days, beginning on the date the notice is served on the employer. The appeal is made to the local District Court judge. If he thinks it is reasonable in the circumstances he may confirm, modify or cancel the notice.

When appealing an improvement notice an employer must notify the Authority, or the enforcing agency as appropriate, of the appeal and the grounds for it. The Authority or the enforcing agency shall be entitled to appear, be heard and adduce evidence at the hearing of the appeal.

If the improvement notice is confirmed or the appeal is withdrawn then the notice comes into effect on the day following that day. If there was no appeal the notice takes effect on the expiration of the period during which an appeal may have been taken or the date specified on the notice whichever is the later. An inspector can withdraw an improvement notice at any time before the date specified in the notice or he can extend or further extend that date at any time while an appeal is not pending.

Prohibition Notice

If there are activities being carried on or likely to be carried on which may involve a risk of serious personal injury to persons at a place of work, an inspector may serve a prohibition notice on the employer or the person in control of the activity. This notice shall state that the inspector holds this opinion and his reasons for so holding. The notice will state the statutory provisions being contravened and it will direct that the activity causing this serious risk shall stop until the risk no longer exists. A prohibition notice takes effect immediately on the person in control of the activity being served with the notice, if the notice so declares. Otherwise the prohibition takes effect after the period during which an appeal can be taken has ended or the day following the day an appeal is withdrawn.

Appeal The bringing of an appeal does not prevent the prohibition notice taking effect unless the appellant applies to court to have the operation of the notice suspended until the appeal has been heard. The court may think it proper to direct its suspension. An appeal may be brought within seven days of receiving the prohibition notice. The District Court judge may confirm, modify or cancel the prohibition notice; even if the notice is confirmed, the District Court judge may suspend the operation of the notice for a length of time he thinks appropriate. An appellant must notify the Authority or enforcing agency of his intention to appeal and they are entitled to appear and adduce evidence at the hearing. If a prohibition notice exists and there is a contravention of it the inspector may apply to the High Court for an order prohibiting the continuance of these activities. The court may grant an injunction if it thinks fit.

Order of the High Court

If the Authority or enforcing agency considers that the risk to the health and safety of persons is so serious then the use of the place of work or that part of it causing the risk, may be restricted or immediately prohibited by order of the High Court. Any such order shall take effect notwithstanding the existence of any other permission for this use.

Obtaining and Disclosure of Information

To obtain information needed by the Authority to discharge its functions, it may serve a notice in writing on an employer requiring that person to furnish the information requested in the notice within a specified time. The information requested must be related to the protection of the health, safety and welfare of persons. This information must be provided unless there is an appeal being taken out against the notice or unless it is still within the time period when an appeal can be taken to the District Court. This time period is within seven days of the request for the information. The information requested must be provided within the time specified in the notice or on such a day that the Authority may agree. The District Court judge may confirm, modify or cancel the notice. He may confirm the notice and still suspend its operation for an appropriate time. The judge has a discretion as to what order to make in relation to the legal costs for bringing the appeal.

An inspector may, in the discharge of his duties, ask an officer of Customs and Excise to detain any articles imported for not more than 48 hours. This detention is for the purposes of examining the articles to ensure that they are not a risk to health and safety. An inspector may obtain information from the Revenue Commissioners in connection with the importation of articles and substances in to the State. The Authority may receive information from the Minister for Health and the Minister for Social Welfare regarding personal injuries to persons at work. However there are some restrictions to this exchange of information, it can only be used for the purposes of this Act.

The 1989 Act provides that consent is not necessary from the person in control of the place of work, usually the employer, before disclosure of information to the Authority, the enforcing agency or a Government Minister. Any information so disclosed may only be used for legal proceedings or an investigation or inquiry held by virtue of this Act. Consent is necessary from the person who furnished the information or controlled the place of work for the use of the information for any other purpose.

An inspector can still inform employees or their representative of factual information to do with their place of work as long as no trade secrets are disclosed. Employers must be given all the information that their employees receive.

Special Reports and Inquiries

The Authority may at any time direct a member of its staff or other competent person to investigate the circumstances surrounding an accident, disease, occurrence, situation or other related matter which happened at a place of work. The investigating person then makes a special report, if he is not an inspector he shall have all their powers. This report may be made public within a reasonable time and in such a manner as he thinks fit. A tribunal may be set up to inquire into the accident or occurrence. The tribunal will have the powers of a District Court judge and of an inspector under the Act. The tribunal shall make a report to the Authority stating the causes and circumstances of the accident and adding observations. This report may be made public.

Offences

Employers and self-employed persons are liable in criminal law if they fail to discharge any of their duties under the Safety, Health and Welfare at Work Act 1989. It is also an offence under the Act to attempt to prevent or obstruct an inspector in the exercise of his functions or if an employer refuses or fails to comply with a bona fide request of an inspector. Similarly it is an offence to fail to submit an improvement plan to an inspector. However, it is a good defence to a prosecution if it can be shown that other measures providing equal protection were taken. Generally, an employer is liable for any obstruction or any false statement which purports to comply with a requirement of the Act, including any intentionally false entry in a book or document.

If an employer is found guilty of an offence for which no express financial penalty is provided, he shall be liable on summary conviction to a fine not exceeding £1,000. If the offence relates to a specific duty then he shall be liable on summary conviction to a fine not exceeding £1,000 or on conviction on indictment, a fine of an amount to be decided by the court. If an employer contravenes a prohibition order, discloses information contrary to the Act or does or intends to contravene a term of a licence existing or undertakes an activity without a licence where one is required, he is liable on summary conviction to a fine not exceeding £1,000. If he is convicted on indictment, the employer is liable to a fine of an unlimited amount or at the court's discretion, a term of imprisonment not exceeding two years or both a fine and a term of imprisonment.

Proceedings may be instituted at any time within one year after the offence. Any summary offence may be prosecuted by the Authority or the enforcing agency whichever is the more appropriate. An employer or the Authority can appeal a District Court order to the Circuit Court. The Circuit Court decision is final.

The Minister may prescribe any work activity as one requiring a licence for the purpose of protecting the health, safety or welfare of persons at work. The Authority has a discretion whether to grant or refuse an application for a licence and may put conditions on the licence granted.

Where there is a special report made, or an inquiry or a coroner's inquest is held concerning the death of any person caused by an accident at work or a disease contracted at work, a person may be prosecuted within six months of the report or inquest for contravening safety or health legislation. If there is a coroner's inquest then the employer has a right to ask questions of a witness subject to the Coroner allowing it as a proper question.

CHAPTER 9

OCCUPIERS' LIABILITY

Edward S. Walsh

Introduction

Over the last two decades, the liability of an occupier of land or premises has expanded beyond all recognition. The old common law approach in relation to occupier liability imposed a duty of care upon occupiers which depended upon the status of the entrant to the land. The four categories of entrant at common law were according to the benefit they endowed on the occupier and the duty owed was determined by that benefit. The categories comprise: contractual invitees, invited on foot of a contract; invitees who entered in pursuance of what was termed a common interest or joint interest; a licensee who was permitted onto the land but whose visit did not confer any material benefit; and finally, a trespasser.

Over the years, there has been a tendency by the courts to approach the issue as to liability of an occupier along the lines of the tort of negligence. This first occurred in the case of *Purtill v. Athlone U.D.C.* [1968] I.R. 205, where a boy who had been on the premises of an abattoir who had stolen some detonators from the premises was injured when he was exploding them at his home. The High Court held the defendant liable in negligence for the injury, subject to a finding of contributory negligence of 15 per cent against the plaintiff. The defendant appealed to the Supreme Court and in the course of the appeal contended that as occupiers of the abattoir, their only duty to the plaintiff, a trespasser, had been to refrain from setting a trap for him and that they were not in breach of that duty.

The Supreme Court, however, was of the opinion that the defendant's liability to the plaintiff could not be determined by an application of the standards of duty owed by an occupier to a person who came to the occupier's premises. Instead that issue should be determined by deciding whether or not the parties were sufficiently proximate to each other at the relevant time to impose on the defendants the ordinary duty to take reasonable care for the plaintiff's safety. The fact that the plaintiff had been a trespasser was not a relevant factor in making that decision.

Purtill v. Athlone U.D.C. was in many respects the wedge in the door through which the Courts subsequently introduced the overall concept of negligence in the law of occupier's liability.

The landmark decision which radically altered the law of occupier liability particularly *vis-à-vis* a trespasser was the later case of *McNamara v. Electricity Supply Board* [1975] I.R. 1. In that case, the plaintiff who was 11 years of age at the time of the accident climbed over a wire fence which surrounded an electricity transformer station. He was injured when, in an effort to catch hold of a drainpipe and slide down from a flat roofed extension within the station, his hand came into contact with a high tension cable some 13 inches distant from the drainpipe. The original station had been built in 1929 and a flat roof extension was built in 1956. In the intervening years, the area around the station had become considerably built up. The E.S.B. were fully conscious of the potential danger which the transformer station posed to children. At the time of the accident, a wire fencing barrier surrounding the station was being repaired and so far from acting as a barrier it in fact facilitated access to the flat roof extension.

In the High Court, the jury before whom the case was tried found that the defendant was negligent, the plaintiff had not been negligent and proceeded to award damages in the sum of £34,772, which the defendant appealed to the Supreme Court. Whilst the Supreme Court set aside the original award on the grounds that the damages were excessive, the court also directed a retrial on all issues. In the course of the Supreme Court judgments, the court was concerned with the duty of care as owed and this Mr Justice Walsh stated to be:

> "[When] the danger is reasonably foreseeable the duty to take care to avoid injury to those who are proximate when that proximity is known is not abrogated because the other party is a trespasser. The duty to those in proximity is not based on any implied term of an invitation or a licence whereupon any warranty for safety which might be thought to be inherent in any such invitation or licence. Rather it is based upon the duty that one man has to those in proximity to him to take reasonable care that they are not injured by his acts. What amounts to sufficient care must vary necessarily with the circumstances, the nature of the danger and the age and knowledge of the person likely to be injured."

The decision of the Supreme Court in the *McNamara* case caused as many problems as it solved, leading to uncertainty as to whether or not the law in the light of the *McNamara* decision favoured the trespasser as compared to the mere licensee or indeed invitee. Mr Justice Niall McCarthy sent a shot across the bows of the old categorised liability of the occupier, which depended upon the status of the entrant, in the case of *Foley v. Musgrave Cash and Carry Ltd*, an unreported judgment of the Supreme Court of December 20, 1985. In the course of his judgment he said:

> "[In] the case of alleged occupier liability I find little assistance in examination of different and somewhat artificial legal relationships. In my view cases of this

kind are better approached on the simple principle of foreseeable risk the duty to take reasonable care to avoid unnecessary risk of injury to persons who may come upon the premises."

Similarly in that case, Mr Justice Griffin stated:

"The plaintiff was on the premises as an invitee of the defendant's. In modern times it appears to me that the duty owed by the occupier to an invitee could best be said to be to take reasonable care in all the circumstances to see that the premises are reasonably safe for the invitee".

Today, in a case of this kind, it seems to matter little whether this test is used or whether the test of foresight or proximity enunciated by Walsh J. in *Purtill v. Athlone U.D.C.* or that of the neighbour principle stated by Lord Atkin in *Donoghue v. Stevenson* [1933] A.C. 562 is applied.

Subsequently, in *Rooney v. Connolly* [1987] I.L.R.M. 768, Mr Justice McCarthy reiterated his disapproval of what he termed to be "the artificial legal relationships" and went on to say that:

"[In] my view the liability, if any, of the occupier of premises to any person injured thereon should be tested in the same manner as any other action laid in negligence – whether or not it was a failure to take reasonable care with such guidance as to the application of that principle as may be necessary in the circumstances of a particular case."

In the light of the concern as to the apparent increased burden on the part of a landowner *vis-à-vis* a trespasser, the farming organisations undertook considerable lobbying of the elected representatives with the result that in 1993 a private members' bill relating to occupier liability was introduced but did not progress beyond the initial stage. A similar attempt in 1994 failed. The Law Reform Commission was instructed to consider the overall position and in turn produced the *Occupiers' Liability Report* (No. 46 of 1994). This report in turn led to the Occupiers' Liability Act 1995. The long title of the Act is:

"An Act to amend the law relating to the liability of occupiers of premises (including land) in respect of dangers existing on such premises for injury or damage to persons or property while on such premises and to provide for connected matters."

In essence, the 1995 Act greatly simplified the legal position of entrants by dividing them into two simple categories:

1. **Visitors** Persons who were present by permission, by agreement or by right, and for whom the occupier must take reasonable care of their safety and other circumstances.

2. **"Recreational Users"** (as distinct from trespassers) Recreational users and trespassers were both entitled to a right not to be injured intentionally or by the occupiers' reckless disregard for their own safety. It was only in the case

of recreational users that an occupier was under the further liability where a structure was provided on the land for the use of such recreational user to ensure that such structure was maintained in a safe condition.

Under section 1(1) of the Occupiers' Liability Act 1995, an "occupier" of a premises is defined as meaning any person exercising such control over the state of the premises that it is reasonable to impose upon that person a duty towards any entrant in respect of a particular danger thereon. Where there is more than one occupier of the same premises the extent of the duty of each occupier towards an entrant depends on the degree of control each of them has over the state of the premises and the particular danger thereon and whether as respects each of them the entrant concerned is a visitor, recreational user, or trespasser.

A premises includes land, water and any fixed or moveable structures thereon and also includes vessels, vehicles, trains, aircraft and other means of transport.

"Recreational activity" means any recreational activity conducted whether alone or with others in the open air (including any sporting activity), scientific research and nature study so conducted, exploring caves and visiting sites and buildings of historical, architectural, traditional, artistic, archaeological or scientific importance.

A "recreational user" is defined as meaning an entrant who with or without the occupier's permission or at the occupier's implied invitation is present on premises without a charge (other than a reasonable charge) in respect of the cost of providing vehicle parking facilities, being imposed for the purpose of engaging in a recreational activity and includes an entrant admitted without charge to a national monument pursuant to section 16(1) of the National Monuments Act 1930, but not including an entrant who is present and is:

(a) a member of the occupier's family who is ordinarily resident on the premises;

(b) an entrant who is present at the express invitation of the occupier or such a member; or

(c) an entrant who is present with the permission of the occupier or such a member for social reasons connected with the occupier or such a member.

An entrant other than a recreational user or visitor is deemed to be a trespasser. Section 2(1) of the 1995 Act provides that subject to section 8, the duties, liabilities and rights provided for by this Act shall have effect and place of duties, liabilities and rights which heretofore attach by the common law to occupiers of premises in respect of dangers existing on the premises to entrants thereon. Section 2(2) of that section went on to provide that the Act would not apply to a cause of action (in any claim or any potential claim) which accrued before the commencement of the Act. The commencement date was one month after the enactment of the Act into law and in consequence the Act operates as and from July 17, 1995.

Duty Owed to Visitors

Under section 3(1) of the 1995 Act, it is provided that an occupier of premises owes a duty of care ("the common duty of care") towards a visitor thereto except insofar as the occupier extends, restricts, modifies or excludes that duty in accordance with section 5 of that Act.

Section 3(2) provides that "the common duty of care" means a duty to take such care as is reasonable in all the circumstances (having regard to the care which a visitor may reasonably be expected to take for his or her own safety and if the visitor is on the premises in the company of another person the extent of the supervision and control the latter person may reasonably be expected to exercise over the visitor's activities) to ensure that a visitor to the premises does not suffer injury or damage by reason of any danger existing thereon.

Duty Owed to Recreational Users or Trespassers

Section 4 of the Occupiers' Liability Act 1995 provides:

(1) In respect of a danger existing on premises, an occupier owes towards a recreational user of the premises or a trespasser thereon ("the person") a duty—

(a) not to injure the person or damage the property of the person intentionally, and

(b) not to act with reckless disregard for the person or the property of the person,

exept in so far as the occupier extends the duty in accordance with *section 5*.

(2) In determining whether or not an occupier has so acted with reckless disregard, regard shall be had to all the circumstances of the case, including—

(a) whether the occupier knew or had reasonable grounds for believing that a danger existed on the premises;

(b) whether the occupier knew or had reasonable grounds for believing that the person and, in the case of damage, property of the person, was or was likely to be on the premises;

(c) whether the occupier knew or had reasonable grounds for believing that the person or property was in, or was likely to be in, the vicinity of the place where the danger existed;

(d) whether the danger was one against which, in all the circumstances, the occupier might reasonably be expected to provide protection for the person and property of the person;

(e) the burden on the occupier of eliminating the danger or of protecting the person and property of the person from the danger, taking into account the difficulty, expense or impracticability, having regard to the character of the premises and the degree of the danger, of so doing;

(f) the character of the premises including, in relation to premises of such a character as to be likely to be used for recreational activity, the desirability of maintaining the tradition of open access to premises of such a character for such an activity;

(g) the conduct of person, and the care which he or she may reasonably be expected to take for his or her own safety, while on the premises, having regard to the extent of his or her knowledge thereof;

(h) the nature of any warning given by the occupier or another person of the danger; and

(i) whether or not the person was on the premises in the company of another person and, if so, the extent of the supervision and control the latter person might reasonably be expected to exercise over the other's activities.

(3) (a) Where a person enters onto premises for the purpose of committing an offence or, while present thereon, commits an offence, the occupier shall not be liable for a breach of the duty imposed by subsection (1)(b) unless a court determines otherwise in the interests of justice.

(b) In paragraph (a) "offence" includes an attempted offence.

(4) Notwithstanding subsection (1), where a structure on premises is or has been provided for use primarily by recreational users, the occupier shall owe a duty towards such users in respect of such a structure to take reasonable care to maintain the structure in a safe condition:

Provided that, where a stile, gate, footbridge or other similar structure on premises is or has been provided not for use primarily by recreational users, the occupier's duty towards a recreational user thereof in respect of such structure shall not be extended by virtue of this subsection."

As can be seen from the provisions of the 1995 Act, the occupier's duty towards a recreational user or trespasser is much reduced. The occupier is not to injure either type of entrant intentionally nor may the occupier act with reckless disregard. What constitutes reckless disregard is something which no doubt will occupy the minds of many lawyers but whilst there is no reported decision as of yet, it appears that in order to be reckless one would have to act in such a manner as to create a substantial and/or unjustifiable risk or in some manner involving culpability to a high degree (*People v. Murray* [1977] I.R. 360).

Under section 5 of the 1995 Act, it is open to an occupier whether by express agreement or by notice to extend his or her duty or to seek by express agreement or by notice to restrict, modify or exclude the duty as owed towards visitors. Where it is sought to restrict, modify or exclude the duty towards a visitor, this will not bind a visitor unless it is reasonable in all the circumstances and in the case of an occupier if it is reported by notice to restrict, modify or exclude that duty, the occupier must take reasonable steps to bring the notice to the attention of the visitor. The 1995 Act specifically provides that an occupier shall be presumed unless the contrary is shown to take reasonable steps to bring the notice to the attention of a visitor when it is prominently displayed at the normal means of access to the premises.

This provision no doubt arose in circumstances where in many cases where such a notice had been previously displayed a case was made that it had not been in fact observed or in fact brought to the attention of the entrant, in consequence it was held generally that the modification/restriction was inoperable in such a situation.

Further, under section 5(5) of the 1995 Act, where injury or damage is caused to a visitor or property of a visitor by a danger in which the visitor had been warned by the occupier or by another person, the warning is not to be treated as absolving the occupier from liability unless in all the circumstances it was enough to enable the visitor, having regard to the warning to avoid the injury or damage so caused.

Under section 6 of the 1995 Act, the duty which an occupier of premies owes to an entrant under the Act is not capable of being modified or excluded by a contract to which the entrant is a stranger, whether the occupier is bound by the contract to permit the entrant to enter or use the premises or not. For the purpose of this section, an entrant shall be deemed to be a stranger to the contract if the entrant is not for the time being entitled to the benefit of the contract, as a party to it, or as a successor by assignment or otherwise of a party to it and accordingly a party to the contract who has ceased to be so entitled shall be deemed to be a stranger to the contract. This section is intended to deal with the situation where the injured person is brought onto the premises by a third party, such as where a repairman who is performing work on behalf of an occupier is accompanied by an assistant. This assistant can still sue regardless of the agreement as between the repairman and the occupier even if the repairman has as such already agreed to waive any right to sue.

Under section 7 of the 1995 Act, an occupier of a premises shall not be liable to an entrant for injury or damage caused to the entrant or property of the entrant by reason of a danger existing on the premises due to the negligence of an independent contractor employed by the occupier if the occupier has taken all reasonable care in the circumstances (including such steps as the occupier ought reasonably to have taken to satisfy himself or herself that the independent contractor was competent to do the work concerned) unless the occupier has or ought to have had knowledge of the fact that the work was not properly done.

The Occupiers' Liability Act 1995 is in many ways is a radical Act which greatly lessens what was the perceived duty of care. But it has been suggested that the effect of the Act is largely to restore the law to its pre-1960 state so that the change is not as dramatic as might be supposed.

It is for that reason that many of the older cases, *i.e.* cases which arose prior to July 17, 1995, on the date of commencement of the Act, may now be of little use in determining how the court should apply the duty of care owed under the Occupiers' Liability Act 1995.

An occupier or owner of land may incur a liability in negligence if such occupier acts in a negligent manner and consequently a person suffers damage.

It is probably best illustrated by a decision of his Honour, Judge Art O'Connor, in the case of *Tarrant v. O'Sullivan* [1949] Ir. Jur. Rep. 46. In that case, the defendant had on or about November 14, 1948, laid poison on his lands at Coole, Millstreet, in the County of Cork. It was alleged that he had neglected to take reasonable precautions against the poison and poisonous substances being removed from the lands with the result that the poison was removed from the land to other lands so that it came into contact with two sow pigs, the property of the plaintiff, which ate the poison and subsequently died.

A claim was brought by the plaintiff against the defendant. The defendant admitted having placed poison on the lands on the nights of November 10, 11 and 12, 1948, but not later. He denied any allegation of negligence and sought to rely upon the provisions of the Protection of Animals Act 1911, as to the giving of personal notice of having poisoned the lands.

In that case, the dwelling house and farms of the parties were separated by a front road. On November 9, 1948, the defendant discovered that a number of his fowl had been killed during the night in a manner which suggested that the killing had been done by dogs. Having found another of his fowl killed on November 10, the defendant gave and posted the required notices in accordance with the Protection of Animals Act 1911, and placed poison on one of the dead fowl which he then tied to his fowl house well away from the public road. The following morning the dead fowl had been partly eaten. On the night of November 11, the defendant placed poison on a dead fowl which he tied to a harrow on his lawn about 21 feet from the public road. The following morning this poisoned fowl was practically eaten. A thick hedge separated the defendant's farm from the public road through which pigs could not pass. The plaintiff was unable to say how the poison could have come into contact with the sow pigs two of which became sick and died on November 14. In the stomach of one pig were found the skins and feathers of a hen.

Mr Justice Art O'Connor in delivering judgment stated:

> "This case is laid in negligence which is the doing of a thing which a reasonable man would not do or failing to do what a reasonable man would do having regard to the circumstances. By virtue of Section 8(b) of the Protection of Animals Act, 1911, nothing in the statute prevents owners or occupiers of land in Ireland from laying or causing to be laid any poison, poisonous matter as therein described after notice has been posted in a conspicuous place and notice in writing has been given to the nearest police station. Accordingly, insofar as this statute operates, a man is entitled to lay poison anywhere on his lands, whether the lands come up to a roadway or not, once he has given the required notice.
>
> The question of common law is where must a line be drawn so as to determine whether a man is negligent or not in placing poison on his lands and in the manner in which he places it. If an occupier of land hides the poison in the ground it is of no value; if he places it in a drain or sewer it may be of value only in killing rats. Where then is he to put it? In the present case the defendant placed poison on his farm on one occasion by the fowl house door and on another

occasion tied to a harrow in the lawn. No evidence has been given if the particular poison used has a smell such as would attract dogs or other animals passing on the roadway...it is clear that the sow pigs did not come into the defendant's lands and the suggestion is that the poison was taken from the defendant's farm by birds or other animals with the result that it came into contact with the pigs. I must hold however in all the circumstances that there is no evidence of negligence against the defendant and if I were prepared to hold that there was negligence I would have to find that the damage sustained by the plaintiff is too remote."

Accordingly, the plaintiff's claim was dismissed.

Negligence

While it seems that the Occupiers' Liability Act 1995 will greatly reduce the liability of an occupier *vis-à-vis* an entrant, it must be remembered that a farmer, in common with every other citizen, has a duty not to act negligently if he knows or foresees or ought reasonably to foresee that injury, loss or damage may be caused to a person by that action. This is best demonstrated by the English decision which came to be the cornerstone of the modern law of negligence, that of *Donoghue v. Stevenson* [1932] A.C. 562, where Lord Atkin outlined what was declared to be a general concept of the relationship giving rise to a duty of care of which the particular cases found in books are but instances, where he went on to state:

> "The rule that you are to love your neighbour becomes in law you must not injure your neighbour; the lawyer's question who is my neighbour? receives a restricted reply. You must take reasonable care to avoid acts or omissions which you can reasonably foresee would be liable to injure your neighbour. Who then in law is my neighbour? The answer seems to be – persons who are so closely and directly affected by my act that I ought reasonably to have them in contemplation as being so affected when I am directing my mind to the acts or omissions which are called in question."

Thus, where a farm owner undertakes an activity, if it is foreseeable that another person may be affected by such activity, even where that person will not in fact enter upon the lands, the land owner is under a duty to take reasonable care to ensure that by his actions the safety of that other person is not endangered.

Consequently, where a land owner is spreading slurry and if in the course of the spreading of slurry he requires to traverse the public road for the purpose of gaining access, such land owner must ensure that he does not cause, allow or permit slurry to be spilt or, for that matter, does not if the slurry is being spread during wet weather, allow mud to be brought onto the public road in such a manner as to interfere with the passage of traffic.

All that is required of a farmer as with any other citizen is that the farmer or citizen be conscious of the fact that in carrying out an activity he may endanger the safety of others and where the presence of such other person is anticipated, care must be taken to guard against any unnecessary risk.

Trespass to Land

The tort of trespass to land consists of intentionally or negligently entering or remaining or directly causing anything to come into contact with land in the possession of another without lawful justification.

Under Article 40.5 of the Constitution, it is provided that:

> "[t]he dwelling of every citizen is inviolable and shall not be forceably entered save in accordance with law".

The slightest infringement of the boundary onto the lands of another will constitute a trespass for which an action may lie.

However, to constitute an actionable trespass, the plaintiff must suffer direct injury rather than consequential. *Salmond and Houston*, the leading textbook on the law of torts, states that:

> "An injury is said to be direct when it follows so immediately upon the act of the defendant that it may be termed part of that act; it is consequential on the other hand when by reason of some obvious and visible intervening cause it is regarded not as part of the defendant's act but merely as a consequence of it."

It is a trespass for a person to place any chattel on the land of another or to cause any object or substance directly to cross the boundary of another's land. Thus, to grow creeper on another's wall or lean a ladder against it will constitute a trespass. Trespass would also arise where a defendant induces an incursion by a person as well as a thing, for example, where one brings or chases a person onto the plaintiff's property.

The plaintiff need show no damage in order to succeed in an action for trespass since trespass to land is actionable *per se*.

A person who places an object on the land of another will be guilty of a continuing trespass if he fails to remove it. However, he will not be guilty of a continuing trespass where as a result of his wrong the plaintiff's land is otherwise damaged. Consequently, a man who cuts down and removes his neighbour's tree or digs a hole in his lawn will have to pay damages of course for his wrong but, unlike the case where he builds a wall in his neighbour's yard, he will not be liable on a continuant basis until the tree is brought back or the hole is filled.

Mr Justice Holmes in *Clark v. The Midland Great Western Railway Company* [1895] 2 I.R. 294, said:

"Continuous torts are simple enough in theory but it is not always easy to distinguish them for practical purposes. A man builds a wall on another's land. This is a continuant trespass and a judgment against the wrongdoer will not bar a second action if the wall is permitted to remain. On the other hand, a man digs a hole or cuts down a tree on another's land then only one action can be brought...what is the principle that underlies (this distinction)? It cannot depend upon the nature of the injuries sustained or upon the fact that such injury is of a continuing character. The right to enjoy one's land free from the encumbrance of a wall does not differ in kind from the right to enjoy it free from the inconvenience of a hole. The element of continuity must, I think, be looked for not in the right interrupted but in the acts that caused the interruption. When a man commits a trespass by placing something on another's land it is reasonable to regard him as responsible for its continuance until he takes away what is in its nature removable or until the owner of the lands by refusing permission to remove it adopts what has been done. A tree cut down is gone forever. Compensation can be made for it but it cannot be brought back. So too in the case of an excavation; it may no doubt be filled up but not so as to make the excavated place what it was before. An equivalent can be given but restoration strictly speaking is impossible. The distinction I have suggested would be found to accord with ordinary thought and language. We naturally think and speak of the man who has built a wall as keeping the wall where he placed it. He has taken possession of certain land by building on it. He retains possession of it as long as the building is allowed to stand. No such idea attaches to the person who makes an excavation or cuts down a tree. He retains for his own use or otherwise disposes of the matter excavated or the timber but his trespass on the land ceases when the act is done."

In that case, liability on a continuing basis was held to attach to the defendants who had interfered with the water supply of the plaintiff some time previously and who had paid damages in respect of this interference already. To remedy the injury, they would have had to have entered the land of the plaintiff. While this did not excuse them, it appears that their liability would cease if the plaintiff on request refused them entry.

If a defendant does not act voluntarily, no liability will be incurred. Thus, if a defendant is carried against his will or sleepwalks onto his neighbour's property he does not commit a trespass. Where a defendant can show that he was neither negligent nor intentional, then and in those circumstances liability will not attach.

Since trespass is essentially an interference with possession, an action in tort will not lie where a person is out of possession at the time of the intrusion in respect of which complaint is made. A landlord may not sue for trespass during the subsistence of a lease where the trespass is to the area demised to the tenant. Nor can a purchaser sue in respect of a trespass which occurs before he in fact takes title.

If, however, the wrongful act of a defendant causes permanent damage to land leading to a reduction in the value of the reversion due to the landlord, then in such circumstances a landlord may sue for trespass. Further, where a person entitled to possession actually enters onto the land and so acquires possession he is deemed to have been in possession from the moment that his right to it accrued. This fiction is known as "trespass by relation" and its effect is that the person may sue for any act of trespass committed while he was out of possession whilst having his immediate right to possession.

In the normal course, it is no answer to an action in trespass to allege that the plaintiff has no right to possession of the lands in question because the right rests in a third party. This defence is known as the *jus tertii*. If, however, a defendant enters the premises with the authority of the person with the true right to possession, such person will have a good defence as against the plaintiff.

Clearly, where a person consents to entry it is not open to the owner of the land to then allege trespass unless it can be shown that the manner in which the entry was effected was in excess of the express or implied terms of the invitation.

Necessity will afford a good defence where there is an emergency, provided same is not caused by the prior negligent conduct of the defendant himself and is of such nature as would justify a person reasonably to take the action that the defendant took even where in the light of hindsight the action proved not to be necessary.

It has been suggested that no compensation should be due where the action is done for the benefit of the public as, for example, to prevent a fire from spreading to a neighbouring village.

In the normal course, if there is a continuing trespass, a plaintiff will be entitled to maintain an action for an injunction subject to proof of title to the land and if loss or damage has been suffered by such plaintiff, that plaintiff will also be entitled to damages in respect of such loss and damage. The court further has a overriding discretion to award aggravated and/or exemplary damages if it takes the view that a defendant has been in flagrant breach of the rights of the plaintiff.

Increasingly, various statutes have conferred on certain specified persons the right of entry onto private property. For instance, a social welfare inspector has a wide power of entry under the provisions of the Social Welfare (Consolidation) Act 1981, where they have reasonable grounds for supposing that persons employed in an insurable employment are employed at a particular premises.

Similarly, an authorised person who has been duly authorised by a Fire Authority has a right to enter premises (at all reasonable times) for the purposes of the Fire Services Act 1981.

Further, under section 28(1) of the 1981 Act, a person in control at a fire or other emergency is permitted to enter any building to cause it to be vacated by its occupants and to pull down the building where necessary. Similar powers of entry arise in the case of water pollution, both under the Water Pollution Acts, which are dealt with elsewhere, and under the Fisheries legislation.

In each instance, it is a matter of determining the nature and extent of the statutory right of entry and in the event that there are preconditions which govern the right to entry, the preconditions must be fully satisfied. If not, then a liability may arise at civil law in trespass. Evidence which is obtained in consequence of such a wrongful entry may be excluded in the course of a criminal trial.

CHAPTER 10

NUISANCE

Edward S. Walsh

"Nuisance in law consists essentially of the unreasonable interference with another person in the exercise of his rights", either to the quiet and peaceable enjoyment of his land and property in the case of private nuisance, or to general comfort and convenience in the case of public nuisance (see McMahon and Binchy, *The Irish Law of Torts* (2nd ed., 1990) pages 446 *et seq.*)

Public or Private

A nuisance may be either a public nuisance or a private nuisance.

Public Nuisance

A public nuisance is a crime. It includes such forms conduct as keeping a common gaming house, or the creation of an obstruction on a highway.

"The essence of the crime is injury to the reasonable comfort and convenience of the public or a section of the public". If a person suffers "particular" or "special" damage over and above that suffered by other members of the public, such a person may bring a civil claim.

Particular or Special Damage   The question of what constitutes "particular" or "special" damage is something which has occupied considerable time and attention in the courts. The general view appears to be that the injury sustained by the plaintiff must be different in kind rather than degree from that suffered by the general public. Recovery may be allowed where the plaintiff's injury is appreciably more serious than that suffered by the general public to such degree that it may be regarded as particular to him.

An unusual case where damages for public nuisance were recovered was that of *Boyd v. Great Northern Railway* [1895] 2 I.R. 555. The plaintiff, who was a medical doctor, had been delayed at a level crossing for some 20 minutes by reason of the default of the defendant's servants. The doctor was "in very large practice" and "whose time was pecuniary value" was held to have suffered "some appreciable damage peculiar to himself beyond that suffered by other members of the public ordinarily using the highway". He recovered the princely sum of 10 shillings in damages.

Another example is that of *Smith v. Wilson* [1903] 2 I.R. 45 where the plaintiff, an elderly small farmer, used frequently to walk to market in Bally-mena on a public road until the defendant obstructed the road by removing a bridge and erecting a fence, as a result of which the plaintiff was obliged to take the longer and more circuitous route and sometimes had to pay for a car in doing so. The claim came before the King's Bench Division, which held that he was entitled to recover damages by a majority decision.

Mr Justice Gibson stated:

> "I think that there is some evidence on which a jury might find that the plaintiff had sustained peculiar, direct and substantial damage in farm business and expenses. No doubt the case is not as strong as if a carriage road had been stopped but still there is some distinctive injury. It may be said that if the plaintiff can sue every other farmer in the neighbourhood who used the path may be able to do the same. This may be so; but every nuisance which affects large sections of the community e.g. nuisance from chemical works or a smallpox hospital or from a collection of explosives is open to the same remark. Everyone who individually sustains particular injury can apply for damages or an injunction."

Public Nuisance on the Highway   Probably the most common type of public nuisance is a public nuisance on the highway such as an obstruction or the creation of a danger.

A public nuisance could be, for example, the leaving of a ladder for an unreasonable period on a public footpath, the digging of a trench in the highway, the leaving of a vehicle on the highway for an unreasonable time, the leaving of railway gates closed longer than reasonably necessary, the allowing of picketers or queues to form so as to obstruct the passage of road users or pedestrians or the access of customers to shops or other premises, the building of a structure which obstructs a road or navigable river or the allowing of a mass of animals to obstruct the highway.

It has been held by Judge Ó Briain in a decision of the Circuit Court in *Hassett v. O'Loughlin* 78 I.L.T.R. 47 that:

> "A nuisance is not confined to an obstruction on the highway; it may consist of anything which makes the use of a highway unsafe or dangerous to the public."

In that case, the defendant was held liable for placing a "tiny heap" of stones on the highway.

Other examples of danger on a highway include leaving an unauthorised "no parking" notice on the footpath; failing to remove a disused gas pipe projecting from the soil or property close to the footpath; damaging the road surface or rendering it hazardous or damaging property under it; placing dangerous materials on or near the highway; holding unauthorised motor bicycle speed trials on an unsuitable road; maintaining a golf club in a manner which allows players to slice the ball onto the highway; projecting a stone step and metal scraper into the highway; letting a wall adjoining the highway fall onto it; reconstructing the side portions of a highway in a dangerous manner, or causing the road or footpath to subside.

Private Nuisance

Separate and apart from the category of public nuisance, there is a private nuisance. Private nuisance occurs in circumstances where a person is discommoded in his user or enjoyment of land to an unreasonable degree.

Chief Justice T.F. O'Higgins, in the case of *Connolly v. South of Ireland Asphalt Co.* [1977] I.R. 99 at 103 stated:

> "It has been said that actionable nuisance is incapable of exact definition. The term nuisance contemplates an act or omission which amounts to unreasonable interference with, disturbance of or annoyance to another person in the exercise of his rights. If the rights so interfered with belong to the person as a member of the public, the act or omission is a public nuisance. If these rights relate to the ownership or occupation of land or some other easement or profit or other right enjoyed in connection with land, then the acts or omissions amount to a private nuisance."

Claim in Nuisance

Mr Justice Henchy, delivering the judgment of the Supreme Court in *Hanrahan v. Merck Sharp & Dohme (Ireland) Ltd* [1988] I.L.R.M. 629 at 634, stated that it was:

> "clear from the authorities on the law of nuisance that what an occupier of land is entitled to as against his neighbour is the comfortable and healthy enjoyment of the land to the degree that would be expected by an ordinary person whose requirements are objectively reasonable in all the particular circumstances."

In order to maintain a claim, actual damage must be proved. The damage may consist of either physical injury to land or a substantial interference with enjoyment of land or an interference with the servitudes (*i.e.* any interference with a right of light or a right of way or other similar type of incident of enjoyment of the property). In determining what constitutes a nuisance the purpose of the conduct in respect of which complaint is made must be taken into consideration. Thus the courts must have regard to what has been termed the utility of the defendant's conduct and the nature of the location or area wherein complaint arises.

The courts have articulated a rule that has regard to the character of the neighbourhood in which the conduct occurs. Mr Justice Barton in the case of *New Imperial and Windsor Hotel Company v. Johnson* [1912] 1 I.R. 327 at 332 stated:

> "One of the necessary incidents of the social life of an industrial city is the certain amount of recreation and innocent amusement taken in the form of social gatherings of the respectable young men and women who do a large proportion of the daily work of the city."

Taking this into account, the court granted an injunction, and ordered the proprietor of the tea-rooms and a restaurant in Belfast whose premises were opposite those of the plaintiff to keep the windows of the premises, which was used for dancing and other entertainment at night, shut after midnight and preventing the patrons who were leaving or entering the premises from making undue noise.

In the more recent case of *O'Kane v. Campbell* [1985] I.R. 115 the court was concerned with a 24-hour shop. The shop in question was positioned on the corner of the North Circular Road and Glengarriff Parade in Dublin. The North Circular Road was described as "a wide busy street both by day and by night". Glengarriff Parade was described as "an old established residential street . . . just removed from the bustle of other more busy places in the area". The shop began to trade on a 24-hour hour basis and an injunction was sought on the grounds that the degree of noise throughout the night disturbed the plaintiff who lived opposite the shop in Glengarriff Parade. The noise was the normal and inevitable result of:

> "ordinary law-abiding people going to and from the shop, revving the engines of their cars or motor bikes, banging car doors and playing car radios. There was no question of disorderly behaviour or breaches of the peace".

Mr Justice Lynch was satisfied that had the shop been on Glengarriff Parade itself, it would have constituted a clear nuisance on account of traffic congestion and noise; conversely, if it had been completely on the North Circular Road and a little distance away from Glengarriff Parade there would be "hardly any doubt that there was no actionable nuisance". In view of the position of the shop at the junction of the two streets, the case was less clear cut, but Mr Justice Lynch was satisfied on the evidence that the trading carried on through the night had "drastically altered the amenity of Glengarriff Parade as a residential street". Accordingly, he granted an injunction restraining the defendant from carrying on business between midnight and 6 a.m.

In the case of *Hollywood Silver Fox Farm Ltd v. Emmett* [1936] 2 J.B. 468, the defendant's farm bordered the plaintiff's fox farm. The defendant objected to a notice board on the plaintiff's property since he thought that it was detrimental to a scheme of his to sell some of his land as plots for bungalows. The plaintiff's proprietor refused to take down the sign. The defendant threatened to shoot on his own property as near as he could to the breeding pens saying "you will not raise a single cub". In time, the defendant carried out his threat. The effect of the noise was that the vixens were put off mating and induced to kill and devour their young. The defendant sought to excuse his conduct by stating that he was attempting to keep down rabbits but the court regarded this explanation as "manifestly untrue" and in consequence the defendant was held liable.

Location

The court has regard to the nature of the location and Friedmann states in "Modern Trends in the Law of Torts" 1 Mod. L.R. 39 that:

> "The first factory in a farming district, the running or by-products of which attract noxious animals which injure crops in the neighbourhood causes obviously a nuisance . . . a second factory may already be in a better position. The standard of comfort may no longer be so clearly that of a farming community and eventually a solitary farmer may possibly be held to cause a nuisance to the workers of a factory nearby through the noise of cattle or the smell of farmyard manure. A parallel problem occurs when a quiet residential quarter is invaded by business and industry."

It is for that reason that a new "development" may be more liable to be enjoined as was evidenced in the case of *Mullin v. Hynes* an unreported decision of the Supreme Court of November 13, 1972, where the court enjoined the proprietor of a large dance hall in a residential area of a country town (Templemore, Co. Tipperary), distinguishing the location of a dance hall in such an area from a dance hall in Belfast as in the *New Imperial and Windsor Hotel Co. v. Johnson* case (see above).

In the normal course, it is no defence to assert that a plaintiff has "come to the nuisance", for example, where a person buys property which he is aware is being subjected to a nuisance from the defendant's land.

This was best illustrated by the decision of *Bliss v. Hall Bing* 4 Ving. N.C. 183 where the court held that that the defendants, Tallow Chandlery, had been emitting offensive smells and vapours onto the plaintiff's property for three years before the plaintiff arrived. It was held that this afforded the defendant no defence since the plaintiff had come to the property.

> "with all rights which the common law affords and one of them is the right to wholesome air".

It has been suggested that it is not reasonable to expect a person to refrain from buying land in a neighbourhood merely because a nuisance already exists nor should such conduct be deemed to amount to contributory negligence unless it is considered that the plaintiff has behaved in an unreasonable fashion.

The courts have emphasised, however, that a person is not entitled to demand an unduly high standard of conduct from a neighbour and in particular as stated by Mr Justice Henchy in *Hanrahan v. Merck Sharp & Dohme (Ireland) Ltd* (see above), the plaintiff:

> "is not entitled to insist that his personal nicety of taste or fastidiousness should be treated as inviolable".

The courts will not grant relief where the damage is in respect of trivial, fanciful or exaggerated inconvenience.

Trees

Where a landowner has a tree or trees on his lands adjoining the highway or his neighbour's lands, he is bound to take such care as a reasonable and prudent landowner would take to guard against the danger of a falling tree causing damage. If he fails to exercise this degree of care, and damage results from such failure on his part, a cause of action will arise against him.

The law in relation to liability in negligence and/or nuisance for trees was considered by Mr Justice O'Hanlon in the case of *Frank Lynch v. Liam Hetherton* [1990] I.L.R.M. 857. In that case the plaintiff had been driving his car along a country road at Kilrush, Clonmellon, Co. Westmeath, when a tree growing on the defendant's land at a point immediately adjoining the highway broke off suddenly at the base of the tree and fell to the ground. There was a dispute as to whether it actually fell on the plaintiff's car or whether the plaintiff drove into it while it was falling or immediately after it fell to the ground. Fortunately the three occupants of the car appeared to have escaped injury but the car was extensively damaged. A branch penetrated one of the front head-lights and continued for some six feet through the engine area and into the passenger area between the two front seats of the car. A claim was brought by the car owner seeking damages in respect of negligence and/or nuisance on the part of the defendant landowner.

On the day when the tree fell, it was not a day of high winds. The tree itself was in a decayed state but the decay, it was found, was not readily apparent. The landowner had a row of wire on the ditch adjoining the highway which connected to the tree and which he had tightened with staples some 10 days before the accident at a point two feet above ground level. The tree at that point was very sound and firm. There was nothing unusual about the tree which was one foot in diameter. No expert had been employed to look at the tree. The area in the centre was rotten but not the outer rings.

The plaintiff succeeded in the Circuit Court subject to a finding of contributory negligence of 30 per cent as against the plaintiff. On appeal to the High Court, Mr Justice O'Hanlon held that the tree had been caused to fall by some inherent defect in the condition of the tree. He considered that a landowner having on his lands a tree or trees adjoining the highway or his neighbour's lands was bound to take such care as a reasonable and prudent landowner would take to guard against the danger of damage being done by a falling tree and if he failed to exercise this degree of care and if damage resulted from such failure on his part a cause of action would arise against him.

For a plaintiff to succeed in such a case, he must establish as a matter of probability that the landowner was or ought to have been aware of the dangerous condition of the tree. Alternatively, it will suffice if the plaintiff can show that proper inspection of the tree at reasonable intervals would have forewarned the owners that it was in a dangerous condition and that measures to prevent the tree falling should have been taken. It was held that on the facts of the case, the defendant had exercised a degree of care that would be exercised by a reasonable and prudent landowner. Even if an expert had been employed, the evidence did not show as a matter of probability that the internal decay of the tree would have been detected as a result of such expert examination.

Roots

Where the encroachment of tree roots onto the property of a neighbouring occupier causes damage, this will constitute a nuisance which entitles the injured party in the appropriate case to seek damages or an injunction or, indeed, to abate the nuisance himself. He is not required to wait until damage is done. He may protect himself by cutting the roots as soon as they project into his property or he may seek a *quia timet* injunction. A *quia timet* injunction is in effect an anticipatory injunction where there is a heavy onus of proof on the part of a plaintiff to show that the damage feared or anticipated is a justifiable real fear.

Where a branch encroaches onto another property and causes damage, the occupier of the property will have the same remedy as in the case of encroaching roots. Where, however, there is branch overhanging a highway and which branch falls as a result of a latent defect not discoverable by any reasonable inspection, liability will not be imposed.

In *Lynch v. Dawson* [1946] I.R. 504 the court was concerned with the branch of a tree which projected onto the highway which became entangled in the top part of a turf lorry resulting in the plaintiff being injured. The court considered that the defendant ought to have been aware of the danger and stressed that changing times could change the level of vigilance required of a defendant. Mr Justice Murnahan stated:

> "This tree about sixteen feet in length and grown as it was would not obstruct much of the present users of the highway and certainly would not have obstructed the user at all forty years ago. Of recent years, however, motor lorries carrying Creels have come into common use. Although the principles of the common law remain the same the application of these principles must move with the times."

The degree of care depends upon the facts in each particular case as is evidenced by the view of Mr Justice Lavery in *Gillen v. Fair* 90 I.L.T.R. 119, where he said:

> "The standard of care required of a farmer in County Mayo having trees growing on his land adjoining a highway might not be as high as that required of an owner of a tree growing beside a highway in a thickly populated built-up area."

Bibliography

For further reference see:
McMahon and Binchy, *The Irish Law of Torts* (2nd ed., 1990)
Salmond and Heuston, *The Law of Torts* (20th ed., 1992)

CHAPTER 11

ANIMALS

Edward S. Walsh

Dogs

At common law, the owner of a dog which caused damage to "cattle" was strictly liable for injury but if it was injury to a human being, liability attached only if it could be shown that the animal had a known mischievous propensity, *i.e.* a vicious temperament of which the owner knew or ought properly to have known.

This anomaly has been removed under the provisions of section 21 of the Control of Dogs Act 1986, which provides:

"(1)   The owner of a dog shall be liable in damages for damage caused in an attack on any person by the dog and for injury done by it to any livestock; and it shall not be necessary for the person seeking such damages to show a previous mischievous propensity in the dog or the owner's knowledge of such previous propensity or to show that such injury or damage was attributable to neglect on the part of the owner.

(2)   Where livestock are injured by a dog on land on to which they had strayed and either the dog belonged to the occupier of the land or its presence on the land was authorised by the occupier, a person shall not be liable under this section in respect of injury done to the livestock unless the person caused the dog to attack the livestock.

(3)   A person is liable in damages for any damage caused by a dog kept on any premises or structure to a person trespassing thereon only in accordance with the rules of law relating to liability for negligence.

(4) (a) Any damage or injury for which a person is made liable under this Section shall be deemed to be attributable to a wrong within the meaning of the Civil Liability Act, 1961, and the provisions of that Act shall apply accordingly.
(b) Sections 11(2)(a) and 11(2)(b) of the Statute of Limitations, 1957, shall apply to such damage."

The Control of Dogs Act 1986 does not as such abolish the old common law *scienter* action under which, if a person was injured by a dog, the person could succeed only if it was shown that the dog had a mischievous propensity and the keeper of the dog knew of this.

However, it is obviously more convenient to frame a claim under the statutory liability as imposed under section 21 of the 1986 Act.

Section 1 of the Control of Dogs Act 1986 defines livestock to include "cattle, sheep, swine, horses and all other equine animals, poultry, goats and deer not in the wild state". There is a statutory presumption to the effect that the occupier of premises where a dog is kept is the owner of the dog as is apparent from the definition of "occupier" as set forth in section 1 of the 1986 Act.

The Control of Dogs Act 1986 also makes provision for the general control and licensing of dogs including greyhounds, for the control and seizure of stray dogs, for the duties of local authorities, the power of dog wardens, the regulation of premises and dogs.

Regulations have been introduced under the Control of Dogs Act 1986 (Guard Dogs) Regulations 1988 (S.I. No. 255 of 1988) which were effective as and from February 1, 1989, controlling the use of guard dogs. The regulations require that guard dogs used at business premises must be accompanied by a handler or security so that they cannot go freely about the premises or escape. A warning notice must be displayed at all entrances to the premises.

Guard dogs must have identification collars and are required to have an electronic device implanted under the skin containing a permanent identification code allotted by the Irish Society for the Prevention of Cruelty to Animals. Section 23 of the 1986 Act introduces a defence in an action for damages for shooting a dog. Section 23(1) provides:

> "It shall be a defence to any action for damages against a person for the shooting of a dog or to any charge arising out of the shooting of a dog if the defendant proves that:—
>
> (a) the dog was shot when it was worrying or was about to worry livestock and that there was no other reasonable means of ending or preventing the worrying; or
> (b) (i) the dog was a stray dog which was in the vicinity of a place where livestock had been injured or killed and
> (ii) the defendant reasonably believed that the dog had been involved in the injury or killing, and
> (iii) there were no practicable means of seizing the dog or ascertaining to whom it belonged; and
> (c) he was the person in charge of the livestock; and
> (d) he notified within forty-eight hours the member in charge of the nearest Garda Station to the place where the dog was shot of the incident."

Section 23(2) of the 1986 Act provides that the provisions of section 23(1)(a) and (1)(b)(i) and (iii) of this section shall be deemed to have been satisfied if the defendant believed that those provisions had been satisfied and he had reasonable grounds for that belief.

Section 25 of the 1986 Act deals with the situation where a nuisance is created by barking dogs. Under section 25(1), where on a complaint being made to the District Court by any person it appears that a nuisance has been created as a result of excessive barking by a dog, the court may:

"(a) order the occupier of the premises in which the dog is kept to abate the nuisance by exercising due control over the dog;

(b) make an order limiting for such period as may be specified in the order the number of dogs to be kept by the respondent on his premises;

(c) direct that the dog be delivered to a dog warden to be dealt with by him in accordance with the provisions of this Act as if the dog were an unwanted dog."

Under section 25(2) of the 1986 Act, before any person makes a complaint to the District Court in relation to a nuisance caused by the excessive barking of a dog, he shall serve notice in the prescribed form within such time as may be specified in the notice of his intention to make such a complaint on the occupier of the premises on which the dog is kept.

Cattle Trespass

Where cattle stray from their owner's lands onto the property of another person, the owner of the cattle is liable for any damage caused irrespective of negligence. This liability arises only where the cattle stray of their own volition. Obviously if the cattle are driven onto the property then liability will be in trespass as distinct from cattle trespass.

The rule applies where cattle break from one field into an adjoining field or where cattle stray from their own field onto the highway and thence on to another person's property. It will not apply, however, where cattle which are being lawfully driven on the highway break onto property adjoining the road. Liability in such circumstances will depend on the plaintiff being able to prove negligence on the part of the owner of the animals, since as a matter of law, it is deemed that landowners adjacent to a highway accept the inevitable risk of damage done by animals lawfully using the highway provided that there has been no negligence.

Under this rule of strict liability, liability attaches only to "cattle" which comprises more than the bovine species and includes horses, sheep, goat, pigs, asses, domestic fowl and domesticated deer, but does not include cats, dogs or wild animals on a person's property.

In consequence, in *Brady v. Warren* [1900] 2 I.R. 632, it was held that a defendant could not be liable for damage caused by rabbits which trespassed onto the plaintiff's property even though it was shown that the defendant, who trapped and exported the rabbits, had encouraged the propagation of the species by importing a foreign strain. The animals were wild and did not belong to the defendant and therefore he was not liable for the damage caused by them.

In that case, however, the court did impose liability on the defendant in respect of damage caused by deer which strayed from his land. The evidence established that the defendant fed the deer during the course of the winter and in such circumstances the court was prepared to hold that the deer were tame and under the defendant's control.

There has been considerable controversy in relation to liability where animals stray from lands which are held on foot of an agistment agreement. In the normal course, under an agistment agreement, the owner of the animals takes the lands on a grazing letting but as part of the agreement the landowner undertakes to herd the cattle.

In *Dalton v. O'Sullivan* [1947] 13 Ir. Jur. Rep. 25 an action was brought against the owner of cattle. The action failed as against the defendant because it was held that he had neither possession of the cattle nor occupation of the land, the defendant living some 100 miles from the land. Ownership of the animals alone was not sufficient to make him liable in cattle trespass.

In *Winters v. Owens* [1950] I.R. 225, there the plaintiff had taken lands under a conacre agreement at Killineer, Drogheda, Co. Louth. The plaintiff suffered loss as a result of the trespass of sheep, the property of the first named defendant, on the said lands, the sheep having escaped from adjoining lands which had been taken by the defendant under a grazing agreement and which agreement provided, *inter alia*, that the owner of the land should be responsible for the herding of the defendant's cattle on and the maintenance of the fences of the lands so taken.

The plaintiff succeeded in the claim in the Circuit Court and which decision was appealed to the High Court before Mr Justice Lavery. In the course of evidence, it was established that the defendant had assumed responsibility for foddering the sheep and this the learned trial judge considered as being important since it showed that the stock generally remained under the care and supervision of the defendant. Mr Justice Lavery was of the view no doubt that if sheep were missing or sick or in need of foddering or other attention, the defendant would have looked after the matter. He considered that the obligations undertaken by the owner of the land to herd was as agent for the owner of the stock. On that basis, he held that the defendant was liable where the sheep had escaped from lands held by the defendant on foot of a grazing agreement, notwithstanding that under the grazing agreement the owner of the lands was liable for the herding of the cattle and maintenance of the fences.

The learned trial judge distinguished the judgment of Ó Briain J. in *Dalton v. O'Sullivan* (see above) and stated that he inferred from the judgment that there was an essential difference in that the cattle there passed into the possession and control of the agister and he considered that the Judge having so found was the basis of the decision.

Mr Justice Lavery further considered that there was sufficient authority that the owner of land may in these cases be liable but it does not follow that the owner of the stock may not also be liable.

This issue was considered in more recent times before his Honour, Judge Sean O'Leary, in a District Court appeal. In *Horan v. Fahy* a case from the Circuit Court at Tullamore (November 7, 1995), the driver of a car collided with a cow straying on a public road. The motorist claimed damages from both the owner of the lands from which the animal had strayed and from the lessor of the lands who also owned the straying animal. Judge O'Leary finding there was no negligence on the part of the motorist, held both the owner of the lands and the owner of the animal equally liable. However, he granted an indemnity, *i.e.* reimbursement against the owner of the animal, in favour of the landowner, which effectively meant the owner of the straying animal was fully liable for the damage caused to the motorist.

The driver of a straying animal will not be liable if the escape is due to something unavoidable, such as an act of God, or inevitable accident or the unforeseen act of a third party.

As a matter of law, the owner of livestock is under a duty to keep it from straying onto the lands of others but this duty is not absolute and has been described as being more, however, than a duty not to be negligent as *per* Lord Justice Somerville in *Sutcliffe v. Holmes* [1946] 2 All E.R. 599.

The wrongful act of a third party may be a defence. So, where a third person left the defendant's gate open so that the cattle of the defendant strayed onto the plaintiff's property it was held that the defendant was not liable in the case of *Moloney v. Stephens* [1945] 11 Ir. Jur. Rep. 37. However, it has been suggested by District Judge Patrick Brennan in a decision of the District Court that in the modern day and age, if the gate in question adjoins a highway, then it may be reasonable for the gate to be secured by means of a lock and in the absence of such lock, the unwarranted and/or unauthorised act of a third party may not constitute a sufficient defence.

Other defences which are available are an act of God or the plaintiff's own fault or inevitable accident. Alternatively, if it can be shown that in some mode or manner the plaintiff has contributed to the loss or damage, it appears that there should be an apportionment on account of contributory negligence under the provisions of section 34 of the Civil Liability Act 1961.

At common law, the owner of an animal was not liable for damge caused by an animal which had strayed onto the highway.

Whilst there had been some erosion of this general principle such as where, for example, animals had been brought onto the highway or alternatively where the animal in question was known to have "such characteristics as to impose upon its owner a duty to take steps to prevent if from endangering the public by getting on the highway and there exhibiting its characteristics to the danger of users of the highway", or where animals had strayed onto the road in sufficiently large numbers to cause an obstruction, the common law principle continued with all its rigours until the enactment of section 2 of the Animals Act 1985.

Section 2 of the Animals Act 1985 provides:

"(1) So much of the rules of the common law relating to liability for negligence as excludes or restricts the duty which a person might owe to others to take such care as is reasonable to see that damage is not caused by an animal straying onto a public road is hereby abolished.

(2) (a) Where damage is caused by an animal straying from unfenced land onto a public road, the person who placed the animal on the land shall not be regarded as having committed a breach of the duty to take care by reason only of placing it there if—
    (i) the land is situate in an area where fencing is not customary and
    (ii) he had a right to place the animal on that land,
  (b) In this subsection "fencing" includes the construction of any obstacle designed to prevent animals from straying and "unfenced" shall be construed accordingly."

In consequence of the enactment of this section, a landowner is now under an obligation to take reasonable care in respect of his fencing and provided he does this, he will not be liable.

The 1985 Act specifically provides that it is no breach of duty for a person to place animals on unfenced land adjoining the highway where the owner of the animal has a right to place them on the land and the area is one where fencing is not customary as, for example, in the case of the Curragh.

This section was considered by Mr Justice Johnson in an appeal to the High Court from a decision of his Honour, Judge David Sheehy, sitting at the Circuit Court at Cavan in the case of *O'Reilly v. Lavelle* [1990] Irish Law Log 177. There, the plaintiff's car had been damaged when it collided with a friesan calf on a public road at 10 p.m. on June 25, 1987. Immediately before the collision, the plaintiff had been driving his car at 50 m.p.h. along a straight line of the road, when the calf and other cattle suddenly ran onto the road from the verge of the plaintiff's left side. The calf belonged to the defendant whose lands adjoined the road on the other side. The area of the accident was one in which it was customary for owners of cattle to fence their lands. Earlier on the same evening, cattle were observed on the side of the road near the scene of the accident. The plaintiff claimed damages from the defendant in the Circuit Court and pleaded that the damage to the car had been caused by the defendant's negligence. Shortly after the accident, the fencing along the boundary between the defendant's lands and the road was examined and found to be intact but no examination was made of the fencing on the defendant's lands along the boundary between those lands and an adjoining laneway giving access to the road opposite the scene of the collision. The defendant pleaded that the accident was caused by the negligence of the plaintiff. The plaintiff's claim was dismissed in the Circuit Court, from which decision an appeal was brought to the High Court.

The matter came before Mr Justice Johnson who allowed the appeal, holding that despite the plaintiff's failure to plead *res ipsa loquitur*, the maxim was applicable and had the effect of placing upon the defendant the burden of proving that he took reasonable care of his animals. It was held that the defendant had failed to discharge that burden and in consequence the plaintiff was entitled to recover judgment.

The maxim of *res ipsa loquitur* which literally means "the matter speaks for itself" is applicable in circumstances wherein the law deems that the onus of proving that there has been reasonable care rests upon a defendant since, in the normal course, the matter in respect of which complaint is made should not occur if reasonable care had been taken. In this specific instance, cattle should not be on the road if the defendant has taken reasonable care to ensure that his fences are intact and his animals secured, and in consequence, if an animal escapes, the burden rests upon the defendant to establish the reasonable care which such defendant had taken to prevent the animal straying from his land.

General Liability

Separate and apart from the specific classes of case above, liability in respect may arise under the general principles of tort such as in negligence, trespass or alternatively by virtue of the duty of care owed by an occupier to lawful entrants.

Negligence

Examples of where liability was found in negligence are numerous. In *Powell v. McGlynn and Bradlaw* [1902] 2 I.R. 154 the defendant, McGlynn, was in the course of saying goodnight to a lady friend and whilst so doing he left a pony and trap unattended. The pony subsequently took fright and bolted and in the course of which the plaintiff was knocked down and injured by the runaway pony.

In *Howard v. Bergin, O'Connor & Co.* [1925] 2 I.R. 110, cattle which were being unloaded at Kingsbridge railway station were allowed to escape onto a road where, after a number of incidents, certain of the cattle collided with the plaintiff causing him injury. It was held that the defendant was negligent because of the unreasonable conduct of the defendant in not using a platform provided for unloading cattle and further, because it had left a gate open onto the public road during the unloading operation and because cattle had been left unattended while a drover had gone in search of assistance. The court considered that this was not a case of quiet animals being allowed onto the road but rather a case where the animals "got wild" in the unloading and thereafter were negligently allowed to get onto the roadway where they "dashed blindly along colliding with or overturning human impediments to their wild progress".

The defendant was held liable in *Kavanagh v. Stokes* [1942] I.R. 596 where the plaintiff was a paying guest at the residence of the defendant. The plaintiff, accompanied by four other girls, had gone to a dance in Gorey and had previously informed the defendant of such intention and had made arrangements with the defendant that the hall door should be left unlatched to enable them to gain entrance. They returned from the dance at about 11.30 p.m. and on their arrival a watch dog, which had been left at large in the grounds of the house, barked loudly. Four of the girls ran into the house on hearing the dog but the plaintiff stayed behind to close the gate and proceeded to pat the dog which then sprang at her and bit her lip. The dog had bitten a child some four or five years previously but there had been provocation on that occasion. The matter came on appeal before Mr Justice Gavan Duffy who held that in leaving the watch dog out in the circumstances, the defendant had failed in her duty to take reasonable precaution to ensure the safety of or prevent danger to the plaintiff and those accompanying her, and in those circumstances the plaintiff succeeded in her claim.

In *O'Gorman v. O'Gorman* [1903] 2 I.R. 573 the defendant who kept about 20 beehives near the plaintiff's haggard was held liable both in negligence and in nuisance when the bees swarmed, while the defendant was taking honey from them and attacked the plaintiff's horse.

Nuisance

In *O'Gorman* (see above) it was considered that apart from liability in negligence there should be liability in nuisance, Mr Justice Kenny stating in the course of his judgment at 582–583:

> "The defendants were entitled to the natural and reasonable use of their own land and the jury had to consider whether this keeping of bees in the manner and place which they did went beyond the lawful use of their own land in relation to their neighbour. It was a jury question and there was in my opinion evidence upon which they could properly act. They found in effect that the defendant set up what was an actionable nuisance and that it resulted in injury to his neighbour. I do not think that finding can be quarrelled with."

In the later case of *McStay v. Morrissey* (1949) 83 I.L.T.R. 28 the plaintiff sought an injunction on the grounds that bees were kept in unreasonable numbers and in an unreasonable place. The court declined to give an injunction but the court was prepared to find that the owner of the bees would be liable for injuries inflicted by the bees on persons living in the vicinity if there was clear evidence that the bees had been kept in unreasonable numbers and in an unreasonable place or, alternatively, if it could be shown that the injuries had been caused as a result of the negligence of the owner in or about the handling and/or management of the bees.

Liability was also imposed in nuisance in the case of *Cunningham v. Whelan* (1918) 52 I.L.T.R. 67 in circumstances wherein which the plaintiff's horse and cart had been overturned when 24 bullocks belonging to the defendant which were unattended on the roadway pressed against the cart. As a matter of law at that time, no liability in the normal course attached for damage caused by animals straying on the road but the court was prepared to hold that it was different where one was dealing with a "combined mass" of animals which caused an obstruction on the highway. In that decision, it appears that the finding of the court was based in nuisance because of the judge's view that it was immaterial as to how the animals had escaped onto the road.

Trespass

Where a defendant drives an animal or causes that animal to enter onto the lands of another, then liability will arise in trespass. This is separate and distinct from the special rule which governs cattle trespass. Cattle trespass arises in circumstances where animals escape or stray of their own volition from the property of the owner of those animals onto the lands of another.

The distinction is important since:

> "First, liability in cattle trespass is strict whereas liability in some kinds of trespass requires at least intention or negligence on the part of the defendant; second, cattle trespass is confined to "cattle", and does not extend to other animals such as cats or dogs; third, the Defences in both torts are not the same." (Extract from the Reform Commission Working Paper No. 3)

In *Ryan v. Glover* [1939] 5 Ir. Jur. Rep. 65 a bullock strayed into a field in which cows were grazing with the result that the animals fought and some of the cows were injured. It was held on appeal to the High Court that the owner of the bullock was responsible for his animal's trespass and that the damage suffered by the owner of the cows was not so remote as to preclude him from obtaining a decree in his favour.

However, where the trespass is directly caused by the wrongful act of a third party in leaving a gate open on a private right of way connecting the lands, the owner of cattle which leave his lands and trespass onto the lands of an adjoining owner will not be liable to the adjoining owner for the resulting damage (*Moloney v. Stephens* [1945] 11 Ir. Jur. Rep. 37).

Occupiers' Liability

There is a general duty on the part of an occupier to take reasonable care for the safety of persons whom such occupier can reasonably foresee being on his property and that duty of care will extend when there are animals present on the property. In such circumstances, where there are animals present within a mart premises, the operator of the mart is under a duty to take reasonable care for the safety of customers who are present within the mart premises to ensure that they are not unreasonably exposed to risk of injury by virtue of the presence of cattle.

Statutory Duty

Under the provisions of the Road Traffic General Bye-Laws 1964 (S.I. No. 294 of 1964), Part V makes provision in respect of animals on the road.

Article 30 provides that a driver meeting or overtaking an animal on a road shall either reduce speed or halt the vehicle if requested to do so (whether by signal or otherwise) by a person in charge of the animal.

Article 31 provides:

"(1) A person in charge of an animal which is being driven along or onto a road shall take all reasonable steps to ensure:

(a) that the animal does not obstruct other traffic or a pedestrian;

(b) that save when being driven to or from land or premises the animal is not on a cycle track or footway; and

(c) that the traffic overtaking the animal has room to do so in safety.

(2) In this bye-law "driven" means conducted without a rein or lead.

Article 32 provides that:

"A person leading a horse along a roadway shall notwithstanding any other provision of these bye-laws do so on the right side of the road."

Article 33 provides:

"During lighting up hours a person in charge of animals on a road shall so carry as to be likely to warn other road users of the presence of the animals a lamp showing a white light visible for a reasonable distance in the direction in which the animals are travelling and a red light visible for a reasonable distance in the opposite direction."

The Road Traffic General Bye-Laws 1964, were made under section 88 of the Road Traffic Act 1961, which section was replaced by section 60 of the Road Traffic Act 1968, which latter section provides that the bye-laws shall continue in force and shall be deemed to be regulations made under that section and shall be capable of being amended or revoked accordingly. The section further provides that a person who contravenes a regulation made thereunder shall be guilty of an offence and the penalty for contravention is provided in the general penalty section.

Separate and apart from these regulations, under section 13(2) of the Summary Jurisdiction (Ireland) Act 1851, any person riding any horse and leading any other horse who shall not keep such led horse on the side furthest away from any carriage or person passing him on any public road or in any street of a town shall be liable to a fine not exceeding 10 shillings.

Impounding of Animals

Under the provisions of section 4(2) of the Animals Act 1985 it is provided:

> "(a) Subject to paragraph (b) a member of the Garda Síochána or any local authority may impound any animal found wandering on a public road or in any public place or trespassing on any public park or open space which is owned or occupied by a Local Authority or a State Authority.
>
> (b) In relation to any such public park or open space the power to impound conferred by paragraph (a) may be exercised only on request by the authority by which such public park or open space is owned or occupied."

Section 4(3) of the 1985 Act provides that the Commissioners of Public Works in Ireland may impound any animal found trespassing on any public park which is under the control and management of the Commissioners.

Under section 4(5) where any animal is impounded in pursuance of the powers conferred by the section, the authority by which the animal is impounded may recover the costs of transporting the animal to the pound from the owner of the animal as a simple contract debt in any court of competent jurisdiction.

In certain circumstances, it is open to the occupier of land to seize any chattel which is unlawfully upon his land which has done or is doing damage there and such citizen is entitled to detain them until payment of compensation for the damage done. This right is known as that of "distress damage feasant". It has been held that this right extends to all chattels whether animate or inanimate. The right of distress damage feasant is vested only in the occupier of the land.

The chattel/object distrained must be on the land unlawfully and there must have been actual damage done by the object. It is lawfully taken and detained only as a security for the payment of compensation. Where there is no damage done there can be no compensation due. There can be no right of distress unless there has been an infringement of right attached to the land whether by trespass or nuisance. If infringement is established, damage need not be done to the land itself or to things forming part of the freehold such as crops, for it is sufficient if the damage is done on the land to property situate thereon or to the person of the occupier. The object intended to be seized must be still on the land. Once it has been removed from the land, the right of distress ceases to subsist even if the object was wrongfully removed.

There is no right of sale on foot of the right of distress damage feasant, the right being merely a right to retain the thing until adequate compensation is made. The exercise of the right of distress damage feasant suspends the right of action for the damage complained of so long as the detention of the property continues. Distress and action are alternative remedies which cannot be concurrently pursued. If, however, the property distrained perishes or is lost without the distrainor's fault, he is remitted to his right of action and so also if the property is restored to the owner.

In general it would appear that there is no right to impound animals which are straying on private property, certainly in circumstances wherein which the owner of the animals is known.

Self-help remedies by a private citizen should be exercised only with the greatest of caution since any act in excess of what is lawfully authorised will constitute trespass for which that person may then become answerable in law.

CHAPTER 12

FIRE

Elaine Hanniffy, Barrister-at-Law

Introduction

At common law, strict liability was imposed on occupiers for the spread of fires. In an Act entitled "An Act for Preventing Mischief that May Happen by Fire" which was passed in 1715, it was provided that no action should be taken against any person in whose "house or chamber" a fire accidentally began.

On November 11, 1938, Roslevan School, which was situate in the townland of Athlone, was destroyed by a fire which had spread to the school premises from the adjoining premises, the property of Athlone Woollen Mills. An action was brought by Hilda Richardson and Elsie Webster against Athlone Woollen Mills Co. Ltd claiming damages based upon the defendant's liability at common law in respect of the damage to property occasioned by the fire. The defendant contended that it was exonerated from any liability at common law by virtue of the 1715 Act and in particular section 1 of that Actwhich provided:

> "No action, suit or process whatsoever shall be had, maintained or prosecuted against any person or persons in whose house or chamber any fire shall . . . accidentally begin".

In the decision of the Supreme Court in the *Athlone Woollen Mills* case [1942] I.R. 581, it was held that the word "house" in section 1 of the statute denoted a dwelling house and did not include a factory and in consequence liability was held to attach to the defendant.

Accidental Fires Act 1943

Subsequent to the decision in *Athlone Woollen Mills*, the Accidenttal Fires Bill was introduced into the Dáil by the then Minister for Industry and Commerce, Mr Sean Lemass, who stated that the legislation:

> "simply proposes to make it clear that the legal position will henceforth be what

until the recent Supreme Court decision it was always commonly assumed to be".

The Bill was passed into law as the Accidental Fires Act 1943.

Section 1(1) of the 1943 Act provides:

> "Where any person (in this section referred to as the injured person) has suffered damage by reason of fire accidentally occurring...in or on the building or land of another person then notwithstanding any rule of law...no legal proceedings shall be instituted in any Court by the injured person or any person claiming through or under him or as his insurer against such other person on account of such damage."

It is clear that the expression "accidentally" means "without negligence".

An occupier will be liable for fires caused by persons on his property with his licence if such fire is other than an accidental fire, *i.e.* one which has occurred without negligence.

An example of negligence is best illustrated by the facts of *McKenzie v. O'Neill and Rowe Ltd*, an unreported decision of Mr Justice Hamilton in the High Court, of June 23, 1977. On a summer's day after a dry spell, a director of the defendant company burned papers that had accumulated on the company's premises on the slopes of the Dublin mountains. The day in question was windy and although after a time the fire seemed to the director's satisfaction to have been extinguished, it later spread to a neighbouring property where it burned gorse, heather and other shrubs planted by the plaintiff. In imposing liability, Mr Justice Hamilton (as he then was) stated that he was:

> "satisfied that having regard to the conditions prevailing at the time, the nature of the wind and the dryness of the conditions and the nature of the growth in the area it was negligent on the part of the Director to light a fire on the defendant Company's premises without taking adequate precautions to ensure that it was extinguished or that no portion of the material being burned or sparks would be blown away by the wind onto the adjoining premises".

Immunity under the 1943 Act extends beyond mere property damage to personal injuries.

Fire Services Act 1981

The Fire Services Act 1981 was enacted in the wake of the Stardust tragedy which occurred in March 1981. The Act made provision for the establishment of Fire Authorities and the organisation of fire services, fire safety, fire fighting and the protection and rescue of persons and property.

Section 18(1) of the Fire Services Act 1981 provides that:

> "The Section applies to premises or any part thereof put to any of the following uses—

(a) use as or for any purpose involving the provision of sleeping accommodation excluding premises consisting of a dwelling house occupied as a single dwelling;

(b) use as or as part of an institution providing treatment or care;

(c) use for purposes of entertainment, recreation or instruction or for any purpose of any club, society or association;

(d) use for purposes of teaching, training or research;

(e) use for any purpose involving access to the premises by members of the public whether on payment or otherwise; and

(f) use for any other prescribed purpose but excluding—
  (i) premises used as a factory within the meaning of the Safety in Industry Acts, 1955 and 1980,
  (ii) premises used as a store and subject to licensing under regulations made under the Dangerous Substances Act, 1972,
  (iii) a magazine store or registered premises within the meaning of the Explosives Act, 1875, and
  (iv) an oil jetty within the meaning of regulations under the Dangerous Substances Act, 1972."

Section 18(2) requires every person who has control over a premises to which the section applies to take all reasonable measures to guard against the outbreak of fire and to ensure that as far as is reasonably practicable the safety of persons on the premises in the event of an outbreak of fire.

Under section 18(3), a duty is imposed on every person being on premises to which the section applied to conduct themselves in such a way to ensure that as far as is reasonably practicable any person on the premises is not exposed to danger from fire as a consequence of any act or omission of his.

It is unclear whether or not section 18(2) can be interpreted as generating a civil liability but to the extent that a statutory duty of care has been imposed it would appear to constitute a significant inroad on the immunity provided by the 1943 Act.

Guesthouses

A farmer who operates a guesthouse may find liability will be imposed in respect of injury to a guest even in respect of a fire which occurs accidentally on premises because of the provisions of section 18(2) of the Fire Services Act 1981.

Wildlife Act 1976

Section 39 of the Wildlife Act 1976 provides:

(1) A person shall not burn any vegetation growing within one mile of—

  (a) a wood which is not the property of such person, or
  (b) land to which an establishment order, a recognition order, a designation order or an agreement under section 18 of this Act relates,

unless such person has, not less than seven years or more than thirty-five days before burning such vegetation, given notice of his intention to do so in writing to both the sergeant in charge of a Garda Síochána station in the Garda Síochána district in which the wood or land is situate and to—

  (i) in the case of a wood, the occupier of the wood,
  (ii) in the case of land to which an establishment order, a recognition order or an agreement under the said section 18 relates, the Minister together with, in case the Minister is not the owner of the land, the occupier,
  (iii) in the case of land to which a designation order relates, the Minister.

(2) Where notice is given under subsection (1) of this section, the Minister or any other person to whom the notice is given may within three days after receiving the notice serve a counter-notice on the person by whom such notice was given objecting to the proposed burning of the ground that it is liable to cause damage to the wood or land concerned.

(3) A person shall not—

  (a) light a fire, or
  (b) do any other act,

which causes, or is likely to cause, the burning of vegetation which is growing within one mile either of a wood which is not the property of such person or of land mentioned in paragraph (b) of subsection (1) of this section.

(4) Any person who burns vegetation, lights a fire or does any other act in contravention of this section shall be guilty of an offence.

(5) Where a person—

  (a) burns any vegetation either in contravention of subsection (1) of this section or after giving the notice required by this section and receiving a counter-notice under this section.
  (b) lights a fire or does any other act in contravention of subsection (3) of this section,

any injury occasioned by such burning, lighting or doing to,

  (c) in case the contravention is a contravention of the said subsection (1), any wood or land in respect of which a notice ought to have been or was served under this section, or
  (d) in case the contravention is a contravention of the said subsection (3),

any wood which is not the property of such person or any land mentioned in paragraph (b) of the said subsection (1),

shall be deemed to have been caused by the negligent act of that person, any damages to the extent of that injury shall be recoverable accordingly in any court of competent jurisdiction from that person by the owner of such wood or land, as the case may be.

(6) In this section wood includes a plantation."

Section 40(1) of the same Act provides:

"It shall be an offence for a person to cut, grub, burn or otherwise destroy, during the period beginning on 15th day of April and ending on 31st day of August in any year, any vegetation growing on any land not then cultivated or in the course of cultivation for agriculture or forestry."

Subsection (2) provides that subsection (1) of section 40 shall not apply in relation to:

"(a) the destroying, in the ordinary course of agriculture or forestry, of any vegetation growing on or in any hedge or ditch;

(b) the cutting or grubbing of isolated bushes or clumps of gorse, firs or whin or the mowing of isolated growths of fern in the ordinary course of agriculture;

(c) the cutting, grubbing or destroying of vegetation in the course of any works being duly carried out by a Minister of State or a body established or regulated by or under a statute;

(d) the destroying of any noxious weed to which the Noxious Weeds Act, 1936, applies;

(e) the clearance of vegetation in the development or preparation of sites on which any building or other structure is intended to be provided;

(f) the removal or destruction of vegetation required by a notice served by the Minister under section 62(1) of the Act of 1946 to be removed or destroyed;

but this subsection shall not operate to exclude from subsection (1) of this Section anything done by burning."

Offences and Penalties

Contravention of either section 39 or section 40 constitutes a criminal offence for which a person shall be liable on summary conviction:

(a) in the case of a first offence under the particular section or subsection to a fine not exceeding £50;

(b) in the case of a second such offence to a fine not exceeding £100; and

(c) in the case of a third or subsequent such offence to a fine not exceeding £200".

CHAPTER 13

DEFAMATION

Edward S. Walsh

Introduction

Defamation is committed by the wrongful publication of a false statement about a person which tends to lower that person in the eyes of right thinking members of society or tends to hold that person up to hatred, ridicule or contempt, or causes that person to be shunned or avoided by right thinking members of society.

Publication means communication to a third party. An exchange between two persons, in which allegations are made by one person of and concerning the other, does not constitute defamation. The essence of defamation is that there must be a false statement made to a third party which statement lowers the person, in respect of whom the allegations are made, in the eyes of right thinking members of society.

While communication is normally by means of words, whether written or spoken, nonetheless under section 14(2) of the Defamation Act 1961 it is provided that:

> "Any reference in that Part to words shall be construed as including a reference to visual images, pictures and other means of signifying meaning."

Slander and Libel

In civil law, slander is defamation in the oral form whereas libel constitutes defamation in the written form and imports an element of permanence. In the normal course, slander is actionable only on proof of special damage, *i.e.* the claimant must prove a specific loss other than certain specific exceptions which are as follows:

1. Slanders which impute unchastity or adultery to any woman or girl.

2. Slanders affecting a person's official professional or business reputation.

3. Slanders imputing a criminal offence punishable by death or imprisonment.

4. Slanders imputing a contagious disease which tends to exclude the sufferer from society.

If the allegation involves any of the circumstances outlined, then even if the person suffers no actual loss, an action may be maintained since, in law, these types of slanders are deemed to be actionable *per se*.

Vulgar abuse is not defamatory provided it constitutes mere vulgar abuse and does not, under the guise of colourful language, tend to make a serious allegation as against the person to whom the words are spoken. Chief Baron Joy in *Donohoe v. Hayes* (1831) Hayes 2265–2266, stated:

> "The principle is clear that a person shall not be allowed to murder another's reputation in jest."

When is Ridicule Defamatory?

The court in the case of *Dunlop v. Dunlop Rubber* [1920] 1 I.R. 280 found that a caricature of a plain and ordinary citizen of Dublin in which he was portrayed "as dressed in a very exaggerated foppish manner wearing a tall white hat, white waistcoat and carrying a cane and eyeglass" was defamatory. Mr Justice Powell in the course of delivering judgment said:

> "The gentleman, for example, who had adopted the stage for his profession could not, I take it, reasonably object that in an advertisement by way of poster of a theatrical performance in which he takes a part he is depicted in the garb proper to the part which he plays, whereas an ordinary citizen who does not aspire to histrionic fame might legitimately object to notoriety of such a kind, even although he were made to represent a personage of some fame and distinction in history, because it would make him merely ridiculous. Again . . . if a man is a public character in respect to whom it might be said that his public life or his great position was calculated to create an interest, it would be unreasonable to suppose that his portrayal in exaggerated form would tend to injure his reputation in the sense of making him an object of ridicule."

In all instances, a distinction must be drawn between defamatory ridicule and what induces mere innocuous humour at a person's expense or a good natured joke or chaff which would not be considered defamatory.

Innuendo

Obviously the question of what is defamatory depends upon the context in which the state in respect of which complaint is made and there may be special circumstances in which an article which is innocuous on its face may be capable of bearing a hidden meaning or hidden significance. If the words are prima facie innocent but because of special circumstances bear a hidden significance or hidden meaning then if such innuendo can be established the words may assume a defamatory context.

In *Berry v. The Irish Times* [1970] I.R. 378 the Supreme Court held that to say of the plaintiff that he was a "twentieth century Felon-setter" and "helped jail republican prisoners in England" was not defamatory on its face and since the plaintiff had not pleaded or proved the innuendo, the plaintiff consequently failed. Chief Justice Ó Dálaigh, in delivering the majority decision of the Supreme Court, stated:

> "If the allegation was that the Plaintiff did it as Secretary of the Department of Justice then he would do so only on the authority of his Minister or of the Government. Alternatively, the allegation might convey that he did so independently of such authority; unless it were claimed that in doing so he improperly and in breach of his trust as Secretary of the Department used information which came into his possession as such officer, for example without the authority of his Minister or of the Government the allegation must not necessarily be held to be defamatory. No such construction was attempted to be put on these words. If it had been so the action would have been of quite a different nature and such accusation would really have been a reflection on the Plaintiff's fitness for his position."

An example of where a plaintiff established the existence of an innuendo successfully was that of *Cassidy v. Daily Mirror Newspaper Ltd* [1931] A.C. 333. The defendant newspaper published a photograph of a Mr Cassidy (otherwise known as Corrigan) with a Miss X and innocently stated that their engagement had been announced. Mr Cassidy was at the time in fact married to although only occasionally living with the plaintiff. The plaintiff claimed that several people understood from the newspaper report that Mr Cassidy was not her husband but was living with her in immoral cohabitation. The English Court of Appeal upheld the jury verdict of £500 in favour of the plaintiff.

The words in respect of which complaint was made were not prima facie defamatory but because of the particular circumstances were capable of bearing a defamatory meaning and inferred whether innocently or otherwise that the plaintiff was not in fact married to the Mr Cassidy in respect of whom the photograph was published by the defendant.

Difficulty in Establishing Defamation

The type of difficulties which are encountered in defamation are best described by the extract from the judgment of Mr Justice Walsh in the case of *Quigley v. Creation Ltd* [1971] I.R. 269, a case brought by the plaintiff, the well known Irish actor, as against a women's weekly magazine in respect of an article which purported to be based on an interview with the plaintiff when no such interview had in fact taken place. The plaintiff's name appeared immediately below the title of the article "They've Left this Isle". The plaintiff claimed that the words used in the article in their ordinary meaning implied that he had left Ireland not for any proper reason such as furthering his art but solely for love of money and "that insofar as he was seeking employment in Ireland he was doing so dishonestly on a false basis since he had decided to make his career overseas".

It was contended that the article, whilst not defamatory in the case of every person, was defamatory in the case of an artist who was primarily interested in giving his art to the people of his own country as opposed to an artist who held himself out as being interested in giving his art to the highest bidder irrespective of his origins or from where he drew his inspiration. Mr Justice Walsh in the course of his judgment said:

> "Basically the question of libel or no libel is a matter of opinion and opinions may vary reasonably within very wide limits. When a jury has found that there has been a libel this Court would be more slow to set aside such a verdict than in other types of action and it would only do so if it was of opinion that the conclusion reached by the jury was one to which reasonable men could not or ought not have come. It is true that if words only tend to lower a person in the minds of a particular class or section of society particularly if the standard of that particular section of society is one which the Court cannot recognise or approve the words will not be held to be defamatory. On the other hand words are defamatory if they impute conduct which would tend to lower that person in the eyes of a considerable and respectable class of the community though not in the eyes of the community as a whole. The test is whether it will lower him in the eyes of the average right thinking man. If it will then it is defamatory if untrue. It follows naturally that in an action in this country the standard would be that of an average right thinking person in this community. The law recognises the right of the Plaintiff to have the estimation in which he stands in the opinion of the right minded people in this community unaffected by false statements to his discredit."

Statement Published Concerning a Class of Persons

Whether one of the class of persons in respect of whom the statement is made can sue depends upon the size of the class and whether the plaintiff can point to facts which show that he was particularly referred to.

In *Le Fanu v. Malcolmson* 1 H.L.Cas.637, an article was published by the defendants suggesting that cruelties were practised upon employees in some Irish factories. Certain other statements in the article included a reference to Waterford amounting to sufficient evidence to enable the jury to identify the plaintiff's Waterford factory as the factory primarily attacked and in consequence of which the plaintiff was held entitled to succeed.

Libel

Where a defamatory statement is made in a permanent form, it constitutes libel. Section 15 of the Defamation Act 1961 provides that:

"for the purposes of the law of libel and slander the broadcasting of words by means of wireless telegraphy (*i.e.* whether on radio or television) shall be treated as publication in permanent form".

Libel is actionable *per se*, *i.e.* without establishing any specific loss or damage other than the fact of publication.

Defences

The defences which are available to a defendant who is sued in a defamation action are as follows:

(a) Justification

(b) Privilege (absolute and qualified)

(c) Fair comment on matters of public interest

(d) Consent

(e) Apology

(f) Offer of amends.

It is not intended to deal with the defences in detail since if someone is sued for defamation, having regard to the complexity of the law, legal advice is an absolute necessity. The defences, however, which are available are set forth in brief below.

(a) Justification

The defence of justification obliges a defendant to prove the truth of the alleged defamatory statement. If the statement is true, then there is no wrong or harm caused to the plaintiff even if people think the less of him because, if true, then the plaintiff had a false reputation at the outset and the law does not protect false reputations.

The truth of the statement is a full defence and cannot be destroyed either by showing that the defendant did not in fact know that the statement in respect of which complaint was made was in fact true or whether or not it was made as a result of malice.

The onus is upon a defendant to prove the truth of the statement. If justification is pleaded and if a defendant fails to establish the truth of the statement, then the plaintiff may receive aggravated damages because the defendant persisted in the lie.

(b)   Privilege

The defence of privilege divides into two categories, absolute privilege and qualified privilege.

(i)   Absolute Privilege

1. The President

    The law in certain circumstances grants total immunity in respect of the publication of a statement even if defamatory. This is known as absolute privilege. Under Article 13.8.1 of the Constitution, the President has absolute privilege and is not answerable to any Court in respect of the exercise and/or performance of the powers and/or functions of the office of President or for any act done or purported to be done by the President in the exercise and performance of these powers and functions. This immunity extends to include a defamatory statement made by the President provided it is made within the context specified by Article 13.8.1.

2. Parliamentary Privilege

    All statements made by members of the Oireachtas in either House and any official report or publication of either House is entitled to absolute privilege under Article 15.12 and 15.13 of the Constitution. Further, under the provisions of the Committees of the Houses of the Oireachtas (Privilege and Procedure) Act 1876, section 2, it provides that the privilege will extend to utterances made before Committees of the Oireachtas by members of either House, to utterances of members, advisers, officials and agents of such Committees, and to documents and reports of such Committees. It is for precisely this reason that members of the Oireachtas may feel free to make allegations of or concerning third parties which clearly reflect adversely upon the third party in respect of whom the publication is made and such third party is without remedy unless there is a repetition of the allegation outside either House in which instance a member of the Oireachtas can be made amenable but not otherwise.

3. Newspaper and Broadcast Reports of Court Proceedings

    Under section 18(1) of the Defamation Act 1961, newspaper and broadcast reports of Court proceedings are absolutely privileged. Section 18(1) provides specifically that:

    > "A fair and accurate report published in any newspaper or broadcast by means of wireless telegraphy as part of any programme or service provided by means of a broadcasting station within the State or in Northern Ireland of proceedings publicly heard before any Court established by law exercising judicial authority within the State or in Northern Ireland shall if published or broadcast contemporaneously with such proceedings be privileged."

4. Judicial Proceedings

All or any statements made during the course of judicial proceedings, whether by judges, counsel, witnesses, solicitors, or the parties to the proceedings are absolutely privileged. The privilege also extends to statements made in the preparation of the trial and to documents and pleadings connected with the proceedings. In *MacAulay & Co. v. Wyse-Power* 77 I.L.T.R. 61, it was held that no action lay where a Circuit Court judge had said of and concerning the plaintiff company in the course of the trial of an action:

> "In my considered opinion the firm of Messrs MacAulay & Co. Ltd of 15 Haymarket, Dublin, is an utterly dishonest and disreputable firm. It is one with which no decent man who has regard for his honour should be associated and its members are men with whom no decent man should socially have resort .. . no person in Connacht should ever again have anything to do with any person even remotely connected with this disreputable firm which earns its profits by battening on the lack of legal knowledge of the simple people of the West."

Also, in the case of *Looney v. Bank of Ireland*, an unreported decision of Mr Justice Murphy of November 3, 1995, it was held that the contents of an affidavit filed in judicial proceedings were absolutely privileged and no action for defamation would lie in respect of them. Complaint had been made as regards the contents of an affidavit filed in a mortgage suit which, it was alleged, was defamatory.

5. State Communications

Absolute privilege is conferred on the executive branch of the Government and extends to communications between members of the Government *inter se*, communications between the Government and the President and communication as between a Minister to a subordinate official or by a military officer to his superior and, it is suggested, to statements made by Secretaries of Government Departments to Ministers. It is less clear whether or not communications by civil servants of lesser rank are entitled to absolute privilege or to qualified privilege only.

6. Communications Between Husband and Wife

Historically, a communication as between husband and wife was not actionable since they were deemed to be one unit in law. This absolute privilege, however, is now explained on the ground that because of the constitutional position of marriage as a matter of necessity the law must deem communication between husband and wife to be absolutely privileged.

(ii) Qualified Privilege

1. There are certain circumstances where the law will recognise the right of a

person to communicate freely provided that it is not done maliciously. A person who makes a statement in such circumstances is entitled to the benefit of qualified privilege provided that he is not motivated by malice. In order to establish qualified privilege the communication must be made bona fide upon a certain matter in respect of which the maker of the statement has a duty to speak or is obliged to protect an interest and regarding which the person in receipt of the communication has a corresponding interest or duty.

An example is that of *Kirkwood Hackett v. Tierney* [1952] I.R. 185. There the President of U.C.D. was held to have a duty to make a full inquiry in respect of a money draft alleged to have been paid out wrongly to a student. A statement alleged to have been made by the President to the student in questioning in the presence of the College Secretary was held to be a privileged communication and was protected in the absence of malice.

So too in the case of *Hartery v. Welltrade (Middle East) Ltd v. Hurley* [1978] I.L.R.M. 38, a complaint to the Garda Síochána and a request that a criminal offence should be investigated were held to have been made on a privileged occasion since they were made, it would appear, in the performance of a legal duty.

The owner of property has an interest in his property and in consequence a communication made to a suspected shoplifter is conditionally privileged. In *Magrath v. Finn* I.R. 11 C.L. 152, it was held that an address from the altar by a parish priest warning parishioners about the plaintiff was not privileged since no privilege attached to a clergyman "rebuking sin".

It is important to note that the defence of qualified privilege will only extend to a person who makes a statement relevant to the occasion and who communicates only to specific persons having a specific interest.

It has further been held that an accusation on a privileged occasion, for example, as against a suspected shoplifter or employee will not necessarily involve the defendant in liability merely because it is accidentally overheard by others who do not have an interest in learning all the accusation. This is best illustrated by the decision of his Honour, Judge James Carroll, delivered on February 6, 1996, in the case of *Sutton v. Savalcake Ltd*. On November 30, 1993, the plaintiff, a mother of two, entered the defendant's premises in the Ilac Centre, Dublin, where the defendant operated a shop selling children's clothes and menswear. She took several garments to a changing room for her son to try on. Having purchased two items she left the shop carrying two bags of shopping and her son's old clothes under her arm. As she left the shop, she was stopped by a security guard employed by the defendant and asked to come back into the store. The words alleged to have been used by the security guard were: "Would you mind stepping back into the shop please?"; followed by: "That garment belongs to us". It is claimed that the ordinary and actual meaning of these words meant, *inter alia*, that the plaintiff was a shoplifter, a thief, or had committed a criminal offence. It was admitted that the words had been spoken but it was denied that they meant what had been claimed, and further it was contended that even if they so did, they were spoken on an occasion of qualified privilege and were reasonable in all the circumstances.

The plaintiff in the course of evidence gave an account of being grabbed by the shoulder and confronted in an aggressive manner and having refused to go back into the shop. She stated when the guard had seen the worn state of the coat, he had hurried back into the store but by this time a crowd had gathered and she was deeply embarrassed. A friend of the plaintiff had witnessed the incident from a distance of several feet. She could see that the plaintiff and her children were distressed but was confused as to why. The security guard in question admitted that he had made a mistake. He had noticed the plaintiff taking several garments into the changing room and when leaving she had appeared to pick a coat from the floor. He insisted that his inquiry had at all times been at a conversational level in tone. He had apologised as soon as he realised his mistake. The plaintiff, however, had become abusive and this was what had drawn the crowd. The assistant manager of the shop told the court that he first became aware that something was wrong when he heard the plaintiff abusing the security guard.

Judge Carroll found that the request which had been made to the plaintiff in view of what the guard had seen was reasonable if made properly. He held that qualified privilege could exist notwithstanding that a third party had heard the allegation. The request to "step inside" was reasonable. The reasonable reaction to this would have been to do so. There was no evidence that the initial communication was made excessively loudly. The plaintiff, an excitable woman, had refused and it was her reaction that had created a scene. Had she behaved reasonably, then the whole unfortunate incident could have been avoided. In those circumstances, the claim was dismissed.

2. Reports

Certain newspaper and broadcasting reports are entitled to qualified privilege under section 24 of the Defamation Act 1961. The reports so protected are mentioned in the Second Schedule to the same Act and comprise:

(a) statements privileged without explanation or contraction; and

(b) statements privileged subject to explanation or contradiction.

In essence, statements privileged without explanation or contradiction comprise fair and accurate reports of proceedings in public of the legislature of a foreign state, any international organisation or conference where Ireland is a member, the International Court of Justice or similar type tribunal, or court proceedings in foreign states, fair and accurate copies of extracts from a public register or notices or advertisements of courts, whether in the State or in Northern Ireland.

Statements which are privileged subject to explanation or contradiction relate generally to trade, business, sporting associations, public meetings, local authority meetings, none of which are specifically relevant for the purposes of this publication.

Where qualified privilege exists, it may be destroyed by malice. This has been described by Lord Justice Brett in *Clark v. Molyneux*, 3 Q.B. 247 in the following manner:

> "If the occasion is privileged it is so for some reason and the defendant is only entitled to the protection of the privilege if he uses the occasion for that reason. He is not entitled to the protection if he uses the occasion for some indirect and wrong motive. If he uses the occasion to gratify his anger or his malice he uses the occasion not for the reason which makes the occasion privileged but for an indirect and wrong motive . . . malice does not mean malice in law . . . but actual malice that which is properly called malice. If a man is proved to have stated that which he knew to be false no-one need to inquire further . . . so if it be proved that out of anger or for some other wrong motive the defendant has stated as true that which he does not know to be true . . . recklessly by reason of his anger or other motive the jury may infer that he used the occasion not for the reason which justifies it but for gratification of his anger or other indirect motive."

The issue as to malice was considered by the Supreme Court in the case of *Mary Hynes-O'Sullivan v. Fachtna O'Driscoll* [1989] I.L.R.M. 349. Here the plaintiff was a consultant psychiatrist practising in Cork. In May of 1982, the defendant, who was acting as a solicitor for a husband in family law proceedings in the High Court, served a *subpoena ad testificandum* on the plaintiff requiring her to travel to Dublin and give evidence. The plaintiff attended as requested but was not called as a witness. Subsequently the plaintiff sent a bill in respect of her fees to the defendant who responded by requiring a breakdown of same. The plaintiff then wrote to the Incorporated Law Society of Ireland complaining of the defendant's conduct and inquiring as to whether there were any guidelines concerning the service of subpoenas on professional persons and asking for assistance in the recovery of her fees. The defendant was then sent a copy of this letter by the Law Society. In reply, he gave his version of events and attacked the plaintiff. The defendant then sent a copy of his reply to the Law Society, to the Irish Medical Association and made a formal complaint thereto, alleging unethical conduct, lack of integrity and professional impropriety in the plaintiff. The Irish Medical Association informed the defendant that it had no jurisdiction in the matter and that such a complaint should be made to the Medical Council whereupon the defendant sent similar letters to the Medical

Council. The defendant pleaded, *inter alia*, that the letters complained of were all written without malice on occasions of qualified privilege. At the end of a hearing before judge and jury in the High Court, the judge withdrew the case from the jury and entered judgment for the defendant. An appeal was brought to the Supreme Court who allowed the appeal and ordered a retrial, holding that the letter as sent to the Irish Medical Association was not protected by qualified privilege notwithstanding any honest or reasonable belief in the defendant that the person to whom he published the words complained of had a duty or interest in the matter referred to therein. It was further held that it was for the trial judge to decide whether the evidence was such as would reasonably entitle a jury to hold as a matter of probability that the publication was actuated by any indirect or improper motive, showing that a reason for which the occasion is recognised as privileged had been violated. Where the plaintiff can point to a number of examples of malice in regard to a publication, the trial judge must allow the case to go to a jury if it would be reasonable for it to hold as a matter of probability that any single instance amounted to malice. If no single instance could reasonably be said to amount to malice, however, the trial Judge must withdraw the case from the jury since it would not be open to it to hold that a number of instances, no one of which of itself could amount to malice, could, treated cumulatively, amount to malice.

(c)   Fair Comment on Matters of Public Interest

This defence is available to a defendant where such defendant can show that the comment was made on a matter of public interest and that what was said was comment as opposed to fact and that such comment was fair in the sense of being honest.

(d)   Consent

In general, if a person agrees to publication, then the fact of such agreement would appear to constitute a full defence. Obviously, the consent of the plaintiff to publication must be real.

(e)   Apology

Although it is not a defence to a defamation suit for a defendant to claim that he had in fact made or had offered an apology, nonetheless under section 17 of the Defamation Act 1961, where a defendant makes an apology before the commencement of an action or as soon afterwards as he has an opportunity of so doing if the action was commenced before the defendant had an opportunity of apologising, such apology is admissible as evidence in mitigation (in reduction) of damages. The apology must be genuine and in an appropriate form and if it is not to the plaintiff's reasonable satisfaction or if it really compounds the original defamation or smacks of insincerity or if it is "half-hearted" or "mean-spirited", the court may not allow this as a defence in mitigation of damages and indeed the apology may in fact constitute an aggravation to the original defamation resulting in increased damages.

Accordingly, in *Kevin Boland v. Irish Independent Newspapers plc*, complaint was made by the plaintiff, a former Government Minister, who had resigned from the Cabinet in 1970, that an article in the *Irish Independent* on January 28, 1993, wrongly stated that he had appeared before the court in the arms trial in 1970, had been dismissed as a Minister by the then Taoiseach, Mr Jack Lynch. On February 5, 1993, the newspaper, in a reference to Mr Boland, said that the article had incorrectly stated that he had appeared in court in the arms trial. It added "Mr Boland was of course charged with no offence and was not a defendant in this trial. We wish to apologise to Mr Boland for any distress or embarrassment caused by our error".

It was claimed that this publication constituted a further aggravated libel in that the words implied Mr Boland was charged with or was guilty of some disreputable act or conduct short of a criminal offence.

The defendant admitted the words in the article were untrue in the sense that Mr Boland did not appear before the arms tribunal. It denied the apology constituted a libel and went on to say that Mr Boland's resignation from Cabinet was a matter of public record.

At the conclusion of the trial, the jury found that the plaintiff had been defamed and awarded damages of £75,000 which judgment was then entered by Mr Justice Kinlen with costs (*Irish Times*, March 9, 1996).

(f) Offer of Amends

Section 21 of the Defamation Act 1961 makes provision in the case of unintentional defamation for the statutory defence of an offer of amends subject to strict compliance with the statutory framework there provided.

CHAPTER 14

SUCCESSION

Elaine Hanniffy, Barrister-at-Law

Introduction

An inevitability facing all people is death. The purpose of this chapter is to provide a brief summary of the principal legal matters relating to death.

If a person dies having made a will disposing of the entire of his/her property that person is deemed to have died testate. A formal document known as a "will" is a formal document whereby the testator (male) or testatrix (female) as the case may be, sets out his or her wishes, as to how his or her estate is to be disposed of. A will is ambulatory in effect, and operates only as and from death. In the normal course, the will comprises one document only but it is open to the testator/testatrix to execute a codicil which will be read in conjunction with the will.

Succession Act 1965

The first requirement of all wills is that they be executed in accordance with the specific formalities as laid down under section 78 of the Succession Act 1965:

> "To be valid a will shall be in writing and be executed in accordance with the following rules:
>
> (1) It shall be signed at the foot or end thereof by the testator or by some person in his presence and by his direction.
> (2) Such signature shall be made or acknowledged by the testator in the presence of each of two or more witnesses, present at the same time, and each witness shall attest by his signature the signature of the testator in the presence of the testator, but no form of attestation shall be necessary nor shall it be necessary for the witnesses to sign in the presence of each other.
> (3) So far as concerns the position of the signature of the testator or of the person signing for him under rule 1, it is sufficient if the signature is so placed at or after, or following, or under, or beside, or opposite to the end of the will

that it is apparent on the face of the will that the testator intended to give effect by the signature to the writing signed as his will.

(4)   No such will shall be affected by the circumstances—

    (a) that the signature does not follow or is not immediately after the foot or end of the will; or

    (b) that a blank space intervenes between the concluding word of the will and the signature; or

    (c) that the signature is placed among the words of the testimonium clause or of the clause of attestation, or follows or is after or under the clause of attestation, either with or without a blank space intervening, or follows or is after, or under, or beside the names or one of the names of the attesting witnesses; or

    (d) that the signature is on a side or page or other portion of the paper or papers containing the will on which no clause or paragraph or disposing part of the will is written above the signature; or

    (e) that there appears to be sufficient space on or at the bottom of the preceding side or page or other portion of the same paper on which the will is written to contain the signature;

and the enumeration of the above circumstances shall not restrict the generality of rule 1.

(5)   A signature shall not be operative to give effect to any disposition or direction inserted after the signature is made.

At the time of execution, the testator must be of sound disposing mind and must act voluntarily. In most instances, the testator will nominate a person to act as the executor/executrix as the case may be.

The person who is appointed executor in a will is not obliged to accept the office. He is free to renounce even if he had agreed during the lifetime of the testator to act as his executor. Once a person extracts the grant of probate then he becomes fixed with the duties and liabilities which he cannot afterwards shake off.

The essential duties and liabilities of an executor are to gather in all assets, to discharge all liabilities and then to administer the estate in accordance with the will. The will itself determines the mode and manner in which the estate is to be distributed after the payment of the debts and liabilities.

Where no will is made, then an intestacy is said to occur. In the case of intestacy, the next of kin are entitled according to their respective priority to extract a letter of administration.

The person who extracts the letter of administration is deemed to be the administrator/administratrix as the case may be and has similar duties to that of the executor/executrix. The term "legal personal representative" includes administrators and executors. A legal personal representative is required to preserve, protect, and administer properly the estate of the deceased.

In the event of an intestacy, the estate is divided according to the provisions of the Succession Act 1965. Section 67 of that Act provides:

"(1)   If an intestate dies leaving a spouse and no issue, the spouse shall take the whole estate.

(2)   If an intestate dies leaving a spouse and issue—

   (a) the spouse shall take two-thirds of the estate, and
   (b) the remainder shall be distributed among the issue in accordance with subsection (4)

(3)   If an intestate dies leaving issue and no spouse, his estate shall be distributed among the issue in accordance with subsection (4).

(4)   If all the issues are in equal degree of relationship to the deceased the distribution shall be in equal shares among them; if they are not, it shall be *per stirpes*.

Section 68 provides:

"If an intestate dies leaving neither spouse nor issue, his estate shall be distributed between his parents in equal shares if both survive the intestate, but, if only one parent survives, that parent shall take the whole estate."

Section 69 provides:

"(1)   If an intestate dies leaving neither spouse nor issue nor parent, his estate shall be distributed between his brothers and sisters in equal shares, and, if any brother or sister does not survive the intestate, the surviving children of the deceased brother or sister shall, where any other brother or sister of the deceased survives him, take in equal shares the share that their parent would have taken if he or she had survived the intestate.

(2)   If an intestate dies leaving neither spouse nor issue nor parent nor brother nor sister, his estate shall be distributed in equal shares among the children of his brothers and sisters."

The essence of distribution *per stirpes* is that issue take the share that their parent would have taken. Consequently, under section 67(4), if there are no surviving children, all surviving children having predeceased the intestate, then all surviving grandchildren would take in equal shares. If, however, the intestate is survived by one or more surviving children and by the children of a predeceased child, then the grandchildren as such will not take in equal shares but rather will take fractions varying in accordance with the size of their branch of the family as if an equal share had been given to each child to be divided equally between his children if he did not survive the intestate.

Status of Children Act 1987

Under the provisions of the Status of Children Act 1987, all children, whether born within marriage or not, have equal rights. Part V of this Act introduced the general principle that relationships between persons are to be determined without regard to whether a person's parents are or have been married to each other insofar as property rights are concerned. On that basis, in the case of an intestacy, a non-marital child is as equally entitled to share as a marital child in the case of the natural parent.

Freedom of Testation

At common law, a testator was free to dispose of his property as he saw fit. The consequence of this freedom was that a testator could act as he wished in determining how and in what manner to dispose of his property under will and, subject to the testator being mentally competent, the law was obliged to admit the will to probate and the estate was administered according to the tenor of the will.

The Succession Act 1965, for the first time in Irish law, made radical changes to the freedom of testation on the part of a testator. The Act was enacted into law on December 22, 1965, but did not in fact come into operation until January 1, 1967. Prior to this Act a spouse or children could be disinherited at the whim of the testator/testatrix.

Legal Right

Section 111 of the Succession Act 1965 introduced the concept of the "legal right share":

> "(1)   If the testator leaves a spouse and no children the spouse shall have a right to one-half of the estate.
>
> (2)   If the testator leaves a spouse and children, the spouse shall have a right to one-third of the estate."

The legal right, as it is known, ranks in priority *below* the rights of creditors of the deceased and *over* devises, bequests or shares on intestacy in the case of a partial intestacy, thus securing priority for the spouse.

The legal right of a spouse may be renounced in an ante-nuptial contract made in writing between the parties to an intended marriage or may be renounced in writing by the spouse after marriage and during the lifetime of the testator.

A renunciation, if made before marriage, must be made by contract in writing between the parties to the intended marriage. Obviously such renunciation must be made by a person who is fully informed and understands the nature, effect and consequences thereof and such person should receive independent legal advice. If the renunciation as made pursuant to a contract is obtained as a result of undue influence and/or fraud and/or duress, or other improper means then can be set aside on the application of the renouncing party.

Where under the will of a deceased person who died testate, there is a devise or bequest to a spouse, the spouse may elect to take either that devise or bequest or the share to which he is entitled as a legal right (section 115 of the 1965 Act). Where a person dies partly testate and partly intestate, a spouse may elect to take either the share of the legal right or the share under the intestacy, together with any devise or bequest to him under the will of the deceased.

The personal representative is under an obligation to notify the spouse in writing of the right of election (section 115 of the 1965 Act). The right is not exerciseable after the expiration of six months from the receipt by the spouse of such notification or one year from the first taking out of representation of the deceased's estate, whichever is the later. In default of election the will applies.

Children

Section 117(1) of the Succession Act 1965 provides that where on application by or on behalf of a child of a testator, the court is of opinion that the testator has failed in his moral duty to make proper provision for the child in accordance with his means, whether by his will or otherwise, the court may order that the child be provided for out of the estate as the court thinks just.

Section 117(2) stipulates that the court shall consider the application from the point of view of a prudent and just parent, taking into account the position of each of the children of the testator and any other circumstances which the court may consider of assistance in arriving at a decision that would be as fair as possible to the child to whom the application relates and to the other children.

An order under section 117 shall not be made except on an application made within 12 months from the first taking out of representation of the deceased's estate.

The Courts

The number of cases in which applications have been brought by children has greatly increased since section 117 of the 1965 Act was first enacted. Section 117 was first considered by Mr Justice Kenny in *Re GM: FM v. TAM* (1972) 106 I.L.T.R. 82. In that case, the testator, who had substantial property interests in the Republic of Ireland and in England, left all his property in Ireland on trust for his wife, and after her death for his two nephews. There were no children of the marriage but in 1941 the wife, with the testator's somewhat grudging consent, had informally adopted the plaintiff/applicant and the adoption had been formalised in 1952 when the Adoption Board made an order under the Adoption Act 1952. Under section 110 of the Succession Act 1965, an adopted child is in the same position as a child born of the marriage. The testator having made no provision in his will for his adopted son, the latter made an application to the court under section 117. The plaintiff/applicant was 32 years old at the time of the application. He was not financially dependent on the testator at the time of the testator's death but, as was pointed out by Mr Justice Kenny in the course of his judgment, section 117 of the Succession Act 1965, unlike comparable legislation in England and certain other Commonwealth countries, is not limited in its application to dependent children. In determining the duty owed, Mr Justice Kenny said:

> "The obligation to make proper provision may be fulfilled by will or otherwise and so gifts or settlements may during the lifetime of the testator in favour of a child or the provision of an expensive education for one child when the others have not received this may discharge the moral duty. It follows I think that the relationship of parent and child does not of itself and without regard to other circumstances create a moral duty to leave anything by will to the child. The duty is not to make adequate provision but to make proper provision in accordance with the testator's means."

Mr Justice Kenny went on to say:

> "When deciding whether the moral duty has been fulfilled [the Court] must take all the testator's property (including immovable property outside the Republic of Ireland) into account but if it decides that the duty has not been discharged the provision for the child is to be made out of the estate excluding that immovable property."

Mr Justice Kenny also considered that the existence of a moral duty to make proper provision for a child must be judged by the facts existing at the date of the death and must depend on:

(a) the amount left to the surviving spouse or to the value of the legal right if the survivor elects to take this;

(b) the number of the testator's children, their ages, their position in life at the date of the testator's death;

(c) the means of the testator;

(d) the age of the child whose care is being considered and his or her financial position and prospects in life;

(c) whether the testator has already in his lifetime made proper provision for the child.

The courts have a wide discretion conferred by section 117 of the Succession Act 1965 and it is open to the courts to take account of all circumstances applicable to an individual case. A child includes an adopted and/or non-marital child and the section operates whether the will was made before or after the commencement date (*i.e.* whether the will was made before or after January 1, 1967).

Exclusion of Persons from Succession

Under section 120(1) of the 1965 Act:

> "(1)   A sane person who has been guilty of the murder, attempted murder or manslaughter of another shall be precluded from taking any share in the estate of that other, except a share arising under a will made after the act constituting the offence, and shall not be entitled to make an application under section 117.
>
> (2)   The spouse against whom the deceased obtained a decree . . . of judicial separation...and the spouse is guilty of desertion which has continued up to the death for two years or more shall be precluded from taking any share in the estate of the deceased as a legal right or on intestacy.
>
> (3)   A spouse who was guilty of conduct which justified the deceased in separating and living apart from him shall be deemed to be guilty of desertion within the meaning of subsection (2).
>
> (4)   A person who has been found guilty of an offence against the deceased, or against the spouse or any child of the deceased (including a child adopted under the Adoption Acts . . . and a person to whom the deceased was in loco parentis at the time of the offence), punishable by imprisonment for a maximum period of at least two years or by a more severe penalty, shall be precluded from taking any share in the estate as a legal right or from making an application under section 117."

Where any share in respect of which a person is precluded from taking under the section is concerned, that share is to be distributed as if that person had died before the deceased.

General

A prudent person will ensure that a will is made during his lifetime so as to ensure that upon his death there is an obvious identified person who is in a position to proceed to extract the grant of probate and that person (*i.e.* the executor) will undoubtedly be a person whom the testator has presumably had good reason to trust and rely upon and who, in the normal course, will be in a position to truly, faithfully and properly gather in the assets and administer the estate in accordance with the directions and instructions as laid down in the will. The absence of a will leads to uncertainty at a time when the surviving next of kin are already distressed.

A prudent testator will have regard for the interests of all next of kin and should have regard to the legal constraints introduced, whether by way of the legal right share to which the spouse is entitled, or to the potential for a claim by a child under section 117 of the 1965 Act if a child considers that there has been a failure on the part of the moral duty to make proper provision.

The execution of a will is a matter of considerable importance and is something for which independent advice should always be sought both in relation to the legal and the financial requirements.

Capital Acquisitions Tax

The subject of capital acquisitions tax is dealt with in chapter 16, but it is something with which a proposed testator should be concerned so as to ensure that assets are not unnecessarily frittered away in circumstances which could otherwise be avoided by careful tax planning.

CHAPTER 15

LEASING OF FARMS

Henry Abbott, S.C.

Introduction

The success of the Land Purchase Acts in establishing universal freehold farmer ownership of agricultural land in the State for many decades, coupled with the statutory ban, repeated in the Land Act 1965, on the letting of farm property, left the farming scene in the Republic of Ireland with hardly any agricultural tenancies until the passing of the Land Act 1984. The undoubted economic pressure for land mobility was catered for by conacre (tillage letting) and agistment (grazing letting) or variations thereof which variously gave interests in lands short of the outlawed tenancy interest.

These conacre and agistment lettings were not alone the creatures of public policy as enunciated in the Land Acts; they also had their roots in practices which facilitated the Irish landed and the landless classes prior to the great land reform of the late nineteenth and early twentieth centuries.

They were typified by the 11-month system, which (despite being a part of the Irish farming scene for up to two centuries) are likely to continue to be a major feature of the land market, by reason of their informality and flexibility and obvious protection against the land being "tied down" in an arrangement that would prevent a strategic sale, gift or inheritance.

The problem with the dual system of a strong freehold ownership with only the 11-month or similar letting system to cater for enlargement of unviable holdings and other needs of land mobility gave rise to the need for the role of acquisition and division of land by the Land Commission by way of re-distribution of large estates, especially in the Midlands, up to the 1970s. For instance, in 1977 the Land Commission acquired 29,816 acres of larger hold-ings generally, and allocated it to farmers who enlarged their holdings, or who migrated eastwards from what were traditionally "congested areas" in the West. Between 1945 and 1978 almost 2,700 "migrations" of individual farmers had been achieved in this way. The Land Commission had in the 1970s a land bank of about 75,000 acres awaiting allocation. The land bank was let to farmers by the Land Commission to farmers on an 11-month, or even monthly, system pending allocation to farmers. With rising land prices and problems of the Land Commission to satisfy the many and often impossibly conflicting demands placed on it regarding redistribution, a consensus emerged that the Land Commission would have to cease this function. Policy makers found it necessary to face the challenge of the re-introduction of the leasing of agricultural land as an option for the Irish farmer.

The passing of the Land Act 1984 was the legislative response to this pressure. While some leasing of land went on, it is fair to say that the system did not catch on as anticipated. As late as 1990 one eminent writer (Wylie, *Land and Tenant Law*) noted that, by then, the new leasing system did not appear to be attracting any significant interest, and this view was echoed by another in 1995 (Supplement to Laffoy's *Conveyncing Precedents*, 1995).

Increasingly, through tax reliefs, and the facility for transferring quotas under the marketing regimes introduced by the EEC in the 1980s and later, the leasing of land became more and more attractive for the farming community. However, by far and away the greatest boost received for leasing of land has been the introduction by the Department of Agriculture of the scheme of early retirement from farming, which came into operation on January 7, 1994. This scheme allows land which is leased to come into the definition of "agricultural holding" for the purposes of the retirement scheme, provided the lease is in respect of a period of at least five years and relates to an area of not less than five hectares.

The land market is thus likely to develop in the foreseeable future on the basis of sales of the farm freehold and medium term leases co-existing with a still active 11-month and tillage market. In the 1970s, the Department of Agriculture estimated that the 11-month and tillage letting market amounted to almost 1 million acres in the State. This figure has probably not changed to date.

Defining Conacre and Agistment

Since many short term conacre and agistment-type lettings are carried out informally, without any written contract, or where the brief contract does not provide for all contingencies, it is necessary to have regard to the common law as it has emerged from the cases decided over a considerable number of years. Apart from the main categories of such arrangements, typified by the 11-month grazing letting and the tillage letting, there are other arrangements which arise. These are the letting of meadow and silage, either by letting it on the shank as it grows in a mature, or almost mature state, ready for cutting or (particularly for silage) allowing the tenant to manure the grass some weeks before the crop is cut. In the more modern context, and with the spread of large cattle sheds, these are either let in their entirety, with or without the services of a person, usually the owner, who may fodder the cattle from silage in the unit, or on the basis of cattle taken in for feeding and paid for at a weekly rate per head.

While landowners and so-called tenants under such arrangements, are most unlikely to seek the advice of their solicitor in relation to every such transaction, it is nevertheless advisable for them to check with their solicitor from time to time, just where the pitfalls lie, in relation to matters such as payment, liability for cattle trespass, occupier's liability and adequacy of insurance cover for both parties. Parties should enquire whether there is in fact an existing agreement proffered by an auctioneer, which is applicable to the letting and whether it has been sufficiently notified to the parties to it, so as to actually be incorporated into a binding agreement.

Payment of "Rent"

In relation to payment and in the absence of agreement to the contrary, payment is only due when the licence for agistment or conacre has been completed. It has been held that there is no lien on either crops or animals in respect of either arrangement regarding unpaid payment for the grazing or tillage. Thus, a standard agreement should provide for staged payments in relation to the letting, at least at the commencement or mid-term, and at the end.

Predominately, auctioneers and estate agents in rural areas not only let the land, but also undertake the responsibility of collecting the payment, under what may or may not be a standard contract. This system is time-honoured and operates efficiently. However it is most unlikely that an auctioneer was anything more than a collecting agent for the owner, and in the event of default in payment by the tenant, the auctioneer would not be found liable: a court would hold that very often auctioneers professional associations, or groups of auctioneers, prepare and operate these standard contracts.

Liability in Respect of Injury to Animals and Crops

At common law and without any written contract, the duty of a person to whom animals are entrusted for grazing or feeding, is to take reasonable care of them and if they are killed through his negligence, he is liable. The duty of the person to whom animals are entrusted on the classic agistment contract without the exclusive user of the licensee of the lands as such, is greater than that of the owner of the lands, which are let on the basis that the licensee has exclusive user of them. The apparent conflict of Irish decided case law on these matters may in large measure, be explained on this basis. Nevertheless in either case, the owner of the lands is under an obligation to ensure that there are proper fences on the lands and that gates are kept properly closed, to prevent straying and there are no obvious dangers.

Liability Arising from Occupation of the Land

The landowner and the licensee should be aware of their liabilities in the event of cattle straying. Under animals legislation, the owner of animals is liable. However, the owner of the lands may be liable in addition to the licensee in the event of the court holding that the animals were in the control of the landowner in circumstances where the landowner was grazing the agister's animals with his own animals, or where the landowner had the obligation to herd the animals or fence the lands. In formal agistment lettings it may be difficult to advise in relation to what exactly the position is without actually looking at the course of trading and the general circumstances of the case.

While it is easy to conclude that there is a degree of uncertainty arising from an unwritten contract, care should also be taken in relation to an agistment arrangement contained in a written contract, where over a period or course of trading, one or other of the parties have waived some of the conditions of the arrangement. A condition or term of an agreement may be waived by a party where that term or condition is solely for the benefit of one party, or it may be waived or altered by the course of trading by agreement of both parties.

Alternatively, a court may take the view that by reason of the failure of one party to insist on the strict terms of an agreement, over a period of years, and the permission of the other party to change its position to its detriment, the party waiving the term or condition may be estopped from asserting it. It is therefore essential that, from time to time parties to written agreements, review them with their solicitors, to find, if in fact, the written agreement represents the course of trading which has developed and whether they are exposed to any possible claims from this area.

Insurance Implications

The preceding paragraph suggests in outline that the exposure of either party to liability may be unpredictable and it shows the need to be quite vigilant in relation to the adequacy of insurance in respect of such claims. Nowadays, farm insurances generally are dealt with on the package-type standard policies offered by various companies, which have the advantage of providing cover for the various types of liability, namely liability to the public who may be injured on the property, liability to employer and liability for storm, fire and theft. Other contingencies may be catered for, such as disease insurance. New occupier's liability legislation passed in 1995 does not remove the need for action in this area.

However, regardless of the comprehensive nature of the package policies, there is always an onus on the farmer and the broker to ensure that the actual farming operations of the farmer are adequately described in the information contained in the proposal and renewal form of the farmer. Very often a package policy taken out many years before, will not reflect the changes in farm operation and thus risks arising from short term licenses, entered into after the initial setting up of the policy, may be overlooked, unless a rigorous checklist is made every year in relation to additional license type arrangements.

Disease Status

In relation to care regarding diseases of animals, there is a statutory obligation to ensure that cattle from one herd are not intermixed with another. With agistment agreements providing for the grazing of some cattle with the owner's herd, the tenant would be exposed to the risk of prosecution for intermixing of animals, unless the animals are changed from the licensee's holding onto the agistment holding under a test period. Similar care should be taken in relation to the movement of sheep, even now under the de-regulated sheep dipping regime. Similarly neither cattle nor sheep should be moved into a herd that is not officially up to scratch, in terms of disease-free status.

E.C. Quota Regime

Both owner and tenant should check whether the agistment agreement actually transfers or impinges on any quota either for milk, sheep or suckler cows on the property. In relation to milk, the ordinary 11-month letting will not operate so as to bring with it the milk quota of the holding. Current regulations under the European Communities (Milk Quota) Regulations (S.I. No. 266 of 1995) require a lease of at least three years to effect such transfer.

Even with the less formal cattle and suckler cow premium quotas, the taking of land on the 11-month system does not automatically pass the quota, and special arrangements should be made in the lease to ensure that the quota, if any, attaching to the land actually passes over to the tenant, as the landowner may quite easily lease it to another person or sell it under the Department of Agriculture and Food schemes.

Care should also be taken with cattle which are taken in for agistment or feeding, to ensure that rules in relation to extensification premia and/or R.E.P.S. are not violated. Rules regarding cereal area aid are very inflexible regarding eligible areas notwithstanding recent liberalisation and knowledge of these rules is vital when taking tillage land for cereals or set-aside.

Local Authority Charges

While the question of whether rates are applicable to agricultural lands in the hands of a tenant in the nature of an arrangement for conacre or agistment are academic in the light of the abolition of rates in agricultural land, nevertheless questions may arise in relation to burgeoning local authority charges for mains water supplies. The occupier is the person who is primarily liable, but this is a matter which can cause difficulties in the event of the authority determining that the owner is in fact the occupier, for the purposes of charging water rates. As agricultural connections may be quite expensive in some counties, and may also be coupled with expensive meter charges, unpaid water charges could be a liability arising after the departure of a licensee, which would be difficult for the landowner to recover from the licensee and hence standard agreements should deal with this aspect.

Also the local authority impinges on landowners in terms of obligation to cut hedges and trees that overhang roads. The Roads Act 1993 imposes liability on landowners who may be liable for allowing water to go on to public roads, and there are some specific disincentives and liability provisions made in respect of the soiling of roads by farm animals and machinery, which should be considered. Under the Pollution Acts, local authority pollution officers may have special arrangements with regard to the spreading of slurry within certain distances of streams and also at certain times of the year. Agents making agreements should have regard to these requirements, so that they do not give rise to difficulties later on.

Agricultural Leases

The passing of the Land Act 1984 lifting restrictions of the last century on farm leases, coincided more or less with a broad initiative of Allied Irish Banks and the Irish Farmers Association, in co-operation with the Incorporated Law Society of Ireland and the Society of Chartered Surveyors in the Republic of Ireland, in proposing a *master lease* for agricultural land.

The object of having such a master lease was to draw on the experience and interest of the various bodies concerned, in an effort to provide a fair system of leasing of land under the new deregulated legislative regime, which at the one time would not unnecessarily tie up owner's land nor leave tenants without compensation for any capital improvements made by them in the event of the tenancy not being renewed, and in the interest of both landlord and tenant, to provide for mutual obligations which would ensure the proper maintenance and development of the land in accordance with modern husbandry methods. The master lease as first introduced, has been revised in 1994, particularly with a view to having same facilitate the farm retirement scheme, introduced in that year.

The sponsors of the draft master lease are anxious to stress that it does not purport to be, and should not be interpreted or construed as, anything other than a draft lease for discussion purposes to assist the parties in reaching agreement in accordance with the particular requirements of each individual case. The notice for practitioners and clients printed with the master lease goes on to warn that it is suggested that each practitioner should put the draft on his/her own word processing system, so that modifications and changes to the text can be made as each individual case requires.

The Gazette of the Incorporated Law Society of Ireland published a check-list for practitioners in relation to the use of the master lease in farm retirement arrangements under the 1994 Scheme which would be of considerable assistance to practitioners, and this is dealt with in a detailed examination of the master lease in this chapter.

The Land Act 1984

Section 3 of the Land Act 1984, which relates to "exclusion of leases of agricultural land from application of certain enactments", introduces a measure of freedom to the ability of owner and tenant to negotiate terms. However the ban on the letting of land without consent of the Land Commission still remains.

The explanatory memorandum of the Land Bill 1984 dealing with section 3 provided a relatively grandiose explanation as follows:

> "As part of its overall land policy, the Government has launched an intensive programme to promote and encourage leasing, so as to get under-utilised land into the management of those who will use it to optimum advantage. However, leasing is a relatively novel concept in Irish agriculture and amongst the factors inhibiting its adoption as a standard land management practice is the apprehension that farmers rights of ownership might be affected if they leased their lands. Such apprehension arises largely from the existence of some nineteenth century landlord/tenant legislation which granted certain statutory rights to lessees. In order to grant equal status to both lessor and lessee and to ensure that leasing arrangements are governed only by the terms of the contract entered into between the two parties and are not subject to overriding statutory provisions, it is proposed to exclude agricultural leases from the application of these provisions."

It is instructive to examine the detailed provisions of the Land Code, the application of which has been excluded by section 3, in the cases of leases of agricultural land.

Section 3(2) of the 1984 Act defines "a lease of agricultural land" as follows:

> "Any instrument in writing (whether under seal or not) containing a contract of tenancy in respect of land used wholly or mainly for the purpose of agriculture, horticulture or forestry."

Section 3(1)(a) of the 1984 Act excludes sections 70 and 71 of the Landlord and Tenant Law Amendment (Ireland) Act 1860 ("Deasy's Act") which Act provided important rights for any tenant who was ejected for non-payment of rent to redeem their holdings on payment of rent and costs, and subject to compliance with other formalities, generally within six months of execution of the order for possession in the ejectment proceedings.

Section 3(1)(b) of the 1984 Act excludes the application of sections 3, 4 and 7 of the Landlord and Tenant (Ireland) Act 1870. These provisions related to the right of the tenant who is ejected or disturbed to compensation for improvements to the holding.

Section 3(1)(c) excludes the application of sections 1, 4, 13 and 22 of the Land Law (Ireland) Act 1881. Of the sections of the 1881 Act excluded by paragraph (c), section 1 related to the right of the tenant of a holding to sell or assign his interest in the tenancy, notwithstanding the objections of the landlord. Section 4 related to providing the tenant whose rent has been increased, or suffers a loss in sale by reason of an increased rent with a right of certain compensation. Section 13 related to regulations regarding the right of the tenant to sell and to have a fair rent fixed by the court, and section 22 contained the extent of the power of a tenant to contract out of the Act.

Section 3(1)(d) of the 1984 Act excluded sections 7(3) and section 30(2) of the Land Law (Ireland) Act 1887. Section 7(3) of the 1887 Act related to the right of a tenant of an agricultural holding to apply for restitution along the lines of sections 70 and 71 of the 1860 Act.

Section 30(2) of the 1887 Act related to the power of the court to stay eviction in the event of payment of instalments of rent in proceedings for the recovery of land for the non-payment of rent.

Section 3(1)(e) of the 1984 Act excludes section 16 of the Land Law (Ireland) Act 1896. This section provided for postponing certain ejectments for non-payment of rent by payment of two years' rent.

It would thus seem that in one swoop, the substantial part of a code of legislation which guaranteed what everyone came to know as the "three Fs", fair rent, free sale and fixed stay of tenure was put at an end by the 1984 Act. At first sight it would seem to be somewhat difficult to reconcile this "laissez faire" approach with the purposeful, if not idealistic introduction of section 3 in the explanatory memorandum of the Land Bill 1984.

This difficulty is resolved somewhat when it is realised that the restrictions in section 12 of the Land Act 1965 against sub- letting were not repealed by the Land Act 1984. A lease of agricultural land to be valid, still requires the consent of the Land Commission, pursuant to section 12 of the 1965 Act and it is through the requirement of consent that leasing will be policed so as to give an element of fairness to the tenant and landlord.

Although it is nowhere stated in the Act, the genesis of the Land Act 1984 depended to a great degree upon a consensus emerging in the time leading up to its enactment, on the contents of the master lease, and it was initially understood that the consent of the Land Commission would only be given in respect of leases substantially along the lines of the master lease and providing the same safeguards for both owner and tenant.

It would appear that the policy of the Land Commission, now very much subsumed administratively into the Department of Agriculture, has remained substantially the same, and a piece of legislation which might otherwise have encouraged a diverse range of leases, some of which could be manifestly unfair in the short term, has prevented the worst problems of de-regulation arising. This type of problem required complex legislation in the U.K. in the 1970s and 1980s. Whether ultimately a profusion of long-term land leases gives rise to the type of social problems which had to be outlawed by the nineteenth-century Land Law Acts or not, remains to be seen.

The Master Lease

The extent of the letting of the master lease, usually relates to all the agricultural lands described therein, excepting and reserving mines, minerals, owner's rights of way and the right of the owner to inspect the condition of the farm at reasonable times.

It is helpful for the reader to know about the main aspects of the master lease. The first schedule of the lease sets out the exact extent of the let farm and the length of the lease.

Paragraph 2 of the lease contains the tenants covenants with the owner. Covenants are basically conditions of the letting.

Covenants 1 and 2 in the lease relate to payment of rent and all existing and future taxes and outgoings, other than Land Commission annuity.

Covenants 3 to 10 in the lease, inclusive, deal with the obligation on the tenant to preserve the property and its contents.

Covenant 12 relates to the avoidance by the tenant of any act or thing which may make void any policy of insurance, or increase risks of fire, etc.

Covenant 13 of the lease relates to the obligation to prevent encroachments and acquisition of rights by anyone. This provision really is not thoroughly essential to protect the owner, but it certainly will protect the owner having to go to law against third parties on the property after the tenant has left at the end of the term.

Covenant 14(a) forbids assignment (sale) by the tenant of a part of the farm, or sub-letting or sharing the possession of the farm or to enter into conacre or agistment agreements. Sub-paragraph (b) is a covenant not to assign without first obtaining the owner's prior written consent. There is a provision that such consent shall not be unreasonably withheld where the proposed assignee (purchaser), is a responsible and suitable person, or a person who has the appropriate qualifications as required by the 1994 Farm Retirement Scheme, and fulfils the relevant conditions laid down by the Retirement Scheme.

Under Covenants 15 and 16, the tenant is prevented from seeking planning permission or a change of the development plan, regarding the zoning of the land and is compelled to facilitate the owner.

Covenant 17 stipulates that the tenant does not carry out the work set out in the third schedule without the prior written consent of the owner, unless the tenant is directed by a third party, by legal order, to do so. The prohibited works envisaged by this covenant are set out in the third schedule and the most notable hazard is the ploughing, or breaking up of permanent pasture, except that described in the second part of the First Schedule. Obviously a mixed or predominantly tillage farm lease must have the First Schedule carefully studied and redrafted so as to leave flexibility for tillage. Likewise tenants likely to engage in more intensive farming may wish to have a special facility, to put in more productive short term leys, if they are to maximise the production of the land for the term involved. Care should be taken to give this freedom to renew old pasture as a basic minimum provision, but additional provisions to the master lease should provide for the quality of the seed and the husbandry which would be necessary to ensure that these leys would survive to the end of the term and beyond. Otherwise the third schedule of the lease forbids all sorts of (perhaps unlikely) activities such as irrigation, hop gardens, orchards, shrubs or trees for commercial production, flowers, vegetables, erection of dwelling house and disposal of stone, gravel, earth, sand and clay.

Noteworthy is category 9 of the covenants of the master lease, of the third schedule which forbids any works not listed in the fourth or fifth schedules. This may be a trap for the unwary unless careful thought is put into what is actually permitted. With alternative farm enterprises and innovation being promoted on all sides as an essential part of rural development, some of these activities should be carefully planned for when first negotiating the lease.

Covenant 19 of the lease is probably one of the potentially most onerous and important covenants of all. This relates to the obligation of the tenant to carry out all works, pursuant to any decree or order of the court, or any laws, statute, statutory instrument, directive regulation, including local authority or E.C. regulation which the farmer, as occupier, is obliged or required to carry out, of which the owner, were he in occupation would be required to carry out.

Nowadays, the pollution control activities of the local authority, the monitoring of standards of milking parlour and milk storage facilities and the provisions of handling facilities for the testing and disease monitoring by the Department of Agriculture, could mean that a farm which is let on a master lease for say 10 years, could prove to be quite a liability in the short-term through the tenant having the obligation to bring these facilities up to date under public authority or Government direction. In addition, the impositions of the Safety Health and Welfare regulations and, (to a lesser extent), the inspections of the Fire Officer of the local authority, would be a hazard in certain situations against which both owner and tenant might be protected by suitable drafting and advice.

Professional advisers should be aware that many farms are in a state of transition or development in relation to the requirements of these controlling codes, which in recent times, have impinged on the operation of farms more and more. It is likely that the production on farms rented on a long lease would be pushed closer to the limit with more intensive production, thereby attracting the attention of the inspecting authorities all the more. In order to be fully protected against risk in this area, professional advisers should consult the prospective tenant or owner in relation to the requirements which may be (needed) during the term of the lease, and whether the tenant is in a position to comply with them.

There follows in the detailed provisions of the lease, a standard proviso for re-entry and covenant for quiet possession. The tenant and owner should understand this to mean that if the tenant misbehaves by not paying the rent or breaking the covenants, the owner may recover possession and similarly if the owner does not allow normal enjoyment of the land by the tenant, the tenant may sue him for damages and sometimes get an injunction.

Clause 3 deals with covenants between the owner and the tenant. Paragraphs A and B relate to insurance and assignment requirements. Clause C deals with the very important issue of the works which the tenant is allowed to do without the consent of the owner. These works are set out in the first schedule. Of these works, the application of slurry to land in accordance with good and proper agricultural practice, is one which may cause difficulty and the implications should be examined before a tenant commences. Spreading of slurry may be subject to planning permission and pollution officer restrictions, in terms of time, space and quantity. The farm may already be a spreading area for some other planning unit under very complicated planning permission arrangements which arise from time to time relating to larger pig units. The lease should contain a warranty that no such spreading arrangements affect the land, as searches by professional advisers may be difficult, unless the planning register in the local authority has been fully written up relating to such restrictions.

Paragraph D of the master lease deals with the determination of the arbitrator as to whether work falls within the third, fourth or fifth schedules.

Paragraph E of the lease relates to a case where the owner withholds consent to the execution of work, such as permanent buildings set out in the fourth schedule, but elects to carry out the works at his own expense. In that case, provision is made for determination by the arbitrator, after service of the usual notice to determine the increase in rent due to the owner by reason of the construction of the buildings. If, after this procedure has been completed and the rent determined, the tenant may, within 14 days of the arbitrator's award, withdraw his application for consent for such buildings subject to the payment of costs. This is an important paragraph and great care would be needed in its operation. Without full specifications, bills of quantities and drawings regarding the work to be done, a great deal of confusion could be generated in the operation of this paragraph and negotiation and arbitration procedure under it.

Paragraph F of the lease deals with determination by the arbitrator of the compensation to which the tenant is entitled, arising from the increase in the letting value of the farm at the end of the lease. It is most likely that such compensation would be for the construction of buildings, for instance, if the tenant received E.U.-type grants which may be given to tenants with holdings of a certain minimum acreage and of five years or more.

Paragraph G of the lease deals with the right of either party to request the President of the Incorporated Law Society to nominate an arbitrator for the purposes of the lease. The provisions of this paragraph are special, in that they dispense with the appointment of an arbitrator by an agreement and opt instead for the appointment by nomination; a course which should make for speed. The paragraph is also special insofar as it sets out in some detail the procedures to be followed by the arbitrator. This means that lengthy legal debates about settling references to arbitration and indeed pleadings might well be dispensed with in such arbitration. However, it would be advisable for the parties to allow the arbitrator to take such steps in the arbitration as would be consistent with Paragraph G, so as to ensure that all the issues and evidence are clarified in the arbitration.

While arbitration is very often put in agreements and leases to achieve speedy resolution of disputes between parties, it has been found in the U.K. that arbitration relating to agricultural leases frequently fails to achieve that aim. Perhaps if this proves to be the Irish experience, through one or other party obstructing the commendable Arbitration procedure set out in the lease, our legislation might provide institutional backing for such procedure, by allocating the function to official administrative bodies such as the Valuation Tribunal or the Rent Tribunal, which may have the twin advantages of set procedures and an ability to accumulate "going rates" for various aspects of compensation and valuation, together with affording experts' records for their research.

Paragraph H of the lease deals with the situation in relation to the tenant holding on to possession and paying rent after the expiration of the term of the lease without the granting of a new lease in formal terms. The basis of such overholding is a monthly tenancy commencing on the day following the end of the term. The rent per month in such a case is one twelfth of the yearly rent of the lease. Such a monthly tenancy arising from overholding may be ended by one calender month's notice, by notice to quit served by the owner.

The question arises, whether the tenancy arising in certain circumstances by implication of over-holding is void, having regard to the provisions of section 12(3) of the Land Act 1965, prohibiting sub-letting without the consent of the Land Commission. Care would have to be taken to ensure that the original consent related to such contingency. Alternatively, it may be argued on the basis of the decision in *Carew v. Jackman* [1965] I.R. 177 that the tenant could seek the consent to such implied tenancy, by forcing the owner to apply to the Land Commission in respect thereof.

Paragraph I of the lease relates to formalities in relation to notice.

Paragraph J specifies that time shall be of the essence in respect of service of notice and other matters relating to consent to assignment, carrying out of works set out in the fourth schedule, either by the owner or the tenant in matters relating thereto and payment by the owner of compensation to the tenant under paragraph F. These are essentially important to lawyers, but of no great concern when considering alterations which may be made to the lease at negotiation stage.

Conveyancing Implications

As the long-term leasing of agricultural land is probably primarily driven by the 1994 Farm Retirement Scheme, it is of considerable assistance to professional advisers that the conveyancing committee of the Incorporated Law Society of Ireland have agreed a basic checklist (published in the Law Society's *Gazette*, November 1994) for the Department of Agriculture of the legal documentation which must be filed in any application for pension. The *Gazette* warns:

> "It should be noted that the check list only relates to the Department of Agriculture requirements regarding getting the pension through and practitioners must also consider the investigations and searches which must be made to ensure that a tenant obtains a good workable title and if acting for the owner, should ensure that the objective of the leasing system in ensuring that the land is not tied up or no undue burden falls on the owner by reason of the leasing is avoided."

The hazards to watch out for on the part of the owner are, first, that care should be taken to ensure that the lease does not relate merely to buildings with ancillary lands which could bring the lands let into the category of tenement within the meaning of the Landlord and Tenant (Amendment) Act 1980 as amended by the Landlord and Tenant (Amendment) Act 1994. This may not be as easy as it seems, and when all the decisions under the Land Law Code relating to whether holdings were substantially agricultural or pastoral or not are considered, it will be realised that questions may arise in relation to larger houses, on small parcels of land and the like.

The question does arise how a tenant of a rural tenement in such circumstances could actually establish a right to a longer tenancy under the 1980 Act as amended, when section 12 of the Land Act 1965 may operate to prevent such a letting. The court would probably make an order granting such new lease, being subject to the Land Commission deciding, pursuant to section 12 of the Land Act 1965, whether a consent ought to be given. In any event in relation to section 12, the definition of "agricultural" in relation to a holding means substantially agricultural or pastoral or substantially agricultural or pastoral in character and it is therefore unlikely that section 12 would provide any bar to the renewal of a lease where a court had found that the land was actually ancillary to the buildings of the tenement within the meaning of the 1980 Act. This aspect is an important consideration for professional advisers in cases where it is possible that alternative farm enterprises may develop with buildings which may effectively downgrade the land to ancillary status.

Practitioners acting for elderly persons should be careful that a long lease does not provide difficulties in liquidating assets in the administration of an estate in the event of the owner not being likely to be succeeded by children or spouse or favoured nieces or nephews for the purposes of capital acquisitions tax, as the presence of a long lease may effectively leave the major part of the value of the farm unsaleable, unless vacant possession may be obtained. With pressure to obtain cash to discharge tax bills, the administration of the estate could be put under unnecessary pressure in those circumstances. The same cautionary approach should be taken in relation to owners, whose debts and other commitments may be such as to require the sale of the land, with vacant possession in the future. Such clients are not ideal subjects for the leasing of land.

The death of a tenant is an important event, about which the lease is remarkably silent. In the absence of any provision that the letting is to end on the death of the tenant, the tenant's interest in the farm will descend to his or her family, or whoever is named in a will. This can give rise to complications and both parties would be well advised to insert some special provisions to cater especially for this possibility and eliminate in so far as possible the uncertainty which might arise from this tragic event. It should be borne in mind that until comparatively recent times, agricultural leases in the U.K. terminated, in many instances, on the death of the tenant.

Care should also be taken in relation to the implications of the Family Home Protection Act 1976, and while the land granted by a lease may not actually contain the family home, sometimes part of the curtilage of the family home could be contained in the lease and thus, where there is no special clause enabling the family home to be "separated" from the rest of the farm, the validity of the whole lease under the Family Home Protection Act 1976 may be in jeopardy.

Also, from an owner's point of view the master lease does not provide any options for the more careful monitoring of whether the quota for milk, ewe or suckler cows and similar quota arrangements attached to the farm may be preserved in certain cases. Modern policy relating to all quotas seems to be moving in the direction of a requirement that the holder of a farm quota should supply a minimum quantity of the product in quota, in order to hold on to the quota. An example of this is the newly introduced rule in relation to sheep quotas where a producer who does not fill the quota for two years may run the risk of the quota falling into the national reserve. The individual quota situation of the owner should be examined carefully and suitable additional provisions should be inserted in the master lease to cater for the timely monitoring of the system in relation to the quota and if necessary, penalties commensurate with the loss of such quota should be provided in the event of the lease being surrendered or terminated, having lost some of the quota rights. Also, such a clause should make provision against the tenant intentionally seeking to transfer the quota, so as to prevent third parties from complicating the picture, regardless of whether they have acquired legal rights or otherwise to the quota.

The operation of milk quotas is dealt with elsewhere and any professional adviser dealing with the lease of an existing dairy farm with quota, on the basis that it will continue as such, should take considerable care to ensure that the quota passes to the tenant with the farm being leased. Provisions for the handling of a situation where there is an additional allocation of quota, (such as an allocation from the National Reserve, during the letting period), should be made so as to reflect what the quota regulations, as administered by the Department of Agriculture indicate in relation to the attachment of such quota to the land. As some leases may now deal with land let on very long terms for forestry, care should be taken to ensure that private foresters actually tend to the forest, so that the capital value thereof is secured beyond the period for claiming grants and premia.

The comments relating to hazards created by the various terms of the master lease indicate that a professional adviser acting for a tenant should be cautious in relation to all of the regulatory hazards now impinging on farm land.

With the possibility of establishing costly buildings on leased property, with an attendant right of substantial compensation at the end of the letting term, the obligation on professional advisers to make thorough searches in relation to title should be the same as that when buying a modern farm.

Again, where substantial additional buildings are constructed on leased land, where alternative farm enterprises are developed, both owner and tenant should be advised that such buildings may lose the farm building exemption from rates as this tends to be defined narrowly so that, for instance, a farmer who develops an equestrian centre or a training stables or certain tourist accommodation, may find that he faces a significant bill for local authority commercial rates.

The implications arising from a tenant with a claim for substantial compensation gives rise to the challenge of securing payment of same in a number of years when the letting comes to an end. The master lease does not seem to provide any security by way of charge on the farm when the letting is at an end for such compensation, and, it may be argued that before tenants are to commit themselves to major works, that they should negotiate arrangements for the registration of such charge on the owner's freehold folio of the farm. This raises the important point of how professional advisers for both owner and tenant may ensure that lending institutions will be in a position to advance to the tenant on a suitable security, money for the purpose of capital improvements.

This problem was envisaged by the *Report of Inter-Departmental Committee on Land Structure Reform* in 1978, when it was suggested that the best way of ensuring that banks would have sufficient security, would be to have both the owner and the tenant join in charging not only the letting, but also the freehold, with the sum borrowed in respect of the improvements. There would also have to be suitable arrangements for set off of compensation against the sum borrowed in the event of inability of the tenant to pay. Obviously, where the tenant sought security for payment in respect of improvements, such security would have to be postponed as a charge on the freehold folio to the lending institutions security. Such arrangements might in due course be standardised by some lending institutions if the need arose.

CHAPTER 16

TAX

Sean McKiernan, Chartered Accountant*

Income Tax

The Tax

Income Tax is charged on the taxable income of individuals each year. Taxable income is total income from all sources calculated in accordance with the Income Tax Acts and after deducting reliefs and personal allowances. Individuals pay income tax and companies pay corporation tax.

Self Assessment

Individuals must submit an income tax return each year before January 31 following the fiscal year to which this return relates. For example, the income tax return for 1995/96 must be submitted before January 31, 1997. Failure to submit a tax return on time will result in a surcharge of between 5% to 10% of the tax payable subject to an overriding limit of IR£50,000. For new start-ups, these surcharges apply from the second year only.

Payment

The payment of income tax which is not deducted at source is due by November 1 in the tax year. So for 1995/96 the payment should be made by November 1,

---

*McFeely & McKiernan, Chartered Acountants, 93 Lower Baggot St., Dublin. This chapter has been written as a layman's guide to the various taxes currently on the statute book and before the Finance Act 1996 is enacted. Tax laws both in the Republic of Ireland and in Europe are constantly changing and we cannot emphasise enough the importance of seeking professional advice specific to the circumstances applicable in any particular case before a final decision is made. The author cannot accept any responsibility for loss occasioned to any person acting or refraining from action as a result of material published herein.

1995 (*i.e.* half way through the tax year irrespective of the possibility that all the income to which the payment relates may not have been earned at this point). Failure to pay the appropriate amount on time may lead to interest at a rate of 1.25% per month being imposed on the shortage.

To avoid interest penalties the preliminary tax paid must be the minimum of:

(a) 90% of the final tax payable; or

(b) 100% of the tax payable for the previous tax year; or

(c) in the case of direct debit participants only, 105% of the tax liability for the pre-preceeding year of assessment, except where this is nil.

In practice there is no requirement to pay preliminary tax in the first year of assessment of a commencing business.

Total Income

In arriving at total income which includes trading profits, professional income, profit rent, interest, dividends, foreign income, pensions and some social welfare payments, there are detailed computational rules laid down in the tax acts and also a considerable body of case law. Where any degree of complexity is involved it is advisable to engage the services of a chartered accountant.

Farmer Taxation

Farmers are assessed to Income Tax under the rules of schedule D Case 1. A simple example is as follows:

		IR£
Profit per Accounts		10,000
Add: Personal Expenses:		
Depreciation	1,500	
Motor and Travel (1/3)	950	
Light and Heat and Phone (1/4)	128	
Goods for own use	280	2,858
Adjusted Trading Profit		12,858
Less: Stock Relief (25%)		1,250
		11,608
Less: Capital Allowances		2,400
Taxable Profit Schedule D Case 1		9,208

Averaging of Farm Profits

A farmer may elect that his farming profits chargeable to income tax are to be computed by reference to an average of the profits arising in each of the preceding three years. Where an election for averaging is made, the election remains in force for all future years, except where the individual decides to opt out of the averaging system.

Opting Out of Averaging   The individual may opt out of the averaging system only if he was charged to tax on the average basis for each of the three years of assessment immediately preceding the year for which he wishes to revert to the normal year basis.

Losses   Where losses are taken into an averaging calculation and the result of that calculation is a loss, one-third of the loss is available for relief against other income under section 307 of the Income Tax Act 1967 or for carry forward under section 309 of the Income Tax Act 1967 against future farm income.

Stock Relief   As stock relief is treated as if it were a trading expense, profits for averaging purposes are the profits after deduction of stock relief.

Capital Allowances   Capital allowances are applied to taxable income after averaging and are therefore not part of the averaging computation.

Stock Relief 25%

Farmers are allowed a deduction from their trading profits of 25% of the increase in stock values in the basis period. There is no claw back of the relief.

Stock Relief 100%

The Finance Act 1995 introduced a special 100% rate of stock relief for certain young trained farmers commencing to carry on the trade of farming for the first time. To qualify the farmer must be under 35 years of age at the start of the year of assessment in which the farming trade commences and must hold one of the specific training qualifications set out in the 1995 Act.

Disease Eradication

The Finance Act 1995 provides special tax treatment for farmers in respect of profits resulting from the disposal of livestock due to statutory disease eradication measures.

– Profits arising from the disposal of herds due to statutory disease eradication schemes will be excluded in computing income for tax purposes for the accounting period in which the livestock depopulation takes place. Such profits will instead be deemed to arise in two equal instalments in each of the next two accounting periods.

– Instead of the normal 25% stock relief, a farmer will be allowed to elect for stock relief of 100% in the two-year period. This stock relief is limited having regard to the amount re-invested in replacement stock.

This special treatment will be applied to compulsory disposals which took place on or after April 6, 1993, and will be available in the case of total cattle herd depopulation arising from statutory disease eradication schemes. Where the disposal is due to brucellosis, a farmer will be treated as having disposed of an entire herd where under the brucellosis eradication rules he disposes of all eligible animals, together with any other animals that must be disposed of in accordance with those rules.

Hobby Farming

Relief for farm losses against other income is claimable only where the farming is carried on, on a commercial basis with a view to the realisation of profits. The relief will only be available for three consecutive years and in special cases, four consecutive years.

If there is no other income, or if relief is denied because of the three/four-year rule, losses may be carried forward for set off against future farming profits.

RELIEFS AND ALLOWANCES

Personal Allowances

Personal allowances are related directly to an individual's personal circumstances, regardless of the nature of the employment.

Single Person's Allowance

Every individual is entitled to a basic tax free allowance which is the single person's allowance. The single allowance in the 1996 tax year is IR£2,650.

Married Allowance

This allowance is available to all married couples who are living together. The married allowance in 1996/97 tax year is IR£5,300.

Age Allowance

If a single or widowed tax payer is over 65 years an additional allowance of IR£200 is available. For married couples the allowance is IR£400, regardless of the fact that only one spouse may be over 65 years.

PAYE Allowance

Persons who have income under the PAYE system are entitled to an annual allowance of IR£800. Since April 6, 1994 this allowance is now available to relatives of their employer. This allowance is not available to proprietors or proprietary directors.

Incapacitated Child Allowance

An allowance of IR£700 is available in respect of each child who is permanently incapacitated by reason of mental or physical infirmity. The child's income must not exceed IR£2,100, as if it does the IR£700 allowance will be reduced by the amount of the excess.

Widowed Person's Allowance

A widowed person is entitled to an additional allowance of IR£500 plus the single person's allowance. If the widowed person had dependent children, they receive a total allowance equal to the married allowance as well as an additional allowance of IR£1,500 in the first year after bereavement. This allowance is reduced to IR£1,000 in the second year after bereavement and to IR£500 in the third year and to nil thereafter.

Single Parent's Allowance

A single parent with a dependent child or children is entitled to an additional allowance of IR£2,650, which renders their total allowance equal to the married person's allowance. Where the dependent child's income exceeds IR£750 per annum this additional allowance is reduced by the amount of the excess.

Housekeeper's Allowance

Where a housekeeper is employed to take care of an incapacitated tax-payer or spouse of the tax-payer, an allowance of IR£7,500 may be claimed. If the amount being paid is less than IR£7,500, the relief is restricted to the amount paid.

Blind Person's Allowance

An allowance of IR£700 per annum is available to an individual or spouse who is blind for all or part of any tax year. Where both spouses are blind this allowance increases to IR£1,600. A further allowance is available in respect of the cost of keeping a trained guide dog, provided the blind person is a registered owner with the Irish Guide Dog Association.

Dependent Relative Allowance

An allowance of IR£110 per year is allowed in respect of dependent relatives of either spouse who are incapaciated by old age or infirmity. This allowance is also available in respect of a widowed mother or mother in law who are not necessarily incapacitated but who are over 65 years of age and resident with the tax-payer.

This allowance is not affected by the dependent's old age pension but will be reduced by the amount of any income which the dependent receives in excess of the old age pension.

Mortgage Interest Relief

Relief is available in respect of interest on money borrowed for the purchase, erection or improvement of a principal private residence, or the residence of a former or separated spouse, or the residence of a dependent relative who is living in the house rent free. The relief is subject to certain restrictions and will be relieved only at the lower rate of tax (*i.e.* 27% currently) from 1997/98 onwards. For the tax payers with income taxable at 48% the effective rate of relief for 1996/97 is 32.25%.

In addition to the restriction in the rate of tax at which mortgage interest is allowable there is a ceiling on the amount that can actually be claimed.

Fees Paid to Certain Private Colleges

For the tax year 1996/97 and future years, allowance will be granted towards fees paid for approved courses in certain private colleges. The courses will have to be full-time undergraduate courses of at least two years duration. The relief is allowed only at the standard rate of 27% tax rate.

Allowance for Payment of Service Charges

For the tax year 1996/97 and future years allowance will be granted towards the payment to Local Authority of service charges. The allowance will be a maximum of IR£150 and will be allowed only at the standard 27% tax rate.

Life Assurance Relief

Tax relief on life assurance was abolished with effect from April 6, 1992, with one exception, namely those policies which form part of a personal pension contract.

Pension Payments Relief

Payments to approved personal pension schemes amounting to no more than 15% of the tax payer's net relevant earnings are fully allowable against tax for persons with non-pensionable incomes.

Allowance for Rent Paid on Private Accommodation

Persons paying rent for private accommodation where the accommodation is the tax-payers only principal residence, are entitled to the following annual allowances:

	Persons over 55 years IR£	*Other* IR£
Single Person	1,000	500
Widowed Person	1,500	750
Married Person	2,000	1,000

Medical Expenses

Tax relief is available on non-recoverable medical expenses incurred by the tax payer, his spouse and children. Certain items are not allowed such as routine maternity, ophthalmic or dental treatment. The first IR£150 claimed in the case of individuals or IR£300 in the case of families is not allowed.

Health Expenses: Dependent Relative

Medical expenses incurred by an individual in respect of a dependent relative can be claimed against tax provided none of those expenses can be recouped. In the case of a dependent relative being maintained in a nursing home or hospital the allowable amount is reduced by 60% of the dependent's old age pension. Full allowances are granted in the case of expense incurred on once-off treatment such as a serious operation.

Medical Insurance

Payments made to recognised medical insurers such as V.H.I. are allowable against tax. From 1996/97 onwards the relief will apply only at the lower rate of tax.

Permanent Health Insurance Premiums

Payments made to a health insurance scheme which provides regular income in the event of sickness or disability are fully allowable against tax. The premiums being paid must not exceed 10% of current income.

Business Expansion Scheme

Expenditure of up to IR£25,000 per annum in an approved fund is fully tax allowable. A married couple may each obtain relief of IR£25,000 subject to various conditions including the fact that they both have sufficient income in their own right.

Relief for Investment in Films

Expenditure of up to IR£25,000 per annum in an approved project is fully tax allowable. Companies may also avail of this relief.

Seed Capital Investment

Individuals who satify certain conditions relating to employment and share-holding may be eligible to obtain tax relief for investment of a sum up to IR£125,000 invested in new ordinary shares in a newly incorporated company engaged in "BES" type activities or research and development. The maximum relief in any one year is IR£25,000, but relief is given against total income of the individual for any of the five years immediately preceeding the year the investment is made.

Exemption Limits

For 1996/97 a single or widowed person or a married person under single assessment whose total income is below IR£3,900 is exempt completely from income tax. This exemption applies to married couples whose total combined income is less than IR£7,800. These limits are increased by IR£450 for each of the 1st and 2nd qualifying children and by IR£660 for each subsequent child. Marginal relief applies where the income does not exceed twice these limits.

INCOME TAX TABLES

Personal Allowances	**1996/97**
	IR£
Single Persons	2,650
Married Couples	5,300
Widowed Person	3,150
One-Parent Family Allowance	
Widowed Person	2,150
Other Person	2,650
PRSI Allowance	Nil
Incapaciated Child Allowance	700
Blind Persons Allowance	
Single/Married – One Spouse Blind	700
Married – Both Spouses Blind	1,600
Employed Person taking care of Incapaciated	
Tax-payer or Spouse (Maximum)	7,500

Income Tax Exemption Limits	**IR£**
Single/Widowed	
General Limit (Under 65 years)	3,900
65–74 years of age	4,500
75 years of age and over	5,100
Married	
General Limit (Under 65 years)	7,800
65–74 years of age	9,000
75 years of age and over	10,200

Tax Bands, Rates and Tables

	Tax Table	*Table Allowance*	*Bands of Taxable Income*
Single/Widowed	A	Nil	First 9,400 @ 27% Balance @ 48%
Single/Widowed	B	4,113	All @ 48%
Married Couples	R	Nil	First 18,800 @ 27% Balance @ 48%
Married Couples	S	8,226	All @ 48%
Marginal Relief Cases	Z	—	All @ 40

Capital Gains Tax

The Tax

Capital Gains Tax (C.G.T.) was introduced in 1975 and seeks to charge tax on the disposal of an investment when the price received for the asset exceeds the cost as adjusted for inflation (indexation relief). The excess of the proceeds over the adjusted cost represent the gain.

Rate

The current rate of C.G.T. is 40% and the only exception is that a 27% rate is applied to gains realised by individuals on the disposal of qualifying shares in certain small and medium sized companies, which have been held for at least five years before disposal. The holding period is reduced to three years for disposals after April 5, 1996.

Basic Example

		IR£
Proceeds (March 1996)		100,000
Incidental Expenses		(1,500)
		98,500
Cost (June 1975)	9,000	
Incidental Expenses	350	
	9,350	
Indexation Factor: 4.764		
Indexation Relief: 9,350 x 4.764		44,543
Gain		53,957
Less: Capital Losses B/F		14,700
		39,257
Less: Annual Exemption (Married)		2,000
Chargeable Gain		37,257
Tax @ 40%		14,702.80

Note that capital losses are allowed against gains and can be carried forward from year to year until utilised but the annual exemption, unless used in the year to which it relates, is lost.

Returns and Payment

Capital Gains Tax is part of the self assessment system and a return of chargeable gains must be made to the Revenue Commissioners on or before January 31 following the tax year of disposal.

Preliminary C.G.T. payments must be made by November 1 following the tax year of the disposal and must amount to 90% of the final liability in order to avoid interest penalties. The Revenue charge interest on all late payments of tax at a rate of 1.25% per month.

Reliefs and Exemptions

Annual Allowance   The first IR£1,000 of chargeable gains accruing to an individual in the tax year (IR£2,000 for married couples jointly assessed).

Tangible moveable property   Tangible moveable property the proceeds of which do not exceed IR£2,000.

Principal Private Residence   The disposal of your main home (and grounds up to one acre) provided that it has been occupied or deemed occupied by the tax-payer during the period of ownership.

Wasting Assets   For example, cars or race horses or other assets the predictable life of which does not exceed 50 years.

Miscellaneous Gains   Gains from Irish government stocks, life assurance policies, betting winnings, lottery winnings, national savings schemes, prize bonds, and compensation for personal injuries are also exempt.

Replacement of Business and Other Assets

A person engaged in a trade, business, profession or employment may defer gains realised on the disposal of certain business assets used solely for the trade throughout the person's period of ownership of them. The tax is deferred where the proceeds of disposal are reinvested in replacement assets for use exclusively in the trade. The chargeable gain arising at the time of disposal is deferred until the replacement assets cease to be used for the purpose of the trade. The following are the assets upon which "roll over" relief may be claimed:

1. Plant and Machinery

2. Buildings

3. Land in certain circumstances

4. Goodwill.

The asset disposed of need not be replaced by an asset of the same category.

The relief is available, in general, where the old and replacement assets are used in the same trade.

Relief is also available where a person ceases to carry on a trade and starts a new trade within two years of the date of cessation provided that the old trade was carried on for at least 10 years.

Normally, the replacement assets must be acquired within a period beginning 12 months before and ending three years after the date of disposal of the old assets. The Revenue Commissioners have discretion to extend these limits.

If part only of the proceeds of sale of the old assets is re-invested in replacement assets, a partial deferral will be allowed but only as long as the amount not reinvested is less that the chargeable gain. The relief for indexation is that applying at the date on which each disposal takes place.

Disposal of Business

A gain arising to an individual who has attained the age of 55 on the disposal of his business or farm or shares in his family company or holding company is ignored where the consideration is less that IR£250,000. In excess of IR£250,000 marginal relief applies, which restricts the tax payable to 50% of the difference between the proceeds and the limit of IR£250,000.

To qualify for the exemption, the individual must have owned the assets for a minimum period of 10 years ending with the disposal and where the business is disposed of through shares in the family company, the individual must have been a working director for 10 years immediately prior to the disposal, of which five years must have been spent as a full time working director. Where the disposal is made to the children of the tax-payer then it is exempt from C.G.T. altogether. But claw-back provisions are in place in respect of disposals by the children within six years.

Sale of Shares – Unquoted Company

If the consideration which an individual obtains for any material disposal by him on or after April 6, 1995, of shares or securities in a trading company, is applied by him in acquiring shares in an unquoted trading company, the business of which consists wholly or mainly of a qualifying trading operation including a profession, he is treated as if any chargeable gain accruing on the disposal did not accrue until he disposes of the new investment. A trade will be regarded as consisting wholly or mainly of qualifying trading operations if not less than 75% of the total amount receivable by the company from all its trading operations is derived from sales made or services rendered by the company in the course of the carrying on of the qualifying trading operations.

A material disposal occurs if throughout the three years ending with the date of disposal, or if shorter, the period during which the company traded, it was a trading or holding company, and the individual had been a working officer or employee of the company.

The conditions under which the relief may be claimed are:

(a) the individual must have held at least 15% of the voting rights of the original company;

(b) the individual must have been an employee or officer acting in a managerial or technical capacity for a period of three years immediately prior to the disposal;

(c) the investment must be made within the period of three years following the disposal of the original shares;

(d) the individual must hold at least 5% of the ordinary share capital of the new company within the period of one year following the disposal of the original shares;

(e) the individual must hold at least 15% of the ordinary share capital of the new company at any time in the period of three years from the date of disposal of the original shares;

(f) the individual must commence work with the new company within one year of the date of sale of the original shares and continue as a full-time working officer or employee of the company for a period of three years from the date of sale;

(g) the new company must not be a subsidiary of or under the control of another company, nor can it form a group with the original company.

The gain which is rolled over may be rolled over again where the new shares are disposed of and the proceeds re-invested in the above manner.

Where part of the proceeds are not re-invested, the amount not re-invested is to be deducted from the gain and any balance of the gain is treated as not accruing until a disposal of the new shares is made.

Relaxation since April 6, 1995

In respect of disposals made on or after April 6, 1995, relief may be obtained where the individual was either a full-time or part-time employee or director of the company. Shares may be quoted or unquoted. There is no minimum voting rights requirement. The relief may be claimed on a disposal of shares in a company carrying on a profession and re-investment may be made in such a company. The individual must be a full-time or part-time director of the company in which the re-investment is made and the company must be unquoted.

The money raised by the company through the issue of the shares must be used for the purposes of qualifying trading operations.

Capital Acquisitions Tax

The Tax

Capital Acquisitions Tax (C.A.T.) applies whenever a person becomes benefi-
cially entitled in possession to property for less than full consideration. The
current relevant legislation is contained in the Capital Acquisitions Act 1976
and subsequent Finance Acts. The tax encompasses both gifts and inheritances
with gifts being charged at 75% of the tax which would relate to the gift had it
been an inheritance (note that if the donor should die within two years of the
valuation date of the gift then it is taxed as if it were an inheritance).

C.A.T. is normally charged on the beneficiary of the gift or inheritance and
the amount of the tax payable depends primarily on the relationship between
the donor and donee. This fact is evidenced by the following table of threshold
amounts below which no tax is payable. It is important to realise that each
exemption limit (threshold amount) is on a cumulative basis, the value of
previous gifts are added to the value of the current gift/inheritance to determine
the applicable exemption.

TAX FREE AMOUNTS FOR C.A.T.

Relationship to the Donor/Testator	Exemption Limit 1996/97
Spouse	Completely Exempt
Child or Favourite Nephew/Niece	IR£182,550
Brother, Sister, or Child of a Brother or Sister	IR£24,340
Any Other Person (Stranger)	IR£12,170

Rates of Tax

Inheritance tax rates are as follows:

Amount	Rate
Exempt Threshold	0%
Next IR£10,000	20%
Next IR£30,000	30%
Balance	40%

Meaning of "Farmer"

A farmer is an individual who is domiciled in the State and 80% of whose gross
(*i.e.* his liabilities are ignored) property in possession is, after the taking of the

gift or inheritance, agricultural property, livestock, bloodstock and farm machinery.

Main C.A.T. Reliefs

Spouses Transfers between spouses are exempt and therefore estate splitting should be considered.

Agricultural Relief

C.A.T. is usually based on the market value of the property passing but where the donee or successor is a farmer as explained above the market value of agricultural property is reduced by 75%.

Agricultural property includes agricultural land and woodland together with houses and farm buildings and also livestock, bloodstock and farm machinery.

Note that in the case of gifts less than IR£360,000 it may be better to apply for agricultural relief under pre-1996 rules which the taxpayer remains entitled to do.

Claw-back

If the agricultural property is sold within six years the full relief is clawed back and if sold after six years but before 10 years then half the relief is clawed back.

Favourite Nephew Relief

If a nephew or niece of the disponer has worked substantially on a full-time basis for the period of five years ending on the date of the gift or inheritance, in assisting in the carrying on of the trade of farming, and the gift or inheritance consists of property used in connection with the trade, or of shares in a company owning such property, then the nephew or niece will enjoy a Class threshold (tax free amount) as if he or she was a child of the disponer, provided that he or she works substantially on the farm or in the farming company.

Small Gift Exemption In any calendar year the first IR£500 from each and any disponor is exempt.

Business Property Relief As a result of the current budget, from January 23, 1996, the relief for business property transferred by gift or inheritance is increased so that 75% of the value of the business assets are excluded from C.A.T. There are various conditions and claw-backs attached to the relief and these are outlined in the Finance Act 1994.

C.G.T. Credit Capital Gains Tax paid on a transaction which is also liable to C.A.T. may be credited against the C.A.T. liability.

Miscellaneous Exemptions

– Pension benefits to an employee

– Compensation payments or damages

– Winnings from lotteries or prizes

– Normal payments to support, maintain or educate a dependent.

Basic Example – Agricultural Relief

		IR£
Market Value		800,000
Liabilities	10,000	
Expenses	5,000	15,000
		785,000
Consideration		35,000
		750,000
Agricultural Relief @ 75%		(562,500)
Valuation for Capital Acquisitions Tax		187,500

Probate Tax

This tax is chargeable at a rate of 2% on the value of estates in excess of IR£10,650 (after deducting normal debts and expenses).

Assets passing to surviving spouses or held in joint ownership are excluded as is the family home.

The tax is normally accounted for by the executor of the estate and is allowed as a deduction in computing capital acquisitions tax.

Residential Property Tax

The Tax

Residential Property Tax (R.P.T.) is an annual tax levied on individuals whose residential accommodation exceeds a certain value and where the household income is over a certain limit. Rented property does not form part of residential property.

Property Value Limit

Where the gross value of all residential property exceeds IR£101,000 as at April 5, 1996 tax becomes payable provided the relevant income limit is exceeded. Where the property is in joint ownership the value is apportioned between the owners but the threshold is split accordingly. Where more than one property is involved it may be worth considering transferring the ownership of that property to a spouse from a R.P.T. viewpoint.

Income Limit

The income limit is not alone that of the house owner but also that of his or her spouse and any other person who resides in the house who is aged 65 or under who is not paying full rent. For the tax year 1996/97 the income limit is IR£30,100. If a person who has employed children residing at home, owns residential property of a value exceeding IR£101,000 it may be possible that a liability to residential property tax arises even though his own income is below IR£30,100. However, if the owner is aged 65 years or over household income is confined to that of the owner only.

Rates of Tax

The first IR£101,000 is not liable to tax. Any amount in excess of IR£101,000 is taxable at 1.5%. The tax payable can be reduced by one tenth for each dependent child resident with the tax payer. Marginal relief is granted where the income exceeds the income threshold by less than IR£10,000 (IR£15,000 where the tax-payer is aged over 65).

Payment of Tax

It is up to each individual to make a residential property tax return if it is the case that the value of their residential property would render them liable to tax. It is not necessarily the case that they will receive a notice from the Revenue Commissioners although in practise most people with incomes in excess of IR£30,100 limit will receive a communication. If a person is in doubt about whether or not be would have a liability he should have his property valued by a reputable valuer and depending on the valuation, act accordingly. The due date of annual payment is October 1. Returns must also be submitted on or before this date.

Tax Clearance Certificate

Anybody selling a house worth more than the threshold value will have to produce a tax clearance certificate indicating that all tax due was paid. Failure to do so will force the purchaser to withhold part of the sale price and pay it over to the Revenue Commissioners. The amount withheld is 1.5% of the excess of the sale price over the threshold amount multiplied by the number of years of ownership of the house by the vendor subject to a maximum of five years.

Stamp Duty

The Tax

Stamp Duty is a tax charged on instruments, *i.e.* written documents (*e.g.* a deed of transfer of property by virtue of which the vendor transfers his interest in the property to the purchaser). The law on stamp duty is contained in the Stamp Act 1891 and subsequent Finance Acts.

Payment

Stamp duty is normally payable within 30 days after execution of the deed at the appropriate rate (Table 1) by the accountable person who is the purchaser or leasee. There are severe penalties for late stamping which are outlined in Table 2.

TABLE 1

Main Stamp Duty Rates

Sale Price/Market Value	Rate
Tranfer of Certain Marketable Stocks and Shares	1%
Other Property	
0 – 5,000	Nil
5,001 – 10,000	1%
10,001 – 15,000	2%
15,001 – 25,000	3%
25,001 – 50,000	4%
50,001 – 60,000	5%
More than 60,000	6%

TABLE 2

Penalties For Late Stamping

Time of Stamping after first Execution	*Penalty in Addition to Duty Payable*
Within six Months	10%
Between six and 12 Months	20%
More than 12 Months	30%

Caution

Where a document has not been stamped it cannot be produced as evidence in an Irish court nor can it be registered by either the Land Registry or the Registrar of Deeds.

Where the statement of value is substantially incorrect then a surcharge is applied to the correct value which can be up to 200% of the original liability.

TABLE 3

Stamp Duty Surcharge

Understatement of value between	*Surcharge*
10% – 30% (Provided this is at least IR£5,000)	50%
31% – 50%	100%
Greater than 50%	200%

Reliefs

The main commercial reliefs are:

(a) Transfers between spouses are exempt.

(b) Transfers between relatives who are lineal ancestors or lineal descendants are at 50% of the normal rate.

(c) Transfers between associated companies are exempt.

Value Added Tax

A farmer need not register for VAT unless:

(a) his turnover from supply of taxable goods (other than farm produce) exceeds or is likely to exceed IR£40,000 in a continuous 12-month period;

(b) his turnover from supply of taxable services (for example, racehorse training, agricultural contracting, guesthouse accommodation) is likely to exceed IR£20,000 in a continuous 12-month period.

A farmer may elect to be a taxable person. But if he wishes to cancel that election he must repay the net VAT gain during the period of the election. He would make the election if VAT on his inputs would normally exceed VAT on his outputs.

Sales VAT Rates

Exempt: Short term letting of land

0%   Food for human consumption, eggs, fruit, vegetables, grain, food producing seeds and exports.

2.8%   Livestock.

12.5%   Agricultural services, guesthouse accommodation.

21%   Racehorse training services, sale of used machinery, sale of live poultry

A farmer may request the Revenue to determine the VAT rate applicable to an activity, and may appeal such a determination.

Cocktail   where a combination of goods and/or services that would normally be chargeable at different rates are supplied together the highest VAT rate applicable to any item in the group must apply to the combined group.

Two thirds rule   where the value of goods (other than 0% food and drink) used in supplying a service exceeds two thirds of the charge to the customer, the transaction must be taxed as a supply of goods, and not as a service.

Taxable Amount   a farmer is generally liable to VAT on the full amount that he becomes entitled to receive in respect of the taxable goods/services he has supplied. A farmer may adjust the taxable amount to take account of bad debts, discounts and returns.

Records

A farmer who is a taxable person must issue proper VAT invoices in respect of taxable goods or services supplied to other taxable persons, keep copies of those invoices and record them along with details of self supplies in a sales book that is kept up to date. An unregistered farmer must issue proper flat rate VAT invoices to other taxable persons and keep copies of these invoices. A farmer must also keep a proper cash book. The records must be kept for six years after the transaction they record. A farmer's records may be inspected at any time by the Revenue Commissioners and the inspector may assess tax he believes is due. There is an appeal procedure available.

A farmer must keep copies of purchases invoices and record them in a purchases book that is kept up to date.

Purchases for Resale

0%   Food producing seeds

2.8%   Livestock

Purchases not for Resale

12.5%   Electricity, repairs

21%   Accountancy services, office equipment, legal services, stationery and telephone

VAT Return

A farmer's VAT liability is calculated by transcribing the figures from the sales and purchases records into a summary and deducting the purchases VAT from the sales VAT. VAT on (properly invoiced) purchases for the business is deductible but no deduction is allowed for VAT on accommodation, cars, car hire, entertainment, food and drink, personal services, petrol or private (non-business) expenses.

Apportionment   If a farmer is carrying on a taxable activity and an exempted activity, only the input tax attributable to the taxable activity is deductible. VAT attributable to both taxable and exempt activities is calculated in the proportion of taxable turnover to total turnover.

Payment   If the sales VAT exceed the purchases VAT, the net tax due must be paid to the Collector General on or before the 19th day of the month after the VAT period. A farmer may be authorised by the Collector General to make an annual VAT return.

Repayment   If the purchases VAT exceeds the sales VAT, a VAT repayment will be due.

Unregistered Farmers

Unregistered farmers may reclaim purchases VAT paid on building work and land reclamation. Form No. VAT 58 should be used, copies of which are available from the Tax Office.

Corporation Tax

Companies resident in Ireland are liable to corporation tax on profits wherever arising.

Losses

Trading losses can be offset against other profits of the same period and the preceding period or carried forward against future profits of the same trade.

Rates

The standard rate of corporation tax is 38%. Close companies in receipt of investment or estate income may be liable to additional corporation tax of 15% on undistributed income.

From April 1, 1996, a new 30% rate of corporation tax will apply to the first IR£50,000 of company taxable income.

Preliminary Tax

A company is required to make a payment of preliminary tax within six months of the end of an accounting period. Where this date falls after the 28th day of the month the tax has to be paid on or before the 28th of the month.

Returns

The corporation tax return must be filed within nine months after the end of the accounting period, otherwise a surcharge will arise and certain reliefs may be restricted.

The surcharge for late filing and the restrictions on claims for certain losses and reliefs are as follows:

(a) Return filed within two months of expiry of deadline:

(i) Surcharge: 5% of tax payable, maximum IR£10,000.

(ii) Restriction: 25% of loss or relief, maximum IR£25,000 (A.C.T. maximum IR£10,000).

(b) Return filed two months or more after expiry of deadline:

(i) Surcharge: 10% of tax payable, maximum IR£50,000.

(i) Restriction: 50% of loss or relief, maximum IR£125,000 (A.C.T. maximum IR£50,000).

10% Rate

A 10% rate of corporation tax applies to manufacturing activities carried on in Ireland until December 31, 2010. The 10% rate also applies to certain trading operations carried on within Shannon Airport.

Distributions

Individuals who are resident in Ireland and in receipt of dividends and other distributions are taxable on the amount received plus the related tax credit. The level of tax credit is:

- Standard Tax Credit: 23/77 x dividend (previously 25/75).

- Distributions out of 10% profits: 1/18 x dividend.

Advance Corporation Tax

Advance corporation tax (A.C.T.) applies where an Irish resident company makes a distribution.

The amount of A.C.T. is equal to the tax credit attaching to distributions made in an accounting period less the tax credits on any distributions received.

A.C.T. can be offset against the company's corporation tax liability in respect of the accounting period in which the distribution is made. Any surplus A.C.T. can be offset against the corporation tax liability of accounting periods ending within the previous 12 months. Any balance can be carried forward indefinitely and set against a future corporation tax liability. Where a company has paid A.C.T., it can surrender the A.C.T. to other companies within the same group.

A.C.T. must be paid within six months of the end of the accounting period in which the distribution is made; otherwise interest will accrue at 1.25% per month or part month. Where the due date falls after the 28th day of the month, the tax has to be paid on or before the 28th day of the month.

A.C.T. does not apply to:

- Certain dividends and interest paid to non resident parent companies.

- Intra-group dividends where a 51% group relationship exists.

- Distributions of profit deemed to arise on shares bought back, redeemed or repaid by the issuing company.

CHAPTER 17

CONTROL AND ERADICATION OF ANIMAL DISEASES

Michael MacGrath, Barrister-at-Law

Introduction

The following is not intended to be a definitive account of legislative and judicial control of disease eradication. Only certain of the more important aspects have been highlighted.

The principal legislative provision for the control and eradication of the disease of animals is contained in the Diseases of Animals Act 1966. Most of the sections of this Act have been in operation for many years. Some sections, however, have only come into operation in recent years, *e.g.* sections 16, 21, 31, 34, 42 to 45, 55 and 57 came into operation on September 7, 1992 (see S.I. No. 249 of 1992).

There are also many Statutory Instruments made pursuant to the 1966 Act and other relevant legislation which are important in understanding the overall regime. There are, however, too many such Statutory Instruments to be mentioned here.

Diseases of Animals Act 1966

The following are some of the provisions of the 1966 Act. The Act provided for measures which the Minister (now the Minister for Agriculture and Food) might take in order to control and eradicate disease.

Notification of Diseases

The 1966 Act provides that the Minister might prescribe that notice be given of the existence or suspected existence of any particular disease. Many orders have been made requiring the notification of diseases (notifiable diseases). Those orders generally provide that any person who has or who has had in his possession or under his charge any animal, poultry, carcass, etc., which is or has been suffering from such notifiable disease, should, as soon as possible, notify either the Secretary of the Department of Agriculture and Food or an inspector at a District Veterinary Office of the Department.

Infected Areas

The 1966 Act also empowered the Minister to declare areas to be infected with a disease or declare a place to be no longer an infected place or area. Pursuant to the Brucellosis in Cattle (General Provisions) Order 1991 (S.I. No. 114 of 1991) and indeed the corresponding tuberculosis regulations the Minister has declared the State to be an attested or disease free area in respect of these diseases.

Section 15 of the 1966 Act authorised the Minister to make orders:

(a) prescribing and regulating the publication, in relation to a place or area declared infected, or the fact of such declaration;

(b) prohibiting or regulating the movement of animals and poultry and persons into, within, or out of an infected place or area;

(c) prescribing and regulating the isolation or separation of animals and poultry being in an infected place or area;

(d) prohibiting or regulating the removal of carcasses, eggs, fodder, litter, utensils, pens, hurdles, dung or other things into, within or out of an infected place or area;

(e) prescribing and regulating the destruction, burial, disposal or treatment of carcasses, eggs, fodder, litter, utensils, pens, hurdles, dung or other things, being in an infected place or area or removed thereout;

(f) prescribing and regulating the cleansing and disinfection of infected places and areas, or parts thereof, and of receptacles or vehicles used for the confinement or conveyance of animals or poultry; and

(g) prescribing and regulating the disinfection of the clothes of persons being in an infected place and the use of precautions against the spreading of disease by such persons.

Classification of Diseases

The 1966 Act makes provision for the classification of diseases in to what are defined as Class A diseases and Class B diseases.

Class A Diseases

Class A diseases are generally speaking more severe and are more severely dealt with in terms of slaughtering. Full compensation is payable subject to certain conditions in respect of the slaughter of such animals. Class B diseases are probably the more common form of diseases encountered in bovine animals, *e.g.* bovine tuberculosis.

The 1966 Act empowers the Minister to cause to be slaughtered any animals or poultry infected or suspected of being infected with specified diseases. With regard to Class A diseases, slaughtering generally extends to any animals or poultry which are or have been in the same field, shed or other place or in the same herd or flock or otherwise in contact with animals or birds so affected or suspected of being so affected or which might appear to the Minister to have been in any way exposed to the infection concerned.

The original list of Class A diseases was as follows:

1. Cattle plague

2. Pleuro pneumonia

3. Foot and Mouth disease

4. Sheep pox

5. Swine fever

6. Epizootic lymphangitis

7. Parasitic mange

8. Rabies

9. Glanders

10. Anthrax

11. Foul pest in any of its forms, including Newcastle disease and foul plague.

This list has been considerably amended, for example by addition of diseases such as Bovine Spongiform Encephalopathy (mad cow disease).

Class B Diseases

Class B diseases were originally defined as including:

1. Sheep scab

2. Bovine tuberculosis

3. Brucellosis in cattle

4. Warble fly infestation.

It was provided by section 19 of the 1966 Act that the Minister could, where necessary for the eradication of Class B diseases, make orders in relation to such disease:

(a) declaraing an area to be an area in whch the disease is to be eradicated (a "clearance area");

(b) declaring an area as to which the Minister is satisfied that the disease is virtually non-existent, to be an attested or disease free area; or

(c) prescribing the conditions under which animals or poultry may be exported, and designating ports or aerodromes, or routes for such export.

Regulations

The principal regulations concerning bovine tuberculosis brucellosis are in the Bovine Tuberculosis (Attestation of the State and General Provisions) Order 1989 (S.I. No. 308 of 1989), and the Brucellosis in Cattle (General Provisions) Order 1991 (S.I. No. 114 of 1991). These Regulations replaced earlier Regulations which were enacted in the 1970s and 1980s.

Section 20 of the 1966 Act and the Taking Possession of Animals

Where a test (a T.B. test) has been carried out which proves to be positive or is deemed to be positive (in the case of inconclusive tests) the holding of animals will be restricted by service of a *restricted holding notice* and *movement permits* will thereafter be required for the movement of animals from the holding during the course of the restriction. Movement permits are also granted for the removal of infected animals to the slaughter house. Since the mid-1970s the Minister has operated an extra statutory scheme for compensation of T.B. infected animals and this scheme has been the subject of litigation from time to time. Section 20 permitted the Minister to make orders in respect of infected animals authorising their being taken into possession on behalf of the Minister by agreement or, in default of agreement, regulating their removal from an area and their slaughter, or their isolation pending their removal or slaughter. Section 20 provides as follows:

> "The Minister may make, in relation to any clearance area or attested or disease free area, orders:
>
> (a) as to animals or poultry affected or suspected of being affected or capable of affecting animals or poultry with the relevant disease:
>   (i) authorising the taking of possession, by agreement, of the animals or poultry on behalf of the Minister;
>   (ii) in default of agreement, securing and regulating the removal out of the area or slaughter of the animals or poultry;

(iii) securing and regulating the isolation and maintenance of the animals or poultry pending their being taken possession of on behalf of the Minister or removed out of the area or slaughtered.

(b) securing and regulating the isolation and testing from time to time of animals or poultry brought on to land or premises;

(c) the prohibition or restriction of the movement of animals and poultry into, out of, through or within the area;

(d) securing and regulating the keeping of records in relation to animals or poultry and the production and inspection of the records;

(e) specifying forms of notices to be served under orders made by virtue of this section;

(f) providing in cases in which there has been a failure to comply with the requirements of any such notice for:

(i) in case the notice requires removal out of the area or slaughter of animals or poultry – the taking of possession of the animals or poultry, their disposal as the Minister thinks fit and the recovery (without prejudice to any penalty that may have been incurred) of the cost of taking possession of the animals for poultry and of thereafter maintaining them and disposing of them;

(ii) in any other case – the carrying out of the requirements of the Notice by or on behalf of the Minister and the recovery (without prejudice to any penalty which may have been incurred) of the cost of carrying out the requirements;

(g) determining, in the case of holdings, situate partly within and partly outside any clearance, attested or disease free area, or situate wholly or partly within two or more such areas, the area in to which such holdings belong;

(h) authorising entry on land or premises for the purposes of any such order; and

(i) for purposes ancillary or incidental to any of the foregoing purposes."

Pursuant to the 1966 Act, the Bovine Tuberculosis (Attestation of the State and General Provisions) Order 1978 was made. These Regulations established a scheme under which the Minister could take possession of and secure the slaughter of diseased animals. However, the scheme did not enable the Minister to take possession of diseased animals by agreement.

As stated above the scheme also provided for the service of notices (see Article 12 of the 1978 Regulations) declaring the holding to be a restricted holding the effect of which was to prohibit the movement of animals in and out of the holding except with the authority of a movement permit issued pursuant to article 12 of the 1978 Regulations.

However, the 1978 Regulations did not provide for or contain provisions enabling the Minister to take possession of diseased animals by agreement. The effect of these Regulations was considered in the case of *Howard v. The Minister for Agriculture* [1990] 2 I.R. 260. There, the applicant farmer owned a herd of cattle which was tested for T.B. and one reactor was found. A *restricted holding notice* was served prohibiting the movement of animals. Subsequently, the

Minister (through his agent) issued a *movement permit* authorising the movement of one of the cattle to the slaughter house. The applicant sought compensation in respect of the destroyed animal and challenged the validity of the
movement permit issued by the respondent. It was the contention of the
applicant that the Regulations which were made by the Minister were made
pursuant to the powers vested in him by section 20 of the 1966 Act and that the
manner in which the Regulations were made did in fact exceed the authority or
power of the Minister under the 1966 Act. It was contended by the applicant
that the Regulations were *ultra vires* (in other words that the Minister had
exceeded his powers under the 1966 Act) in making the Regulations in the form
in which they were made in that they did not allow the Minister to take
possession of the diseased animal by agreement before proceeding to take
possession compulsorily in default of such agreement as was thought to be
envisaged by section 20. During the course of the case before the High Court,
there was considerable debate as to the source of the Minister's powers to make
such Regulations. Murphy J. held that the source of the Minister's authority lay
in section 20 of the 1966 Act. He further held:

> "1. that the proceedings under article 13 of the Regulations of 1978 which allow
> the respondent to permit the disposal of reactor cattle but which did not
> entitle the respondent to take possession of the affected animals fell within
> the terms of section 20 of the Act;
>
> 2. that the respondent could not invoke the provisions of section 20(a)(ii)
> otherwise than in the context of the entire scheme of section 20 because the
> provisions of paragraphs (a) (i), (ii) and (iii) were interdependent and could
> not be invoked separately from each other;
>
> 3. that the operation of section 20(a)(ii) depended on the failure to reach
> agreement under section 20 and that since article 13 of the 1978 Regulations
> did not provide for any procedure to be adopted by agreement with the owner
> of the animals, the entire scheme of article 13 was *ultra vires* the Statute."

Mr. Justice Murphy further held that the provisions of the article could not
be severed from the entire of the Regulations of 1978 and accordingly the entire
Statutory Instrument was invalid. Subsequently the Minister made new Regulations – namely the Bovine Tuberculosis (Attestation of the State and General
Provision) Order 1989. The purpose of these Regulations was to amend and
rectify deficiencies in the 1978 Regulations.

Compensation

A system of compensation was established by the 1966 Act in respect of animals
dealt with under section 17 (being Class A disease animals) or under section
20 (being Class B disease animals). Section 17(2) provided that the Minister

should, subject to section 58, pay compensation for animals and poultry (with certain exceptions) which had been slaughtered under the section. Section 22 provided that the Minister shall once again subject to section 58 pay compensation for animals and poultry taken possession of on his behalf pursuant to an order under section 20.

Section 58 empowers the Minister, with the consent of the Minister for Finance, to make provision for:

"(a) the making and determination of applications for and the mode of assessment and payment of compensation;

(b) the inclusion of provisions for the fixing of compensation by agreement between the applicant and the Minister or, in default of agreement, by a valuer appointed by agreement between an applicant and the Minister or in default of such agreement by a valuer appointed by the Minister; and

(c) the inclusion of provision, in the event of the Applicant disputing the determination of the application, for the settlement of the dispute by arbitration."

However, section 58 provided that where a person was convicted of an offence under the Act in relation to animals or poultry slaughtered or taken possession of he should be disentitled to compensation in respect of such animals or poultry but the Minister could make an *ex gratia* payment to him of such amount as the Minister thought fit in lieu of compensation.

Extra-Statutory Scheme

The operation of the compensatory provisions of the 1966 Act have been the subject of much debate, particularly in the context of bovine tuberculosis. As stated above, the Minister has operated an extra statutory scheme of compensation since approximately 1976. This was considered in the case of *McKerring v. Minister for Agriculture* [1989] I.L.R.M. 82. In the *McKerring* case, the plaintiff applied for payment of sums he claimed were due to him from the Minister in respect of reactor cattle (*i.e.* bovine tuberculosis reactor cattle) which had been slaughtered. Under the scheme, which was known as the Bovine Tuberculosis Eradication Scheme, the Minister paid sums of monies to farmers whose cattle were slaughtered when found to be reactors.

The schemes, however, were operated by reference to conditions which were printed on the back of a permit document relating to the movement of the reactor animals for slaughter. One of the conditions provided that the Minister might at his discretion refuse payment in whole or in part where he was satisfied that the owner had not complied with the provisions of the Disease of Animals Act 1966, and the other requirements of the scheme. The plaintiff had been convicted on a number of occasions of offences under the 1966 Act which were unconnected with the cattle involved in the present claim. During the course of his judgment in the High Court, Mr Justice O'Hanlon commented "about the remarkably informal" way in which the scheme had been organised. He did not accept that the payments were entirely ex gratia. He held that the provisions of the scheme as set out in the conditions conveyed an impression of a promise to pay, subject to conditions, and there was sufficient consideration from the plaintiff in being required to comply with the conditions, even though some of them might have been a matter of legal obligation as well; and therefore payments could not have been regarded as purely *ex gratia*. The Minister was not entitled to withhold payment whenever it seemed proper for him to do so. However, in this case, he felt that in view of the plaintiff's convictions under the 1966 Act and his refusal to keep proper records and to disclose relevant information, the Minister was entitled to refuse payment of any sum to the plaintiff.

Further consideration was given to this extra statutory scheme by the Supreme Court in the decision of *Rooney v. The Minister for Agriculture and Food* [1991] 2 I.R. 539. There, 20 of the plaintiff's cattle were slaughtered as reactors. He was paid certain monies by the Minister in respect of the animals pursuant to the extra statutory scheme. In 1985, a further 26 animals were slaughtered but no monies were paid in respect of these as the plaintiff had failed to comply with certain other conditions set out in the extra statutory scheme. He issued proceedings claiming he was entitled to compensation in accordance with the 1966 Act (as opposed to payment of grants pursuant to the extra statutory scheme). His claim was dismissed in the High Court. He also claimed that the Minister, by failing to activate the relevant provisions of the Disease of Animals Act 1966 (*i.e.* sections 22 and 58) had breached an alleged constitutional right to compensation.

It was argued by the Minister that he was not obliged to activate the relevant provisions and that to do so would oblige him to take possession of diseased animals, as opposed to the position which then obtained under the scheme whereby animal owners brought their cattle to the slaughter houses and this together with the administrative costs which would be entailed would greatly increase the cost to the exchequer of disposing of diseased animals. The Supreme Court found against the plaintiff. It was held that in the absence of *mala fides* or abuse of power on the part of the Minister the court was not entitled to review his decision to create and operate an extra statutory scheme.

It was further held that even if the court did have the power (and this was doubted) to force the Minister to make orders under section 20 of the 1966 Act that it would not do so in the absence of *mala fides* or bad faith or abuse of power on the part of the Minister. Furthermore, it was held that as the Minister had in place a reasonable scheme for providing financial assistance to owners of diseased cattle, it was not necessary in the circumstances to decide whether there was a constitutional requirement to provide for compensation sought.

Black Spot Area

The provisions of the 1978 Regulations were further considered in the case of *Carroll v. Minister for Agriculture and Food* [1991] 1 I.R. 230. There, the plaintiff owned lands in an area of high disease incidents which had been designated by the Minister as a black spot area. The consequences of such designation was that veterinary inspectors were instructed that a test for bovine tuberculosis which would, in other areas, be regarded as inconclusive, should result in the service of a restricted holding notice if carried out in a black spot area. The designation of the black spot area of the entirety of the district electoral division within which the applicant's holding was situate had been advertised in local newspapers. The applicant's cattle were tested by a veterinary surgeon and an inconclusive result was obtained from one animal. The animal was declared to be a reactor and the applicant sought to have the animal re-tested. This was refused.

The applicant challenged the validity of the test on the basis that it was not carried out in a fair and proper manner and that he did not have a right of appeal and therefore was in breach of constitutional and natural justice. The application was refused. Mr Justice Blayney stated that given the designation of the area as a black spot area with a high incidence of disease, and the fact that the test carried out had been inconclusive, the veterinary inspector who received the test results had reasonable grounds for suspecting that there was a reactor on the holding. He continued:

> ". . . given the importance of the Disease Eradication Programme, the need to eliminate delays in identifying and isolating reactors, the fact that the tests were carried out by independent Veterinary Surgeons and the minimal risk of error involved in the test procedure, the absence of a right of appeal or a right to require an independent re-testing of the reactor was not a breach of constitutional guarantee of basic fairness of procedures".

During the course of that case, the evidence was that the term "black spot" had no legal basis but was used by E.R.A.D. to define areas in relation to which E.R.A.D. had decided that a stricter standard of interpretation should apply, *i.e.* areas where a high incidence of bovine tuberculosis was present.

Movement of Animals by Sea, Air, etc.

Under the 1966 Act, the Minister is also entitled to make orders regarding the movement of animals and poultry, the carriage of animals and poultry by sea or air, the importation of animals and poultry, provisions in regard to imported animals, quarantine, etc., and the prevention of sheep scab.

Offences

Section 48 of the 1966 Act provides that if a person without lawful authority or excuse contravenes the provisions of the Act or order of the Minister or if he fails to do or to comply with other matters which are referred to in that section he shall be guilty of an offence.

CHAPTER 18

MILK QUOTAS

Michael MacGrath, Barrister-at-Law

Introduction

The following is intended as a brief overview of the milk quota system.

Regulations were recently introduced, namely the European Communities (Milk Quota) Regulations 1994 (S.I. No. 70 of 1994), which made provision for alterations to the milk quota system. These Regulations have now been replaced by the more comprehensive European Communities (Milk Quota) Regulations 1995 (S.I. No. 266 of 1995). However, before analysing the 1995 Regulations, in order to understand better the milk quota regime, it is intended to look at the background to the introduction of milk quotas.

Section 1

Background

The background to the introduction of milk quotas or milk levies was very succinctly summarised in the decision of *Lawlor v. The Minister for Agriculture* [1990] 1 I.R. 356 by Mr Justice Murphy when he stated:

"The European Economic Community recognised that the Community as a whole was suffering from surpluses as a result of imbalance between supply and demand for, amongst other things, milk and milk products. Various Regulations were made which had the effect of introducing what was known as a uniform co-responsibility levy on all milk delivered to dairies and on certain dairy products sold direct from the farm with a view to correcting this imbalance. These measures did not resolve the problem. In March 1984, the Council of the European Communities decided to introduce an additional levy on quantities of milk delivered beyond the guaranteed threshold. The general scheme determined by the Council was to establish the figure for the quantity of milk or milk equivalent representing the level of internal consumption and then current export possibilities of the Community as a whole and, having done so, to distribute that figure among the member states on the basis of milk deliveries within their territories during the 1981 calendar year. Among the many refinements made to this simple concept was the provision that the base year for Ireland and indeed Italy should be the calendar year 1983. Whilst the scheme envisaged a Community target and national limits for the member states, the fundamental concept was to penalise the producer who exceeded that part of the national quota or reference quantity ascribed to him. This super levy scheme was introduced by Council Regulation (EEC) No. 856 (1984) of 31st March 1984 and duly published in the official journal of the European Communities on the 1st of April, 1984. That Regulation, having clearly stated that its purpose was to curb the increase in production, went on to provide that the levy system could be implemented in each of the territories of member states in accordance with one or other of two formulas, the first of which imposed the levy on the producer in the first instance and the other provided for the imposition of the levy on the purchaser of the milk or milk products in excess of the relevant quantity. However, in the latter event there was express provision requiring the purchaser to pass on the levy to those producers who had increased their deliveries above the appropriate quota. Levies were also to be imposed on producers who sold quantities for direct consumption in excess of the reference quantity."

The European Community Regulations which originally governed milk quotas were contained in Council Regulation 857/84/EEC. Pursuant to those Regulations and indeed to other regulations which had been made in 1968 the Minister for Agriculture made the European Community (Milk Levy) Regulations, 1985 (S.I. No. 416 of 1985) which came into operation on December 12, 1985. The General Regulations provided that the quota (or as it is more technically referred to the reference quantity) should be equal to the quantity of milk or milk equivalent delivered by the producer (where formulae A was adopted) or purchased by the purchaser (where formulae B was selected) in the base year. The levy was to be determined by the Commission.

The Base Year

As stated above, 1981 was the reference year which was decided upon for most countries. However, the Council recognised at the time of the making of the Regulations that the year 1983 would apply to Ireland because "in Ireland the dairy industry contributes directly or indirectly to about 9 per cent of the gross national product, a proportion materially higher than the Community average." Further, it was recognised that the development of alternative agriculture production in place of dairy production would in Ireland encounter obstacles which would be difficult to overcome and therefore in the circumstances the guaranteed quantity for Ireland should be fixed by reference to the 1983 deliveries.

The Relevant Formulae

The formulae referred to above were established by article 1 of the 1984 Regulations (855/84). That section provided that the levy system should be implemented in each region of the territory of the Member State in accordance with one of the following formulae:

> "Formula A – a levy shall be payable by every milk producer on the quantities of milk and/or milk equivalent which he has delivered to a purchaser and which for the twelve months concerned exceed the reference quantity to be determined.
>
> Formula B – a levy shall be payable by every purchaser of milk or other milk products on the quantities of milk or milk equivalent which have been delivered to him by a producer and which during the twelve months concerned exceed a reference quantity to be determined.
>
> – the purchaser liable to the levy shall pass on the burden in the price paid to those producers who have increased their deliveries, in proportion to their contribution to the purchasers reference quantity being exceeded."

As stated, Ireland, opted for Formula B.

Transfer of Reference Quantities – Original Rules

The initial rules for the transfer of reference quantities or milk quotas were contained in a Commission Regulation 1371/84/EEC. Article 7 of those Regulations provided the following rules:

1. Where an entire holding is sold, leased or transferred by inheritance, the corresponding reference quantity shall be transferred in full to the producer who takes over the holding;

2. Where one or several parts of a holding is sold, leased or transferred by inheritance, the corresponding reference quantity shall be distributed among the producers operating the holding in proportion to the areas used for milk production or according to other objective criteria laid down by Member States. Member States may disregard transferred parts the area of which used for milk production is less than the minimum size which they shall determine; and

3. The provisions of sub-paragraphs 1 and 2 above shall also be applicable in other cases of transfer which, under the various national rules has comparable legal effects as far as producers are concerned. Member States may apply the provision of sub-paragraphs 1 and 2 in respect of transfers taking place during and after the reference period.

The Regulations themselves made it possible for a producer (*i.e.* generally

speaking the farmer) to transfer his reference quantity from an existing purchaser (*i.e.* generally speaking the co-operative) to a new purchaser with effect
from specified dates.

Article 12 of the European Communities (Milk Levy) Regulations 1985 (S.I.
No. 416 of 1985) made it a criminal offence for any person to sell or transfer
land or any part of land without at the same time assigning to the purchaser or
transferee of that land or part of the land the relevant reference quantity. It was
further provided that any person who purported to lease land, or any part of
land, for a period of not less than three years without at the same time assigning
to the lessee of the land or that part of the land the relevant reference quantity
should also be guilty of an offence. Further, a person who purchased the land
or who took a lease of land without actually acquiring an assignment of the
relevant reference quantity was also deemed to be guilty of an offence. The
Regulations did not, however, apply to sales, leases or transfers of lands where
an agreement in writing had been concluded prior to the Regulations coming
into force.

The Regulations regarding transferring quotas have from time to time been
altered. The European Communities (Milk Levy) (Amendment) Regulations
(S.I. No. 51 of 1987) provided that if the owner of land to which reference
quantity attached transferred not more than 25 per cent of his land, the entire
of that reference quantity might with the consent of the transferee be retained
by such owner provided that such owner was engaged in the production of milk
on the residue untransferred of his land; and the retention of such reference
quantity was necessary to maintain the viability of such production of milk.

Quota Attaches to Land – Not Unconstitutional

In *Lawlor v. The Minister for Agriculture, Duffy & Duffy* [1991] I.R. 356 it was
contended by the plaintiff that the 1985 Regulations were unconstitutional,
being an unjust attack on his property rights. There, the plaintiffs had sold a 90
acre dairy farm to the second and third defendants. No reference was made to
the farm's milk quota. In August, 1986, the Minister informed the plaintiff that
the second and third named defendants were entitled to the quota which was
attached to the farm. The plaintiff challenged this but his claim was dismissed.
It was held that the Regulations did not constitute a general attack on the right
of private ownership of property guaranteed by the Constitution. It was further
held by Murphy J. that whilst the Regulations curbed the right to enter into and
to expand dairy production, and therefore did to a certain extent delimit certain
rights of ownership, such limitation was clearly with a view to reconciling the
exercise of those rights with the common good. In any event, it was held that
the Regulations did conform with the Constitution in that they carefully and
correctly balanced the interests of all the parties whose rights required to be
considered and were in no sense arbitrary or unjust.

Special Cases

At the time of the introduction of the milk quota system, it was recognised that there were certain special cases which had to be catered for. Therefore, purchasers of milk (*i.e.* co-operatives and dairies) could make provision for producers, for example whose deliveries in 1983 were affected by disease problems such as brucellosis and tuberculosis, for farmers who had invested heavily in milk production and who might be severely penalised if confined to the base quota, and for new entrants to milk production during the period January 1, 1993 to May 21, 1984. The first category were confined to farmers who had a certain percentage of their dairy herd affected by disease and would be subject to a maximum of the quantity delivered in each case in 1981 or 1982. The second category was subject to a maximum of the annual target in the farmers milk improvement plan, with priority being accorded to producers in the rescue package. The third category was subject to a maximum equal to the average yield per cow in the co-operatives area concerned multiplied by the farmers cow numbers in January 1994, in the case of a farmer who commenced milk production in 1983 and cow numbers in May, 1984, in the case of a farmer who commenced milk production in 1984.

The quotas to be allocated to the above category of producers were effectively to be obtained from a national reserve. The national reserve was established by quotas freed by producers of milk who participated in the Milk Cessation Scheme. This scheme provided for the payment of a premium to producers who undertook to discontinue milk production for as long as the super levy system operated.

A restructuring scheme was introduced in 1987/1988 under which it was open to co-operatives or dairies to purchase quotas from producers who wished to give up milk deliveries and to re-sell these to certain categories of producers within the same co-operative or dairy. However, re-sale had to be made to farmers who fell within certain categories and the allocation was prioritised.

Claw Back

A further reserve was established in circumstances where quotas were being transferred by means of land transactions (other than inheritance). A reserve was established by means of deductions or claw backs from quotas which were being transferred and from that reserve permanent quotas would be allocated to certain special category producers.

Temporary Leasing of Milk Quotas

A further scheme for the temporary leasing of milk quotas was introduced in

1988/1989. Under that scheme producers could offer for lease to other producers within the same co-operative or dairy a portion of their quotas which they
considered they would not require in the particular year. The portion of these
could not exceed 70 per cent except in the case of a producers whose herd was
depopulated under the Disease Eradication Schemes in 1987.

Mulder Quotas

Further allowances were made for the allocation of quotas to milk producers
who participated in the Non-marketing of Milk Scheme or the Dairy Herd
Conversion Scheme during the relevant reference year and who thereby lost
out (*i.e.* Mulder producers). Indeed, the operation of this scheme was itself
subjected to litigation and special quotas were introduced to deal with such
producers.

The Levy

Article 5 of the 1985 Regulations (see above) provided that any amount due on
foot of the levy which was payable pursuant to these Regulations should, within
the lime limits prescribed by the Regulations, be paid to the Minister by the
person from whom it is due and that such sum would be recoverable in a court
of competent jurisdiction as a simple contract debt. It was also provided by
Article 6 of the 1985 Regulations provided that a person who was liable to pay
a levy and who failed and neglected to pay same would be guilty of a criminal
offence and liable on summary conviction to a fine. Indeed, it was further
provided that a purchaser (*i.e.* the co-operative) who failed to recover all or any
portion of the levy for which he was liable would also be guilty of an offence
and liable on summary conviction to a further fine. The 1985 Regulations also
laid down detailed provisions concerned the enforcement of the super levy
system.

Section 2

European Communities (Milk Quota) Regulations 1995

The 1994 Regulations are in some ways more definitive than the 1985 Regulations. These regulations were comprehensive and were known as the European Communities (Milk Quota) Regulations 1994. They came into operation
on April 1, 1994. The 1985 Regulations were revoked save to the extent that
they ceased to have effect. Furthermore it was specifically provided that the

revocation effected by the 1994 Regulations did not affect the operation of the 1995 Regulations as regards cows milk produced on or before March 31, 1993; and the imposition of any levy thereon. The 1994 Regulations have in turn been replaced by the European Communities (Milk Quota) Regulations 1995, which came into operation on October 4, 1995. The 1994 Regulations will still apply to cows milk produced before October 3, 1995 and the imposition of levies thereon.

It is now proposed to look at these 1995 Regulations in some detail.

Transfer of Holdings

(a) The General Rule

Article 4 of the 1995 Regulations provides that where any holding or part thereof is transferred by sale, lease or inheritance the milk quota attached to that holding or part thereof shall be transferred to the producer to whom that transfer is made. There are certain formalities which have to be complied with. These are set out in the Regulations. There are some exceptions to this general transfer rule. For example, the Regulation governing transfer as outlined in Article 4 does not apply to a licence to occupy land or a lease for a period of less than 12 months.

(b) Land Used for Milk Production

Land used for milk production is defined in the 1995 Regulations as meaning any area used for the purpose of maintaining a milk production enterprise, including land used as pasture for cows producing milk and replacement heifers, and land used for forage production for feeding to a dairy herd.

(c) Expiring Leases

Where a lease of any land to which a milk quota attaches expires, it is provided that the milk quota shall be transferred to the lessor of such land on such expiration. Where a lease of any land to which a milk quota attaches expires on a date other than the last day of the milk quota year, the amount of the milk quota to be transferred to the lessor of such land for the remainder of the milk quota year in question will be calculated in accordance with procedures laid down by the Minister.

(d) Special Milk Quotas

The special milk quotas referred to in Council Regulation 3950/92/E.C. (SLOM II Quota) or referred to in Council Regulation No. 2055/93/E.C. (*i.e.* SLOM III

Quota) also have their own special rules. It is specifically provided that notwithstanding the general transfer provisions, where a producer who holds an SLOM II Quota sells or leases all of his holding before June 30, 1996, then a proportion of that quota will be added to the national reserve and the proportion to be so added will be in the same proportion to the total SLOM II Quota as the part sold or leased is to the entire holding.

With regard to the SLOM III Quota a different date was provided – namely October 1, 1996. Where a producer who held an SLOM III Quota sells or leases all of his holding before October 1, 1996, then that SLOM III Quota shall be added to the national reserve. If part of the holding was sold or leased before October 1, 1996, then a proportionate part of the quota will be added to the reserve.

Milk Quota Attaching to Land

For the purposes of the Regulations a milk quota shall be deemed to be attached to the land used for milk production in the last milk quota year, prior to the milk quota year in which the transfer took place in which the amount of milk production was equal to or greater than 90 per cent of the quota in question less:

(a) Any quota added in the year of transfer or in the year before the year of transfer by means of certain reallocations which are permissible in accordance with the Regulations; and

(a) Any quota added in the year of transfer or in the year before the year of transfer by allocation from a national reserve.

The Regulations also deal with a calculation of the milk production quota in the case of leased lands or milk produced on lands held under licence and gives the Minister certain powers in relation to certifying the quota to be attached to lands in certain situations.

Restricted Quota in Less Favoured Areas

In the case of less favoured areas (*i.e.* areas described in Council Directive 85/350 of June 27, 1985 and Council Directive 91/466 of July 22, 1991), where a transfer takes place by way of sale, lease or inheritance, the only milk which may be recorded against the milk quota attached to that holding (or part therof) which is transferred, is the milk produced from a dairy herd which is permanently maintained on transferred land, or on other lands operated by the transferee, or on both such lands which are situated, where the distance between the lands does not exceed 48 kilometres.

Recording of Milk Quota Transfers

Where a transfer takes place by way of sale, lease or inheritance, the transferee must within two months of the date of transfer furnish the co-operative with a "Delivery Milk Quota Transfer Form". The Milk Quota Transfer Form is not necessary where the milk quota is transferred to a lessor as a result of the expiry of a lease.

Transfers to Public Authorities and for Non-Agricultural Purposes

The Regulations also provide that where a producer who is entitled to a milk quota wishes to transfer his holding (or part thereof) to which that quota is attached:

1. to a public authority (which is in itself defined in the Act as meaning a Minister of the Government, the Commissioner of Public Works in Ireland, a Local Authority, a Harbour Authority, a Health Board, a V.E.C., a board or body established under statute, a company in which all the shares are held by or on behalf of or by directors appointed by a Minister of Government or a company in which all the shares are held by a board, a company or other body established by statute or in which the shares are held by the Minister); or

2. for use in the public interest; or

3. for a non-agricultural purpose, or

4. where a public authority possessing compulsory purchase powers has given formal notice of intention to exercise those powers in respect of such a holding;

and where the producer intends to carry on the production of milk, he can apply to the Minister for a *certificate of retention* of the milk quota (*i.e.* where it is proposed that the milk quota shall attach to the land being retained) or a *certificate of transfer* (*i.e.* where it is proposed that the milk quota be transferred and attached to land being purchased or leased or inherited by the transferor within one year of the date of transfer) or indeed both certificates in respect of different parts of the quota. Such certificates are referred to as Number I Certificate of Transfer and Number I Certificate of Retention.

There are a number of conditions which must be complied with before the Minister can issue such certificates. These are provided for in detail in the Regulations and include, amongst other things, a written undertaking that the applicant intends to continue in milk production and the Minister must of course be satisfied that such intention is bona fide. There are strict time limits applicable to the application for such certificates and indeed for their operation thereafter.

Where a person seeks a Number I Certificate of Retention respect of a restricted quota (*i.e.* a milk quota attached to lands situated in a less favoured area) the certificate of retention will not be granted unless the distance between the lands to which the restricted quota is attached and the lands to which the milk quota is to be attached does not exceed 48 kilometres. This restriction does not apply however where a public authority possessing compulsory purchase powers has given formal notice of its intention to exercise those powers in respect of the holding to which the restricted milk quota is attached.

Where part of a holding (not more than half a hectare in size) to which a milk quota is attached, is transferred by sale for use for a non-agricultural purpose, the milk quota attached to the transferred portion will be retained with the remainder of the transferor's holding, provided that the remainder is capable of producing that amount of quota and that the instrument of transfer contains a declaration by the transferee that he does not intend to use the land so transferred for agricultural purposes. He must also consent to the retention of the milk quota by the transferor.

Improvement of Structure of Milk Production Holding

Where a producer wishes to improve the structure of milk production on his holding by either a transfer of all of his holding with a subsequent purchase or inheritance of other land in fee simple, or by a transfer of part of his holding, whether with or without a subsequent purchase or inheritance of other land in fee simple, he may apply to the Minister before the proposed transfer for:

(a) a Number II Certificate of Retention – *i.e.* a certificate that the milk quota attaching to the part of his holding which he proposes to transfer, shall, in the event of such transfer, be attached to such other part of his holding as may be specified in the certificate; or

(b) a Number II Certificate of Transfer – *i.e.* a certificate that such milk quota shall, in the event of such transfer, be attached to land being purchased or inherited by the transferor within one year and three months of the date of the certificate; or

(c) a Number II Certificate of Retention and a Number II Certificate of Transfer in respect of different parts of such milk quota.

Once again, there are a number of conditions of which the Minister must he satisfied before he can grant a certificate. And these include the Minister being satisfied that the producer will improve the structure of milk production on his holding as a result of the proposed transfer and that the applicant gives a written undertaking of his intention to continue in milk production. The Minister must be satisfied that such intention is bona fide. Furthermore, where a Number II Certificate of Retention is sought, the Minister must also be satisfied that such a milk quota is capable of being produced in the lands being retained.

In the context of restricted quotas similar distance limitations apply (48 kilometres) to Number II Certificates of Retention as apply to Number I certificates.

Expiring Leases – Where Lessee has established the Quota

Where there is a lease or licence or other limited interest in land due to expire without any possibility of renewal or similar terms, the person entitled to such interest may apply in writing to the Minister for a declaration that all or part of the milk quota concerned shall be transferred to him and the Minister may make a declaration that all of part of the milk quota shall be so transferred. In this regard, the applicant will apply for what is known as a Number III Certificate of Attachment. This Regulation applies to persons who had established a quota.

National Reserve

The 1995 Regulations also provide that the Minister may replenish the national reserve. He may do this by reducing a specified percentage of each individual milk quota in order to grant additional or specific milk quotas to producers determined in accordance with objective criteria agreed between the E.C. Commission and the Minister.

Transfer of Milk Quota Between Purchasers

A producer may transfer his delivery quota, in whole or in part, from an existing purchaser to a new purchaser beginning January 1, April 1, October 1, by commencing deliveries of milk to the new purchaser provided he furnishes specified notices to the purchasers concerned.

Register of Milk Purchasers

Article 17 provided that the Minister shall establish and maintain a register of purchasers to be known as the register of milk purchasers. It is an offence for a person to purchase milk unless he is a registered purchaser. Specific provisions deal with sole purchasers, group purchasers and joint purchasers.

Dormant Milk Quotas

The co-operative must provide the Minister with a list of producers who have quotas and who have not made milk deliveries during the previous milk quota year, in circumstances where such producers did not make a temporary transfer of milk quota pursuant to the 1995 Regulations. In respect of such persons, and indeed in any other case where the Minister hás reason to suspect that a producer has not marketed or delivered milk produced on his holding in the milk quota year, the Minister may serve a notice on him informing that he is considering adding that person's milk quota to the national reserve and giving him 30 days to submit observations. The Minister may thereafter make an addition of that quota to the national reserve. Where a producer whose quota has been added to the national reserve pursuant to this regulation resumes production of milk, he will be granted a quota no later than April 1 following the date of his application.

Where the reason for the non-production/delivery arises as a result of a dispute about entitlement to a milk quota and if such dispute has been referred to arbitration or is the subject of court proceedings, the Minister cannot exercise his power to add that quota to the national reserve. If the arbitration or proceedings are not being prosecuted with reasonable speed, however, the Minister may in fact exercise his power to add the quota to the national reserve.

Definitive Discontinuation of Milk Production

A producer who has surrendered his milk quota pursuant to a scheme for the purposes of the definitive discontinuation of milk production and who delivers or markets milk is deemed to be guilty of an offence.

Miscellaneous

The Regulations also provide for the payment of levies, the recovery of interest on late payments, the provision of statements from purchasers regarding delivery quotas, the keeping of records, and the employment of officers to carry out the Minister's functions under the said Regulations.

Authorised Officer

An authorised officer is given quite wide powers including the power, at all reasonable times, to enter and inspect any premises in which he has reasonable grounds for believing that any books, records or other documents relating to the production, delivery, processing or disposal of milk or milk products or to the payment of, or otherwise relating to the levy, are kept. An authorised officer may require the person on such premises to provide such information or books, etc.

Offences

Any person who purports to transfer or to acquire a milk quota other than in accordance with the 1995 Regulations or who makes a transfer and who purports to retain an entitlement to a milk quota is deemed to be guilty of an offence. Further, the transferor will also be guilty of an offence if he attempts to subvert the provisions of the Regulations.

CHAPTER 19

FINANCIAL AID TO FARMERS

Peter Bland, Barrister-at-Law

In this chapter it is proposed to discuss some of the legal aspects of the payments available to Irish farmers. It is outside the scope of this work to detail the requirements for eligibility to each of the existing means of funding, though special attention shall be paid to the three major schemes which are of particular current relevance to the Irish farmer.

The Common Agricultural Policy

The European Economic Community was established by the Treaty of Rome in 1957. Under the EEC Treaty a common policy in the sphere of agriculture was adopted by the Member States. The objectives of this policy are set out in Article 39(1):

(a) to increase agricultural productivity by promoting technical progress and by ensuring the rational development of agricultural production and the optimum utilisation of the factors of production, in particular labour;

(b) thus to ensure a fair standard of living for the agricultural community, in particular by increasing the individual earnings of persons engaged in agriculture;

(c) to stabilise markets;

(d) to assure the availability of supplies;

(e) to ensure that supplies reach consumer at reasonable prices.

The interests of the consumer and the farmer are traditionally opposed yet Article 39(1) ostensibly protects both sectors. Political and economic concerns have favoured the farmer and the resultant body of C.A.P. legislation concentrated on fixing prices to assure farmers an adequate income within the common markets that were established for each agricultural product. The objectives of the production of cheap food and the modernisation and structural improvement of European agriculture were not addressed in the law of the C.A.P. to the same extent as the provision of income for farmers. As a result, the European Court of Justice has tended to recognise the priority of attaining a fair standard of living for the farmer over reasonable prices for consumers: see Case 24/62, *Germany v. E.E.C. Commission* [1963] E.C.R. 63.

When Ireland joined the EEC in 1973 she became bound by the C.A.P. as it had been developed over the previous 16 years, or, as it has been said, she jumped aboard a moving train. The basic principle of the C.A.P., the support of agricultural incomes by market and price policy, has benefited Ireland greatly. The C.A.P. continues to develop by means of the adoption of decisions, regulations and directives by the European Council and delegated legislation by the Commission. Though the C.A.P. policy and legislation is created by these institutions, the responsibility for administration and implementation of the C.A.P. in Ireland is a matter for the Irish authorities. Advances of funds are paid to the Minister for Agriculture, Forestry and Food to enable the Minister to make the payments to farmers under Irish schemes implementing C.A.P. legislation. As a Member State establishes the scheme which implements the E.C. legislation, the subsequent administration of the scheme is subject to the national law of the particular Member State.

Contractual Basis of Aid

Under the various systems of subsidies, grants, premia and schemes the Minister may be seen as making offers to pay certain sums on certain conditions to eligible farmers. Where this is the case a contract binds the Minister and the farmer. There is not always the creation of this contractual relationship. As Costello J. said in *Kylemore Bakery v. The Minister for Trade, Commerce and Tourism* [1896] I.R.L.M. 529 at 535:

> "I am aware that government departments administer a great variety of different schemes by means of which public funds are paid to producers and manufacturers and I am not suggesting that every time a firm or individual applies for payment of a grant or subsidy a contractual relationship arises forthwith. The terms of each scheme and the circumstances of each application must in every case be considered."

This said, in the normal course, where a farmer is informed of, applies for and complies with the terms and conditions of a scheme a contract or a number of contracts are formed between the farmer and the Minister.

The terms and conditions of the contract can be found in the explanatory literature and the application forms. This offer can be withdrawn at any time by the Minister. The Minister may also vary the offer by amending the terms and conditions, the application form or the rates of payment available. Obviously the farmer may decline to accept the offer, or depending on the terms of the offer, having accepted it for a period may decline to accept it for any further period. The consideration given by the farmer is the compliance with the terms and conditions of the offer.

The leading case of *McKerring v. The Minister for Agriculture* [1989] I.R.L.M. 82 concerned a refusal by the Minister to pay monies to Mr McKerring under the Bovine Tuberculosis Eradication Scheme and the Bovine Brucellosis Eradication Scheme following the slaughter of Mr McKerring's cattle. First, the Minister claimed that Mr McKerring had failed to comply with the conditions for payment which were to be found on a permit document relating to the movement of reactors for slaughter. Secondly, the Minister claimed that the grants were never intended to be a matter of legal obligation but were made purely on a *ex gratia* basis at the discretion of the Minister. In other words, it was claimed that the Minister was entitled to withhold payment whenever it seems proper for him to do so. O'Hanlon J. thought it an extraordinary fact that although the schemes had been in operation since 1976 with an expenditure of hundreds of millions of pounds they were not subject to statutory regulation and there was real confusion as to their legal status. He examined the conditions on the permit document and concluded that the conditions conveyed a promise to pay if they were complied with. The arrangement was therefore a contract and not an ex gratia payment.

O'Hanlon J. went on to decide the question of whether the conditions of the contract entitled the Minister to refuse payment in the circumstances of the case. Condition 9 on the back of the permit stated that:

> "The Minister may at his discretion refuse payment in whole or in part where he is satisfied that the owner has not complied with the provisions of Animals Act 1966."

Mr McKerring had been convicted of certain charges referring to the Eradication Schemes under the Animals Act 1966 and to that extent the Court recognised that there was "a black mark against the plaintiff".

Department officials gave evidence that he had consistently played fast and loose with the requirements of the schemes, failing to disclose information and refusing to keep records as he was obliged to do under the schemes. It was suggested that he had deliberately introduced reactors so as to take advantage of the mechanics of the scheme whereby diseased animals could be more profitable than healthy ones. O'Hanlon J. concluded that his convictions and his cavalier attitude towards the schemes entitled the Minister to refuse the payment of any sum to Mr McKerring under Condition 9.

The question arises as to when the Minister is entitled to recoup all monies paid where there has been a breach of the conditions of a scheme. In each case the particular breach must be considered in the light of the particular conditions. In *Kylemore Bakeries v. The Minister for Trade, Commerce and Tourism* [1986] I.R.L.M. 529 it was held that where the breach was the failure to pass on the full subsidy to the consumer as required under the scheme did not entitle the

Minister to recoup all sums paid on foot of *all* claims. Rather the Minister was entitled to recoup and deduct the amounts of the subsidy not passed on.

Judicial Review

A person who wishes to challenge the legality of a decision of the Minister may make an application for judicial review in the High Court under Order 84 of the Rules of the Superior Courts 1986. A judicial review of an administrative act is a separate matter from adjudicating whether the Minister has acted in accordance with his contractual obligations.

Any decision as to a farmer's eligibility to any payment must be made according to law. There must be legal authority for the decision and it must be in compliance with the natural and constitutional justice principles of fair procedure and equality before the law. As we have seen, the Minister for Agriculture, Forestry and Food is responsible for making grants to farmers and it is his decision how to implement the relevant E.C. legislation. The Minister commonly issues guidelines in respect of the schemes he administers and it is from these publications that the farmer learns the conditions which he is obliged to meet to participate in the scheme or receive the grant or subsidy. These documents may claim further discretionary powers of refusal on behalf of the Minister, but it should be remembered that an administrative body must always exercise its discretion in a reasonable and bona fide manner. The Minister is obliged to take only reasonable matters into account and to ignore irrelevant considerations. An example of a condition for eligibility is the requirement for the production of a current tax clearance certificate under the Scheme for Installation Aid. Following the decision in *The State (Melbarien Enterprises Ltd.) v. Revenue Commissioners*, unreported, Hamilton P., High Court, April 19, 1985, the refusal by the Revenue Commissioners to provide the certificate is open to challenge if irrelevant considerations were taken into account. In that case the company was not in arrears but was connected with a company that owed monies to the Revenue Commissioners. In the circumstances, the consideration of that connection was held to be irrelevant. Similarly, where the Minister for Industry and Commerce refused to pay a subsidy to a baker because he had been convicted of an offence connected with the sale of bread, the Supreme Court declared that the Minister was not entitled to disqualify the applicant as there was no published condition disqualifying such persons: *Latchford v. The Minister for Industry and Commerce* [1950] I.R. 33. Murnaghan J. stated that the Minister was free to alter the conditions for the payment of the subsidy, "but until altered or withdrawn, the conditions apply, and persons who have complied with the condition are entitled to claim that they have qualified for payment of subsidy".

The doctrine of legitimate expectation requires the Minister to act consistently with an arrangement, even if that arrangement does not give rise to a contract, where the arrangement gives the farmer a legitimate expectation that the payment will be made or will continue to be made. This doctrine was explicitly recognised as forming part of Irish law in a number of recent cases, including the Supreme Court decision of *Wiley v. Revenue Commissioners* [1993] I.L.R.M. 482. Where the Minister acts inconsistently with the agreement he may be found to have abused his power and be judicially reviewed on the grounds of unfairness. However the mere fact of derogation from the agreement will not always in itself render the decision unfair. The doctrine is limited in its application and the courts are unwilling to expand it's boundaries. The courts have recognised the reality that administrative policy is often subject to rapid changes, as farmers grappling with revised Area Aid applications will be familiar. Further, the doctrine may be defeated by an invocation by the Minister of the wider public interest.

Common Agricultural Policy Reforms

On June 30, 1992 the Council of Agriculture Ministers approved major reform measures to the C.A.P. In general terms, the reform represented a change of emphasis from intervention purchasing towards direct compensatory payments and capital grants to producer in most agricultural sectors. Included in the reforms was a requirement for every farmer who wishes to apply for arable aids or livestock premium/headage payments to submit an Area Aid application setting out how it is intended to use the land for the purposes of the funding. Two important new schemes were introduced in Ireland as accompanying measures to the C.A.P. reforms, the Rural Environment Protection Scheme and the Scheme of Early Retirement from Farming. A third scheme, the Scheme of Installation Aid, has been revised to apply to the installation of eligible young farmers after January 1, 1994. It is believed that participation in these schemes has been hindered by misconceptions as to the legal conditions for eligibility and for this reason it is proposed to deal in turn with the relevant requirements for participation.

Scheme of Early Retirement from Farming

The Early Retirement Scheme implements Regulation 2079/92 and has the objectives of facilitating the enlargement and generational turnover of farms by providing older farmers with a pension and to reassign agricultural land to non-agricultural use where it cannot be farmed under satisfactory conditions of viability. A farmer is eligible for a pension if he: is between 55 and 66 years of age; is farming not less than five hectares of utilisable agricultural area (U.A.A.); has practised farming as a main occupation for the preceding 10 years; and has agreed to dispose of the relevant agricultural holding, buildings and quota rights by sale, transfer or lease to a "farming transferee".

The retiring farmer or "transferor" may retain his dwellinghouse and a maximum of 10 per cent but not more than one hectare of his agricultural holding. He must undertake to cease all farming activity.

If the transferor can prove to the satisfaction of the Minister that a farming transferee can not be found he may transfer the holding (without any milk quota rights) to a "non-farming transferee". Alternatively he may reassign the land to non-agricultural purposes, forestry or the creation of ecological reserves. A farming transferee is defined by reference to criteria as to age, agricultural qualifications or experience, expansion of the holding and undertakings to farm the land for five years (or as long as the pension lasts) as a main occupation. A non-farming transferee, which may include a corporate body, for non-farming purposes, forestry or the creation of ecological reserves. In each case the released land must be used in harmony with environmental protection legislation.

The objective of producing enlarged agricultural holdings is implemented by requiring a farming transferee either: following the transfer to expand the holding by five hectares U.A.A. or 10 per cent, whichever is the greater; or hold in full ownership or under lease at least five hectares U.A.A. which was not the subject of a transfer from the transferor on or after July 30, 1992.

This requirement causes difficulties for the transferee who cannot afford to purchase or lease the land for expansion. It is worth noting that there is no requirement for land intended to satisfy this requirement to be contiguous to the transferred holding. Thus it appear that, for example, a lease of five hectares in Leitrim may be used to expand a holding in Kildare. It is also of advantage for a transferee to acquire a five hectare U.A.A. holding before the transfer, rather than afterwards. This is because enlargement after the transfer must be 10 per cent of the transferred holding where that transferred holding is in excess of 50 hectares. If A wishes to transfer his 200 hectare holding to his son, B, to satisfy the requirement B can acquire five hectares the day before the transfer. However if he leaves the enlargement until after the transfer B must acquire 20 hectares. Where transfers after July 30, 1992, are, in the opinion of the Minister, not in accordance with the spirit of the scheme, the Minister reserves the right to reject the application.

The scheme also provides for pension payments for two agricultural workers (which may include family helpers) for each transferred holding on the undertaking to cease all farming activities completely and definitely.

Scheme of Installation Aid

The Scheme of Installation Aid is another scheme designed to encourage the earlier transfer of farms, though here the financial incentive is to the young farmer. To be eligible for a payment of a premium of £5,600.00 the applicant must be set up as a full time farmer when under 35 years of age and have or acquire within two years the required occupational skill and competence. A full time farmer is defined as a person:

1. who derives at least 50 per cent of his total income from farming on his farm;

2. who devotes at least 50 per cent of total working time to farming on his farm; and

3. the labour requirement of the farm is at least 0.5 of a Man Work Unit.

The income requirement can be part satisfied by income from craft, tourism or forestry activities carried out on the farm provided that at least 25 per cent derives from direct farming activities. He must farm the lands on a full-time basis for at least five years from the date of setting up. The farm must have within two years of the setting up a labour requirement of one man working unit. The young farmer must have obtained a freehold estate in the farm lands or a lease to run for at least five years from the first setting up.

The application for the payment under the Scheme is required to be accompanied with the application fee, the applicant's original birth certificate, his agricultural education certificates, current tax clearance certificate and where there is non-farming income a letter from the employer and a statement of tax liability and/or confirmation of statement of P35, evidence of herd/flock/cereal/IACS Number and documentary evidence of the transfer of the land. As the applicant should show that he is in control of the farm taken over farm accounts or tax returns may be requested in any case. The applicant must provide for the year immediately prior to the transfer certificates of all herd tests, ewe premia and of permanent milk quota and actual milk supplied. Where any land was rented, leased or let in the year prior to application evidence of such dealings must be furnished.

The documents which must be submitted in the case of registered land are certified copies of the Land Registry folio and stamped deed of transfer, together with (if applicable) a Land Commission purchase agreement/letter of confirmation. In regard to unregistered land a deed of conveyance or assent which is stamped and memorialised in the registry of deeds shall be sufficient evidence of ownership. Where the applicant benefited from the will of a deceased person he is obliged to produce a certified copy of the grant of probate and the executor's assent; if he benefited on intestacy a certified copy of the grant of administration and the administrator's assent. Where appropriate a family home statutory declaration should be provided. Curiously, the Department also have requested a letter from the applicant's solicitor stating:

1. the amount of land owner prior to the transfer;

2. the amount of land transferred to the applicant; and

3. the amount of land if any retained or transferred to other family members.

Rural Environment Protection Scheme

The Rural Environment Protection Scheme (R.E.P.S.) implements Council Regulation 2078/92 and is designed to establish farming practises which conserve and protect the environment, to protect flora and fauna and to produce quality food in an extensive and environmentally friendly manner. As of April 1996, £45.6 million has been paid to 13,000 farmers participating in R.E.P.S.; the projections are for an allocated £230 million by 1997 with a proposed total expenditure of £750 million. The basis of participation in R.E.P.S. is an undertaking by the applicant to carry out his farming activities in accordance with an agri-environmental plan for a period of five years. A failure to comply with the stipulated five year term would appear on the face of the specifications to entitle the Minister to recoup the payments already made (see *Gaeltarra Éireann v. George Stephenson*, unreported, High Court, Barrington J., March 23, 1980). The agri-environmental plan is drawn up by a planning agency approved by the Department. In consideration for this undertaking by the farmer the Department makes a basic annual payment of 125 ecu per hectare, subject to a maximum of 40 hectares.

The Department of Agriculture, Food and Forestry have published a detailed document entitled "Agri-environmental Specifications" which set out the requirements for participation in the scheme. These specifications are undergoing revision at the time of writing; further revisions are expected following E.C. legislation.

R.E.P.S. payments are calculated by reference to lands owned farmed by the applicant. To fulfil his obligations under the plan the farmer must be in control of the lands the subject of his application. In his application form he declares all land farmed and the manner in which they are held. He is considered to be sufficiently in control of lands which he owns, co-owns or has leased. Land which is taken under a conacre or agistment agreement may be calculated for the purposes of R.E.P.S, provided such lettings are of at least seven months and include the months of April to October. The farmer who lets out the land will not be eligible for R.E.P.S. payments in respect of that land. A farmer who has turbary rights may not include the this land in his application, nor may the farmer who owns the land subject to the turbary rights. However a farmer who has a right of pasture (or "commonage") may include a proportionate amount of the lands subject to the right in his application.

To establish his ability to carry out the plan the farmer must provide for inspection his documents of title. The documents which may be required are specified as follows:

(a) in the case of registered land, a copy of the relevant land registry folio, or where a transfer of land has taken place but registration is not completed, a certified copy of the stamped deed of rransfer;

(b) in the case of unregistered land, a stamped deed of assignment;

(c) Land Commission purchase agreement;

(d) grant of probate, including the deed of assignment;

(e) where the farmer is the beneficial occupier but is unable to produce any of the above, an affidavit setting out the fact that the farmer has been in undisputed occupation of the land for at least the previous five years;

(f) where the farmer has a leasehold interest in the lands, a certified copy of the lease agreement, registered with the Land Commission and stamped by the Revenue Commissioners;

(g) for conacre, agistment and oral leasehold agreements, the farmer must produce a Form R.E.P.S. 1A which shall be completed by his R.E.P.S. Planner.

The R.E.P.S. planner completes the agri-environmental plan in accordance with the specifications contained in measures 1 to 11 of the Scheme. These measures relate to matters such as waste management, grassland management, the maintenance of farm and field boundaries, the retention of wildlife habitats, the protection of features of historical and archaeological interest and the keeping of records by the farmer. There are a further six supplementary measures under which the farmer may be eligible for additional payments, such as organic farming, where the lands are in a national heritage area or where the farmer rears animals of local breeds in danger of extinction. Further documentary evidence is required as proof of eligibility for some of these supplemental measures. Supplementary measure 5 provides for 150 ecu per hectare up to a maximum of 40 hectares where a farmer enters into a contract with a local development organisation or comparable group under which he shall provide public access to his land for environmentally friendly leisure and sporting activities where such activities were not previously carried out on the farm. The Department has listed five criteria in circular 10/95 to planners which limit the eligibility under supplementary measure 5. Though the contract must be with an organisation access must be given to the public as a whole and is designed to facilitate agri-tourism. Payments shall not be made in respect of access where a right of way already exists. The applicant farmer must satisfy the Department that he has in place adequate public liability insurance.

The Department have viewed as abuses of the Scheme certain leasehold agreements entered into by prospective participants in R.E.P.S. For example, the leasing of land designated a national heritage area or the leasing of "degraded commonage" by a farmer who does not farm in the vicinity of such lands have been identified as not being within the spirit of the scheme. However, there is no condition in the 75 pages of specifications and appendices which disqualifies farmers who enter such arrangements from the scheme. A farmer who has contracted to lease lands designated as within a national heritage area in order to gain extra supplementary measure payments will suffer a loss if his

R.E.P.S. application is refused. It may be that, given the omission of any condition informing the farmer of this administrative practise and it's inconsistancy with the practise in other schemes, such a decision could be open to judicial review.

INDEX

Agriculture
definition of, 22
Animals
cattle,
trespass by, 158, 159, 160, 161
dogs,
damage caused by, 156, 157,
158
general liability of, 162
negligence, for, 162
nuisance, for, 163, 164
occupiers, for, 164
trespass, for, 164
impounding of, 166, 167
livestock,
definition of, 157
road, on, 165
Animal Diseases
animals, movement of, 241
black spot area, 241
diseases,
classification of, 234
class A, 235
class B, 235, 236
compensation, 238, 239
extra statutory scheme, 239, 240
infected areas, 234
notification of, 233
offences, 242
regulations, 236
tuberculosis test, 236, 237, 238

Banking
banker,
definition of, 72
bank,
account,
closing of, 84
combination of, 82, 84
current, 79, 70
operation of, 79

customer of, 72
relationship of, with 73
fiduciary as, 74, 78
confidentiality, 78, 79
family home and, 91, 92
guarantee, 92, 93
loans, 87, 88
mortgage, 89
equitable, 90, 91
judgment, 94, 95
overdraft, 85, 86
withdrawal of, 86, 87
refer to drawer, 80, 81
security, 89

Contract
acceptance, 96
auction sales, 104
breach of, 106
remedies for, 106
damages, 106
injunction, 107
quantum meruit, 107
recission, 106, 107
specific performance, 107
capacity to, 97
caveat emptor, 99, 100, 102
consideration, 96
conditions of, 99
implied, 101, 102
contents of, 98
duress, 97
evidence of, 97
exemption clauses in, 103
finance houses,
liability of, 103
goods,
correspond with description of,
101
fitness of, 102
sale of, by sample, 102, 103

Contract—*cont.*
  hire-purchase contracts, 104
  implied, 96
  insurance contracts, 105
  merchantable quality, 101, 102
  motor vehicle,
      sale of, 103
  nature of, 96
  orally made, 99
  representation, 98
  Sale of Goods and Supply of
        Services Acts 1893–1980,
        100 *et seq.*
  seller's title, 101
  supply of services, 105
  termination of, 106
  terms,
      express, 99
      implied, 99, 105
  undue influence, 97
  warranties in, 99
      implied, 103
  word of mouth by, 96
  writing, in, 96, 97, 99

Defamation
  class of person,
      statement published concerning,
          176
  defences for,
      apology, 183, 184
      consent, 183
      fair comment, 183
      justification, 177
      offer of amends, 184
      privilege, 178
          absolute, 178, 179
          qualified, 179, 180, 181,
              182
  establishing,
      difficulties in, 175, 176
  innuendo, 174, 175
  libel, 173, 176, 177
  nature of, 173
  ridicule, 174
  slander, 173, 174
  vulgar abuse, 174

Employers' Liability, *see also*
    Employment
  employer
      duties of, 122 *et seq.*
  offences, 133, 134
  safety,
      emergency procedures, 127
      information , disclosure of, 132,
          134
      inspectors, 130
          improvement plan of, 130, 131
          prohibition notice by, 131
      lifting and carrying, 127, 128
      machinery, 129
      maximum weights, 129
      promotion of, 129, 130
      representative, 126
      statement, 125, 126
      special reports, 133
      work, at, 124, 125

Employment, *see also* **Employers'**
    Liability
  contract of, 109
      implied terms of, 109 *et seq.*
      termination of, 120, 121
  discrimination
      direct, 115, 116
      indirect, 116
  dismissal, 112, 113, 114, 117
  employee,
      duties of, 110
  employer
      duties of, 109
  Employment Equality Agency, 116,
          117
  like work, 117
  Minimum Notice and Terms of
        Employment Act 1973,
        purpose of, 111
  minimum periods of notice, 111
  part-time employees
      employment of, 119
  pay,
      right to same rate of, 117
  redundancy payments, 117, 118
      calculation of, 118
      entitlement, 118

Employment—*cont.*
 terms of,
  written statement of, 112
 unfair dismissal, 112, 113, 114
  remedies for, 114, 115
 wages,
  payment of, 109
 work,
  availability for, 110
  provision of, 109
 young persons,
  employment of, 119
  protection of, 119, 120
Environment, *see also* **Planning and Pollution**
 areas of scientific interest (A.S.I.s), 18, 19
 conservation orders, 16
 environmental impact assessment (E.I.A.), 28, 47, 66, 67
 environmentally sensitive areas (E.S.A.s), 20
 importance of, 15
 land use plans, 15
 national parks, 20
 natural heritage areas (N.H.A.s), 19
 special amenity area orders, 16
  contravention of, 16
 special areas of conservation (S.A.C.s), 20
 special protected areas (S.P.A.s), 18
 tree preservation orders (T.P.O.s), 17
 Wildlife Act 1976,
  orders under, 17, 18
 zoning, 15, 16

Farming
 definition of, 57
Fee Simple
 absolute, 3, 6
 definition of, 3
 modified, 3
Fee Tail, 3, 4
Financial Aid
 common agricultural policy, 256
  reforms of, 260
 contractual basis of, 257, 258, 259

 early retirement schemes, 260, 261
 judicial review, 259, 260
 rural environment protection scheme, 263, 164, 265
 scheme of installation aid, 261, 262
Fire
 accidental, 168, 169
 guesthouse, 170
 liability for, 168
 offences, 172
 penalties, 172
 safety, 168, 169
 wildlife, 171, 172
Freehold Estates, *see also* **Land**
 estates less than, 4
 fee farm grants, 5
 leases for lifes, 5, 6
 leases for term certain, 4, 5
 periodic tenancies, 4, 5
 tenancies at sufferance, 4, 5
 tenancies at will, 4, 5

Land
 agistment, 8
 boundaries, 11
  roads as, 11
 compulsory purchase of, 54
 co-ownership, 6, 7
 conacre, 8
 estates in land, 2, 3
  acquiring of, in, 7
 definition of, 9, 10
 easement, 12, 13
  acquisition of, 13
  dominant tenement, 12
  extinguishment of, 14
  servient tenement, 12
 freehold estates, 3–6
 future interests in, 6
 incorporeal hereditaments, 11, 12, 13
 ownership of, 9, 10
 profit à prendre, 12, 13
  acquisition of, 13
  extinguishment of, 14
 tenure, 2
 title deeds, 7, 8
 seisin of land, 3, 4

Leasing of Farms
agistment, 193, 197
    definition of, 194
agricultural leases, 198, 199
animals,
    disease status of, 197
    injury to,
        liability for, 195
conacre, 193
    definition of, 194
conveyancing implications, and,
        205, 206, 207, 208
crops,
    injury to,
        liability for, 195
E.C. quotas, 197
insurance,
    implications of, 196, 197
letting of land,
    Land Commission permission,
        without, ban on, 199
local authority charges, 197, 198
master lease, 201, 202, 203, 204,
        205
occupation of land,
    liability arising from, 196
rent,
    payment of, 195
tenants,
    ejectment of, 199
Life Estate, 3, 4

Milk Quotas
authorised officer, 254
background to, 243, 244
base year, 244
claw back, 247
dormant, 253, 254
expiring lease, 253
land, attach to, 246, 250
levy, 248
milk production, discontinuation of,
        254
milk production holding,
    structure of, 252, 253
mulder quotas, 248
national reserve, 253
offences, 255

reference quantities, transfer of,
        245, 246
register of milk purchasers, 253
relevant formulae, 245
restricted, 250
special cases, 247
temporary leasing of, 247, 248
transfer of, 245, 246, 251, 252
    purchasers between, 253
    recording of, 251
transfer of holdings,
    expiring leases, 249
    general rule, 249
    land used for milk production,
        249
    special milk quotas, 249, 250

Nuisance
claim in, 150
damage,
    actual, 150, 151
    particular, 148
    special, 148
location, 152
private, 148
public, 148, 149
    highway, on, 149
roots, 154
trees, 153

Occupiers' Liability
entrant
    categories of, 135, 137
land,
    trespass to, 144, 145, 146, 147
negligence, as, 135, 136
    liability in, 141, 142, 143
occupier,
    definition of, 138
premises,
    definition of, 138
recreational activity, 128
recreational users, 137, 138
    duties owed to, 139, 140
trespasser, 135, 138
    duties owed to, 139, 140
visitors, 137
    duties owed to, 139, 140

Planning Law
  agricultural land,
    other uses for,
      alteration of a hedge, 68
      halting sites, 70
      public enjoyment of, 68
      public rights of way, 69
      roads, 69, 70
      services, 70
      special amenity orders for, 68
      tree preservation orders, 69
  An Bord Pleanála,
    appeals to, 45
  building law, and, 48, 49
  compensation, 51–55
    claim for,
      blocking of, 53
      entitlement to, 52
      restrictions on, 52, 53
  change of use,
    material, whether, 21, 39
  development of land, 38
    definition of, 39, 42
    exemption for, 22, 23, 42, 43, 44,
      58
      rural areas in, 23, 24, 25, 26,
        27
      specific, 59–65
    permission required for, 21
  development plan, 41, 58
    contents of, 41
    enforcement of, 49–51
      court action, 51
      notice for, 50, 51
      prosecution, 49
      warning notices, 49
    material contravention of, 46
    procedure for making, 42
  integrated pollution control licences,
    47, 48
  planning authority
    powers of, 40, 41
  planning grievance,
    rights of action for,
      judicial review, 55, 56
      reference on point of law, 56
      private action, 56
      section 27 injunction, 56

  planning permission, 42, 58
    development not requiring, 43, 44
    development requiring, 44, 45
    interpretation of, 46
    retention permission, 47
  purchase notice, 53, 54
  use of land,
    definition of, 39
  works,
    definition of, 38
Pollution, *see also* **Environment**
  agricultural wastes, 67, 68
  air, 30, 33, 34
  common law remedies for, 29, 30
    misfeasance of public office, 29
    negligence, 29
    nuisance, 29, 30
    statutory duty, breach of, 29
    trespass, 29
  civil liability for, 32-35
  criminal offences of, 30
  damages, actions for, 34
  defences for, 30, 31
  liability for, 29
    avoidance of, 35
  licences for, 31, 32
  penalties for, 31
  water, 30, 32, 33
  waste disposal, 35
    main liabilities for, 36, 37

Succession
  administrator
    duties of, 186
  administration,
    letter of, 186
  capital acquisition tax, 192
  children,
    courts, application to, by, 189,
      190
    rights of, 187, 188, 189
  exclusion from, 191
  executor,
    duties of, 186
    liabilities of, 186
  intestacy,
    estate, division of upon, 186, 187
    occurrence of, 186

Succession—*cont.*
  legal right share, 188
  per stirpes, 187
  testation,
    freedom of, 188
  will,
    execution of, 185
    nature of, 185

Tax
  capital acquisitions tax
    agricultural relief, 223
    application of, 222
    business property relief, 223
    claw back, 223
    credit capital, 223
    farmer, meaning of, 222, 223
    favourite nephew reliefs, 223
    miscellaneous exemptions, 224
    rates of, 222
    reliefs, 223
    small gift exemption, 223
  capital gains tax,
    assets, replacement of, 219, 220
    business, replacement of, 219,
      220
    disposal of business, 220
    example of, 218
    exemptions, 219
    nature of, 218
    rate of, 281
    relaxation, 221
    reliefs, 219
    returns and payment, 219
    sale of shares in unquoted
      company, 220, 221
  corporation tax,
    10% rate, 231
    advance, 231, 232
    distributions, 231
    losses, 230
    nature of, 230
    preliminary tax, 230
    rates, 230
    returns, 230, 231
  income tax,
    allowances,
      age, 213

income tax—*cont.*
  allowances—*cont.*
    blind person's, 214
    business expansion scheme,
      216
    dependant relative, 214
    fees paid for certain private
      colleges, 214
    health expenses of dependant
      relative, 215
    housekeeper's, 213
    incapacitated child, 213
    married, 212
    medical insurance, 215, 216
    PAYE, 213
    payment of service charges,
      214
    permanent health insurance
      premiums, 216
    personal, 212
    rent paid on private
      accommodation, 215
    single parent's, 213
    single person's, 212
    widowed person's, 213
  disease eradication, 211, 212
  exemption limits
  farm profits,
    averaging of, 211
  farmer taxation, 210
  hobby farming, 212
  payment of, 209, 210
  relief,
    life assurance, 215
    medical expenses, 215
    mortgage interest, 214
    pension payments, 215
    seed capital investment, 216
  self-assessment, 209
  stock relief 25%, 211
  stock relief 100%, 211
  tables, 217
  total income, 210
  residential property tax,
    income limit, 225
    nature of, 224, 225
    payment of, 225
    property value limit, 225

Tax—*cont.*
  residential property tax—*cont.*
    rates of, 225
    tax clearance certificate, 226
  probate tax, 224
  stamp duty,
    late stamping, penalties for, 227
    nature of, 226
    payment of, 226
    rates of, 226
    reliefs for, 227

  stamp duty—*cont.*
    surcharge, 227
  value added tax,
    nature of, 228
    purchases for resale, 229
    purchases not for resale, 229
    records, 229
    return, 229, 230
    sales VAT rates, 228
    unregistered farmers, 230